This page has been perforated so that it can be removed and used as a bookmark

The Farne Islands in Northumberland are home to thousands of puffins.
Competition entry from Chris Carthern

Turning the pages of an inspiring year

Each and every entry in your *Handbook* is packed with information to help you get the most from every visit. The symbols will help you navigate things easily. Here's what they mean …

These symbols tell you something about the place
You'll find them above its description.

- 1939 Acquisition date
- Historic house
- Castle/fort
- Church/chapel
- Watermill
- Windmill
- Other buildings
- Public house
- Archaeological site
- Farm/farm animals
- Garden
- Countryside/park
- Coast
- Nature reserve
- Places to stay
- Campsite
- Licensed for weddings
- Available for functions

These symbols tell you about accessibility
You'll find them towards the end of each listing.

- Designated parking
- Drop-off point
- Transfer available
- Accessible toilet
- Catering accessible
- Shop accessible
- Induction loop
- Photograph album
- Virtual tour
- Seats/seating available
- Braille (guide or menu)
- Large print (guide or menu)
- Steps/uneven terrain
- Ramped access or slopes
- Level access/terrain, paths
- Lifts
- Stairclimber
- Stairlift
- Narrow corridors
- Wheelchairs available
- Powered mobility vehicle
- Accessible route and/or map available

This table shows you when places are open

Example place		M	T	W	T	F	S	S
House								
11 Feb–4 Nov	11–5	M	T	W	T	F	S	S
5 Nov–28 Nov	12–5	M	T	W	T	F	S	S
1 Dec–9 Dec	10:30–4:30	M	T	W	T	F	S	·

Last entry to house and tea-room 20 minutes before closing.

These are opening times.
A letter means the place or facility is **open** on this day.
A grey dot means it's **closed**.
Any special notes about opening times are shown down here.

This page has been perforated so that it can be removed and used as a bookmark

Celebrating 125 years of discovery

On 12 January 1895, the National Trust was founded. Home to 100 members paying ten shillings each, the organisation looked after 4 ½ acres of land at Dinas Oleu in North Wales. Our first President, the Duke of Westminster, told co-founder Octavia Hill 'mark my words, Miss Hill, this is going to be a very big thing'.

He was right.

In 2020, as we celebrate our 125th anniversary, we have more than 5.9 million members, and we care for places that anyone can come and discover – from captivating castles to historic houses and magnificent meadows.

Our greatest strength is that each of these places offers something to inspire everyone, whether that's sitting in a beautiful garden, hiking through open countryside, or exploring the hidden history of a great house.

For the past 125 years, people have been discovering new experiences and making special memories with us. I hope this *Handbook* inspires you to do likewise in 2020.

Here's to looking after nature, beauty and history for everyone, for ever.

Hilary McGrady
Director-General

Celebrating **125** years

Where will your membership take you?

This year's National Trust *Handbook* is brimming with unique places. Over the following pages, you'll find hundreds of them, each of which you can visit as often as you like, taking advantage of the constantly evolving seasonal changes, long opening hours and, of course, free car parking. Not only that, but if you visit off-peak – for example early morning, midweek or autumn – you'll probably find places even more peaceful.

There's so much to look forward to that it might be hard to know where to start. So here's a bit more information about the places we look after, and what you could do there.

When you scan, we can ...

As a member, you can park for free at nearly all the places we look after.

But please remember to scan your membership card at a parking machine, if there is one.

That place will then receive money from National Trust central funds to spend on improvements.

So when you scan, we can do all sorts at the places that matter to you.

Gardens that grip you

Space to think. Space to stroll. Space to play. Space to picnic. We know a garden needs to be all these things and more. The gardens in our care include some of the most famous in the country, by illustrious designers like 'Capability' Brown. As a member, you have the freedom to lose yourself (or find yourself) in these tranquil spaces whenever the mood takes you.

'There isn't a day in a garden that isn't unique and each garden is totally different. The seasons, weather, nature's power, history and our gardeners' creativity all combine.'

Rosie Fyles,
Head Gardener at Ham House

Countryside that calms

As Europe's largest conservation charity, the National Trust is your gateway to a lifetime of countryside. Rivers to revive the spirits, forests to feel at one with, mountain views to move you, wildflower meadows to while away the hours ... there's nearly a thousand square miles of countryside to enjoy as often as you like. (And 39 pubs to reward yourself with afterwards.)

Put special places in your pocket

Inspiration for a great day out is just a smartphone away – the National Trust app brings you maps, opening times, events and more, while our website, podcasts and social media channels (not to mention staff and volunteers on the ground) are also brimming with bright ideas.

Download our app from the App Store or Google Play

Buildings
that bewitch

From Jacobean to Georgian, medieval to Modernist, bomb shelters to Beatles' homes, we care for a huge variety of buildings. Whether you're looking to indulge a love of architecture and history, or simply feel refreshed by a change of scene, your membership is the key to some of the best-known buildings around – and some of the best-kept secrets too.

'What makes a building are the everyday stories of people; these can often remind us that within those walls, there's real social history.'

Muks Miah, Senior Visitor Experience Officer at the Birmingham Back to Backs

Seasides
that stir you

The rising screech of gulls, the lazy gaze of a basking seal, the crash of waves, the soaring splendour of sheer cliffs and ... well ... the smell of fish and chips. There's nowhere quite like the coastline of England, Wales and Northern Ireland, and we're honoured that 780 miles of it (and counting) will be looked after by us for ever.

Fun for all the family ...

It's hard keeping the whole family entertained all at once, but it *can* be done at lots of the places we care for.

There's '50 things to do before you're 11¾' for the youngsters, not to mention family nature trails, adventure playgrounds and seasonal events – all of which can help children connect with nature and the great outdoors.

Meanwhile, any adults not on childcare duty could sneak off for a well-deserved cuppa or a stroll round the house.

... including four-legged friends

A bracing hike across the fells or a soothing stroll around the gardens – whatever you're doing, we want your four-legged friend(s) to be able to enjoy it with you. So we welcome dogs wherever possible, and we're looking for more ways to do this, including at holiday cottages (see page 10). But we also realise that lots of people enjoy dog-free spaces, and of course we can't allow Rover to roam all over. So before you promise the pooch the best walkies ever, find our latest dog access information online, or check the 'Things to see and do' section of the place you're visiting.

Get more from your membership

We bring you more than 'just' inspirational places; we also offer special events, holidays, shopping, lots of opportunities to help with our work … and that's only the start of it.

Don't be beaten getting off-the-beaten track

Even in the age of satnavs and apps, some places still require more than a postcode to find. This can mean these hidden corners are all the more peaceful when you do finally arrive.

But to maintain your inner peace en route, you might need a copy of our *Getting Here* guide, which you can get free at **nationaltrust.org.uk/ gettinghere** or **on 0344 800 1895;** it's packed with detailed directions and maps.

Get with the programmes

We look after so many places that there can be literally hundreds of special programmes and events going on at any given time. From live music and open-air theatre to sports events and conservation walks, there's something for everyone.

Find out what's happening near you at **nationaltrust.org.uk/ visit/whats-on**

Go on, treat yourself

After a long hillside hike, a refreshing plunge in the sea, a gentle potter round the house or just some quiet reflection in the garden, what could be better than a drop to drink or a bite to eat, freshly made in the café? Or, indeed, a quick trip to the shop for unique gifts, like textiles and homeware inspired by the special places in our care? Everything you buy from our cafés and shops will help our charitable work too.

If you can't decide on the day, there's always our online shop at **nationaltrust.org.uk/shop**

'I have always loved cooking, even from a young age I knew I wanted to be a chef. What brought me to work for the National Trust was that we make great food from scratch. I really enjoy using fresh ingredients and knowing everything is authentic.'

Alex Huntington,
Head Chef at Sizergh

Stay in places that stay with you

If you're looking to stay somewhere unique, have a look at our range of holiday accommodation. Grand manor houses, cosy cottages, rustic bunkhouses, picturesque campsites – they're all here, and more than 200 of them are dog-friendly. Many properties are at places we look after, so you can often have the grounds to yourself after hours. And wherever you stay, all the money goes to a good cause: helping us carry out conservation work in the surrounding area.

'We loved wandering around after the Castle had closed. The grounds were so varied, so extraordinarily picturesque.'

Alison Petch,
The Bothy, Powis Castle

Enjoy rich history, peaceful parklands and a warm welcome

As a National Trust member, your support makes a huge difference; we simply couldn't do all of our conservation work without help from people like you. But, to keep up with the ever-increasing costs of looking after places, we need other ways of support too.

In 2008 we were gifted the company Historic House Hotels Ltd, and all their interests in three special properties. More than 10 years on, the income that Bodysgallen Hall (top and page 402), Hartwell House (middle right and page 125) and Middlethorpe Hall (bottom left and page 372) continue to generate as hotels is helping lots of vital conservation work.

Give something back

Lots of members join because they're just as excited by our cause – looking after unique places for everyone, for ever – as they are by the promise of unlimited great days out. That's why so many of them also volunteer, donate to their favourite places, organise fundraising events, buy gift membership for others, go to conservation events, or leave gifts in wills.

'If I have this joy, surely I want to do what I can to enable others to have that joy.'

Agnes Segal on keeping her memories of the Llŷn Peninsula alive for ever by leaving a gift in her will

Have your say

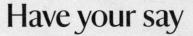

Every autumn, we hold our Annual General Meeting (AGM), which is a great opportunity to learn about our strategy and voice your views on how we work. You can also vote in various elections and resolutions – **look out for voting papers in your autumn** *Magazine* **or vote online.**

Still can't get enough?

Ok, so you've tried everything else on these pages. 'That's it,' you're thinking, 'I've really got the most out of my membership.' Well, actually there's more.

You can get free or discounted entry to places looked after by similar heritage organisations abroad. And you can join local supporter or volunteer groups full of like-minded people, enjoying visits, talks, volunteering and lots of other activities together.

In fact, we could probably fill this entire *Handbook* with membership perks, but we figured you'd rather we filled it with places to visit, so that's what we've done. Still, have a look at our website and you'll find loads more unexpected benefits to your membership.

Cornwall

'There's nothing I enjoy more than sharing my love for this special place with our visitors. I was diagnosed with Parkinson's at 37, but when I'm here I'm a volunteer wildlife ranger and I couldn't be happier.'

Heidi Reynolds reflects on her volunteering role on the Lizard peninsula in Cornwall. She loves immersing herself in nature and helping visitors experience the incredible wildlife on the UK's most southerly point

Heidi (second from left) exploring the Penrose estate and Lizard peninsula by bike

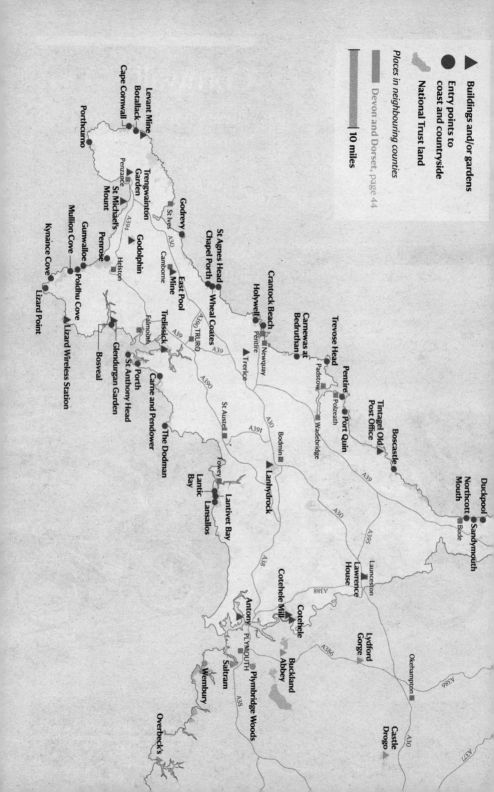

Buildings and/or gardens

Entry points to
coast and countryside

National Trust land

Places in neighbouring counties

Devon and Dorset, page 44

10 miles

Cape Cornwall
Botallack
Levant Mine
Porthcurno
Penzance
Trengwainton Garden
St Michael's Mount
Godolphin
Penrose
Gunwalloe
Mullion Cove
Poldhu Cove
Kynance Cove
Lizard Point
Lizard Wireless Station
Bosveal
Glendurgan Garden
Carne and Pendower
St Anthony Head
Porth
Helston
Trelissick
Camborne
East Pool Mine
Godrevy
St Ives
Chapel Porth
St Agnes Head
Wheal Coates
Holywell
Crantock Beach
Pentire
Newquay
Trerice
TRURO
Falmouth
St Austell
The Dodman
Fowey
Lantic Bay
Lansallos
Lantivet Bay
Lanhydrock
Bodmin
Wadebridge
Padstow
Polzeath
Trevose Head
Carnewas at Bedruthan
Port Quin
Pentire
Tintagel Old Post Office
Boscastle
Northcott Mouth
Bude
Sandymouth
Duckpool
Launceston
Lawrence House
Cotehele Mill
Cotehele
Antony
PLYMOUTH
Saltram
Wembury
Plymbridge Woods
Buckland Abbey
Lydford Gorge
Okehampton
Castle Drogo
Overbeck's

Antony

Torpoint, Cornwall PL11 2QA

🏠 ✴ 1961

Parking: 250 yards.

Centuries-old portraits preside over glimpses of present-day life in this house full of personal treasures, which is still lived in today by the Carew Pole family. Playful topiary, a cone-shaped fountain and intriguing sculptures accompany sweeping views in the garden. Antony is a great place to lose track of time.

Access: 🅿️ 🚻 ♿ 🔍 📷 🚪 ♿ ::
House ♿ ♿ **Grounds** ♿ ➡️ ♿

Find out more: 01752 812191 or antony@nationaltrust.org.uk

Eat, shop, stay: a tea-room in the colonnade courtyard offers light lunches and afternoon tea. Indoor and outdoor seating available. Picnics welcome. Gift shop selling souvenirs and plants. Small second-hand bookshop.

Antony		M	T	W	T	F	S	S
1 Apr–28 May	12–5	·	T	W	T	·	·	·
2 Jun–30 Aug	12–5	·	T	W	T	·	·	S
1 Sep–29 Oct	12–5	·	T	W	T	·	·	·

House: open 12:30 to 4:30 (timed ticket entry may be in operation). Also open Good Friday, Easter Sunday, Saturday 9 May, Sunday 24 May and Bank Holidays, excluding Christmas and New Year.

Things to see and do: Indoors Family trails. Activity room – games, books and dressing up. **Outdoors** Seasonal trails and events. Croquet. Den-building. Garden sculpture. '50 things'. **Dogs**: assistance dogs only.

With a magnificent landscape garden and treasure-filled house, it is easy to lose track of time at Antony, above and below

Boscastle

near Tintagel, Cornwall

🏚️ 🚶 🛏️ 1955

Satnav: use PL35 0HD. **Parking**: 100 yards, pay and display, not National Trust (charge including members).

There has been a fishing and trading port here for centuries, with boats coming and going between the high cliffs that guard the snaking harbour entrance. Much of Boscastle can be discovered on foot, with footpaths leading in all directions. You can walk in the footsteps of the young Thomas Hardy through the wildlife-rich ancient woodland in the Valency Valley, or explore the rare medieval field system known as 'the Forrabury Stitches' high above the village. The striking lookout building on Willapark headland, and the historic churches of Minster and Forrabury, are nearby.
Note: toilet by main car park (not National Trust).

Boscastle, above and below, has been a fishing and trading port for centuries

Eat, shop, stay: harbourside café with courtyard seating. Large shop and visitor centre offering a wide range of gifts, seasonal plant sales plus a wealth of guides and information about the local area. Second-hand bookshop. Five holiday cottages. Free Wi-Fi throughout.

Things to see and do: children's quiz/trail. Coasteering (not National Trust). Visitor centre shows film about the 2004 flood. Why not combine with a visit to Tintagel Old Post Office, 4 miles down the coast? **Dogs**: welcome on walks and in café courtyard.

Access: 🅿️ 🚻 🛗 Grounds 🚶

Find out more: 01840 250010 or boscastle@nationaltrust.org.uk

Boscastle		M	T	W	T	F	S	S
Shop, café and visitor centre								
Open all year	*	M	T	W	T	F	S	S

*Opening times vary throughout year, ranging from 10:30 to 4 in winter to 10 to 5:30 in high summer. Closed 25 and 26 December.

Bosveal

near Mawnan Smith, Falmouth, Cornwall 1980

Walks from here take in wooded valleys, secluded coves and soft, sheltered shores of the Helford River and Falmouth Bay.
Note: toilets and refreshments at nearby Glendurgan Garden. Holiday cottages at Bosloe and Durgan. For satnav use TR11 5JR.

Find out more: 01326 252020 or bosveal@nationaltrust.org.uk

Botallack

on the Tin Coast, near St Just, Cornwall

🏠🏛️⛱️♿🚻🍽️ 1995

Satnav: use TR19 7QQ. Beware, some satnavs misdirect. Keep to the B3306 until you reach Botallack village. **Parking**: just beyond Botallack Count House.

On the wild Tin Coast, the famed Crowns engine houses cling to the foot of the cliffs in a landscape transformed by its industrial past. From here Cornish miners changed the world, and today it's part of the Cornish Mining World Heritage Site. **Note**: industrial landscape, mine shafts/exposed cliffs – please keep to paths.

Eat, shop, stay: light refreshments, pasties and ice cream available in the Botallack Workshop Café. Picnic blankets to borrow. Botallack Count House Cottage, sleeping two, has dramatic coastal views.

An engine house at Botallack on the wild Tin Coast

Things to see and do: augmented reality technology allows you to view Botallack as a bustling 1860 mining landscape. Outdoors trail and easy clifftop walk to Levant. **Dogs**: welcome on short leads. Please take care near mine shafts and cliff edges.

Access: ♿🅿️🚾♿♿♿♿

Find out more: 01736 786932 or botallack@nationaltrust.org.uk

Botallack	
Botallack Workshop Café	
Open every day all year*	10–5**

*Excluding 24 and 25 December. **January, February, November and December: open 11 to 3.

Cape Cornwall

on the Tin Coast, near St Just, Cornwall

🏛️⛱️♿🚻 1987

Rugged Cape Cornwall is a good place to watch wildlife

Satnav: use TR19 7NN for Cape Cornwall car park. Beware some satnavs misdirect. Follow the signs in St Just town to Cape Cornwall. **Parking**: at Cape Cornwall, Porth Nanven (Cot Valley) and Ballowall.

The distinctive headland of Cape Cornwall juts out into the ocean where two great bodies of water meet. Once a heavily industrialised landscape, it is now part of the Cornish Mining World Heritage Site, and a wild and rugged home to the many seabirds that nest on the Brisons Rocks. **Note**: narrow lanes, unsuitable for caravans. Industrial landscape – please keep to paths for your own safety.

Eat, shop, stay: light refreshments (not National Trust) every day from Easter to October. Toilets in car park. Holiday cottage in nearby Cot Valley.

Things to see and do: beach for rock-pooling and swimming. Working cove for crab and lobster fishermen. Short walk to the top of the Cape for Isles of Scilly views. **Dogs**: welcome, but not on beach and slipway from Easter to October.

Access: 🚾

Find out more: 01736 786932 or capecornwall@nationaltrust.org.uk

Carne and Pendower

near Veryan, Cornwall

🏠🏖️🚶🛏️ 1961

Carne and Pendower on the Roseland peninsula

Satnav: for Carne use TR2 5PF; Pendower TR2 5PF (turn right at sign for Pendower Beach). **Parking**: car parks at both Carne and Pendower.

Two of the best beaches on the Roseland peninsula: fine stretches of sand and rock pools, popular with families. Walks along the coast and inland reveal the area's wildlife – great for butterflies in summer and birds in winter. Lots of history to discover nearby, from Bronze Age to Cold War. **Note**: seasonal toilets in both car parks.

Eat, shop, stay: seasonal refreshments available (concession). You can stay close to Carne Beach at the five holiday cottages at Gwendra and Caragloose.

Things to see and do: ideal beaches for swimming and rock-pooling. Path leading inland to Carne Beacon, one of Britain's largest Bronze Age barrows. Downloadable walking trails to wider area. **Dogs**: seasonal dog restrictions on beaches (please keep under control near livestock).

Find out more: 01872 501062 or carne@nationaltrust.org.uk

Carnewas at Bedruthan

near Padstow, Cornwall

🚶🛏️ 1930

Satnav: use PL27 7UW. **Parking**: on site.

Since Victorian times this has been one of the most popular destinations on the Cornish coast, known for its spectacular clifftop views of giant rock stacks striding across Bedruthan Beach (not National Trust). Those with a head for heights can climb down the cliff staircase to the beach (closed during the winter) but beware of being cut off by the tide. For a longer walk, follow the coast path to Park Head and the sheltered cove of Porth Mear beyond. Carpets of spring and autumn squill bedeck these clifftops, and birds nesting from March include linnets, stonechats and skylarks. **Note**: unsafe to enter the sea here at any time.

Carnewas at Bedruthan: the view from the cliff staircase

Places may occasionally close for events or bad weather, check at nationaltrust.org.uk

Eat, shop, stay: shop offering gifts, many locally sourced and produced, and popular tea-room (concession) with adjoining clifftop tea garden. Picnic area. Holiday cottages offering expansive sea views at Park Head.

Things to see and do: children's quiz. Carnewas awarded 'dark sky status', so ideal for stargazing. Why not combine with a visit to Trevose Head (7 miles) or Trerice (9 miles)? **Dogs**: welcome under control.

Access: ♿🅿🚻💺 Car park and clifftop ♿➡

Find out more: 01637 860563 or carnewas@nationaltrust.org.uk

Carnewas at Bedruthan		M	T	W	T	F	S	S
Tea-room								
10 Feb–15 Nov*	11–4**	M	T	W	T	F	S	S
21 Nov–20 Dec†	11–4	·	·	·	·	·	S	S
Shop								
8 Feb–8 Nov	10–5**	M	T	W	T	F	S	S
14 Nov–20 Dec†	10:30–4	·	·	·	·	·	S	S

*Tea-room and shop: also open 1 to 5 January; tea-room open weekends in January and February. **Tea-room: open 10:30 to 5 from 28 March to 1 November (shop open 10:30 to 4 before 28 March). †Tea-room also open 27 to 31 December (shop 28 to 31 December). Cliff staircase closed from 9 November to mid-February.

Chapel Porth

near St Agnes, Cornwall

⛱ 🏊 1957

Satnav: use TR5 0NS. **Parking**: car park (very busy in summer), accessed down single track with passing places. Additional parking at nearby Wheal Coates and St Agnes Head.

At the foot of a steep valley between high heathery cliffs, Chapel Porth Beach is a shingle strip at high tide and a huge expanse of sand at low tide. The area is steeped in mining history, with many remains to be discovered on walks. **Note**: seasonal toilets. Take care not to get cut off by incoming tide. Seasonal lifeguards.

Eat, shop, stay: Chapel Porth Beach Café (concession) open daily in summer and most winter weekends (01872 552487). Picnics welcome.

Things to see and do: coast path and inland paths link with Porthtowan, St Agnes Head and World Heritage Site mining remains at Charlotte United, Wheal Coates and Trevellas. **Dogs**: seasonal dog ban on the beach (Easter Sunday to 30 September inclusive).

Access: 🅿🚻💺♿ Beach ♿

Find out more: 01872 552412 or chapelporth@nationaltrust.org.uk

The popular beach at Chapel Porth

Cotehele

St Dominick, near Saltash, Cornwall PL12 6TA

🏠 ✝ 🖼 🌀 👥 🐾 🍽 1947

Satnav: follow postcode until Tavistock, then brown signs. **Parking**: at house and on quay.

This rambling granite and slate-stone home, high above the River Tamar, was built by the Edgcumbes and remained in their family for nearly 600 years. Time has stood still. The hall, with its ancient timber roof and displays of weaponry, and the warren of tapestry-clad rooms beyond have changed little since Tudor times. The 5-hectare (12-acre) garden features historic daffodils, terraces, ponds and orchards with 150 local apple varieties. The Valley Garden, with medieval stewpond and dovecote, leads to Cotehele Quay – thriving in Victorian times – where you'll find the 1899 Tamar sailing barge *Shamrock*, lime kilns and Discovery Centre. **Note**: the house has no electricity, so feel free to bring a torch.

Eat, shop, stay: restaurant near house serving hot lunches and cakes. Tea-room on quay offering light lunches, cakes and cream teas. Gift shop and plant centre. Art and craft gallery featuring West Country artists. Second-hand bookshop. Picnic area. Eight holiday cottages on estate.

Things to see and do: Indoors 'Around the world at Cotehele' highlights collection items with transatlantic connections to commemorate the anniversary of the *Mayflower* voyage. **Outdoors** Play area. Year-round family trails, events and walks. **Dogs**: welcome on estate walks, restaurant and tea-room. Assistance dogs only in formal garden.

Access: 🅿 ♿ 🚻 🔊 ♿ 📷 ⬇ ♿ ·· 🅰
Building 🅰 🅰 🅰 Grounds 🅰 🅰 ➡

Find out more: 01579 351346 or cotehele@nationaltrust.org.uk

Cotehele		M	T	W	T	F	S	S
House								
7 Mar–1 Nov	11–4	M	T	W	T	F	S	S
Christmas Garland*								
2 Nov–31 Dec	10:30–4**	M	T	W	T	F	S	S
Garden, estate, restaurant, tea-room, gallery and shop								
1 Jan–6 Mar	10–4	M	T	W	T	F	S	S
7 Mar–1 Nov	10–5	M	T	W	T	F	S	S
2 Nov–31 Dec	10–4**	M	T	W	T	F	S	S

*Hall of house and Breakfast Room only. Hall prepared and garland constructed between 2 and 20 November.
**Everything closed 25 and 26 December.

Exploring the garden by the north-west tower at Cotehele, a later 17th-century addition to the largely Tudor house

Cotehele Mill

St Dominick, near Saltash, Cornwall PL12 6TA

🏛️🍴🏠 1947

Parking: on Cotehele Quay (at the mill by arrangement only). Shuttlebus from Cotehele house (dependent on volunteer availability).

A peaceful walk alongside the Morden stream from Cotehele Quay takes you to the restored 19th-century Cotehele Mill. On Thursdays and Sundays you can watch corn being ground into flour. Traditional woodworker and potter on site, as well as recreated wheelwright's, saddler's and blacksmith's workshops. Look out for baking days. **Note**: nearest toilets and parking at Cotehele Quay.

Eat, shop, stay: Cotehele flour, gifts and ice cream for sale. Edgcumbe tea-room at nearby Cotehele Quay serves light lunches and cream teas. Kiosk at quay. Picnics welcome in meadow. Two holiday cottages.

Things to see and do: **Indoors** Events, including milling and bakery demonstrations, as well as dress-up days. Opportunity to mill grain at the hand quern. **Outdoors** Family trails. **Dogs**: welcome, but assistance dogs only in bakery and mill.

Access: 📶🚿📷🖨️🎵 Building 🏠 Grounds 🏠

Find out more: 01579 350606 (mill). 01579 351346 (Cotehele) or cotehele@nationaltrust.org.uk

Cotehele Mill		M	T	W	T	F	S	S
7 Mar–27 Sep	11–4:30	M	T	W	T	F	S	S
28 Sep–1 Nov	11–4	M	T	W	T	F	S	S

Crantock Beach

near Newquay, Cornwall

🏖️ 1956

Satnav: use TR8 5RN for Crantock Beach and TR8 5QS for Treago Mill. **Parking**: on site (height restriction barrier when unmanned) and at Treago Mill for Polly Joke Beach (also known as Porth Joke).

Close to Newquay, this feels like a different Cornwall: Crantock Beach is an expanse of golden sand, great for sandcastles and surfing. Wonderful walking country – through the dunes on Rushy Green, along the banks of the Gannel Estuary, or around the headland of West Pentire, carpeted with wild flowers. **Note**: danger, unpredictable currents.

Eat, shop, stay: seasonal refreshments on beach (one concession, one not National Trust). Other non-National Trust refreshments in Crantock, West Pentire, and Fern Pit café across the estuary (by seasonal tide-dependent ferryboat/footbridge).

Things to see and do: surf school and board hire. Spot seals from the coast path. Summer wild flowers to discover in fields above nearby Polly Joke Beach. **Dogs**: welcome under control everywhere, including the beach.

Access: 📶

Find out more: 01208 863046 or crantockbeach@nationaltrust.org.uk

Crantock Beach: perfect for surfing and sandcastles

The Dodman

Penare, near Gorran Haven, Cornwall 1919

The highest headland on Cornwall's south coast, with massive Iron Age ramparts. Great walking, wildlife and beaches on either side. **Note**: park at Penare – footpaths to Hemmick Beach and Dodman Point. For satnav use PL26 6NY – go past Treveague Farm and continue downhill.

Find out more: 01872 501062 or thedodman@nationaltrust.org.uk

The winding engine in action at East Pool Mine

Duckpool

near Bude, Cornwall 1960

Remote beach with rock pools at the mouth of the wooded Coombe Valley, overlooked by cliffs carpeted with wild flowers. **Note**: toilets open seasonally. For satnav use EX23 9JN.

Find out more: 01208 863046 or duckpool@nationaltrust.org.uk

East Pool Mine

near Redruth, Cornwall

🏠 🏛 1967

Satnav: for main site, use TR15 3NH; for Trevithick Cottage use TR14 0QG. **Parking**: for main site, use Morrisons' car park (far end). Additional parking at Michell's Engine House nearby.

East Pool celebrates the extraordinary lives of people who worked at the very heart of what is now the Cornish Mining World Heritage Site. With two giant beam engines, preserved in towering engine houses, this is a place for all the family to discover the dramatic story of Cornish mining.

Eat, shop, stay: small shop selling gifts, minerals and Cornish history books. Hot and cold drinks, snacks and ice cream available to enjoy outside on picnic benches, or inside the Discovery Centre.

Things to see and do: historic engines and hands-on exhibits. Family activities, trails and free guided tours. Trevithick Cottage, home of Cornish engineer Richard Trevithick, is nearby at Penponds. **Dogs**: welcome in outdoor areas.

Access: 🅿 ♿ 🚻 ♿ 🔎 🎫 ♿
Taylor's Engine House ♿ Grounds ➡
Michell's Engine House ♿ ♿

Find out more: 01209 315027 or eastpool@nationaltrust.org.uk
Trevithick Road, Pool, Cornwall TR15 3NP

East Pool Mine		M	T	W	T	F	S	S
Taylor's Engine House and Discovery Centre								
3 Mar–31 Oct*	10:30–5		T	W	T	F	S	
Michell's Engine House								
3 Mar–31 Oct*	12–4		T	W	T	F	S	
Trevithick Cottage								
1 Apr–28 Oct	2–5			W				

*Also open Easter Monday and Bank Holiday weekends in May and August.

Glendurgan Garden

Mawnan Smith, near Falmouth,
Cornwall TR11 5JZ

[icons] 1962

Parking: on site.

Glendurgan Garden was described by its creators, the Quakers Alfred and Sarah Fox, as a 'small peace [sic] of heaven on earth'. Visitors can find out why it proved to be just this for the Foxes and their 12 children by exploring Glendurgan's three valleys, running down to the sheltered beach at Durgan on the Helford River. There's a puzzling maze, created by Alfred and Sarah to entertain the family. You can enjoy camellias, magnolias and primroses in early spring, then rhododendrons and bluebells in May, followed by the exotic greens of summer and dramatic autumn colour in the trees. **Note**: steep paths, steps, uneven terrain.

Eat, shop, stay: tea-house (concession) serving homemade cakes, soups, sandwiches and light lunches. Well-stocked plant centre and small shop. Second-hand books in Durgan Fish Cellar. Holiday lets close by – from waterside cottages for two, to country houses for eight or more.

Things to see and do: you can find out about local history from friendly volunteers in Durgan Fish Cellar and explore Durgan Beach on the Helford River. Seasonal children's trails and activities in the orchard. **Dogs**: assistance dogs only in garden. Walks in surrounding countryside (details available at Glendurgan).

Access: [icons]
Garden entrance [icon] Garden [icons]

Find out more: 01326 252020 or glendurgan@nationaltrust.org.uk

Glendurgan Garden		M	T	W	T	F	S	S
15 Feb–31 Jul	10:30–5:30		T	W	T	F	S	S
1 Aug–31 Aug	10:30–5:30	M	T	W	T	F	S	S
1 Sep–1 Nov	10:30–5:30		T	W	T	F	S	S

Last entry one hour before closing. Closes dusk if earlier.
Open Bank Holiday Mondays.

Glendurgan Garden: the sheltered beach at Durgan, above, and a colourful sweep of wild flowers, below

The Side Garden at Godolphin, where fashions have come and gone, leaving little changed since the 16th century

Godolphin

Godolphin Cross, Helston, Cornwall TR13 9RE

🏚 🏛 ⛅ ✤ 🐾 👤 2000

Parking: 300 yards.

Hidden in shaded woodland, Godolphin escaped modernisation and contemporary fashions. The granite-faced terraces and sunken lawns of the Side Garden have seen little change since the 16th century, and Victorian farm buildings tell the story of Godolphin as a tenant farm. The estate, once busy with prosperous tin mines, is now part of the Cornish Mining World Heritage Site and is wonderful walking country, rich in archaeology, rare plants and wildlife. There are panoramic views from the top of Godolphin Hill. The historic house is a holiday home, where you can stay and experience the splendour that mining riches bought. **Note**: house is open to visitors on limited dates between holiday bookings (please check before visiting).

Eat, shop, stay: small tea-room in the Piggery serving drinks, sandwiches, cakes, ice cream. Local gifts and souvenirs. Picnic benches in the orchard or borrow a blanket to relax in the garden. You can soak up the atmosphere by staying in Godolphin House.

Things to see and do: gardener's potting shed has information on flora and fauna. Free guided tours and waymarked walks. Discover the active conservation programme of the farm buildings. Barefoot trail from Easter to October. **Dogs**: welcome outdoors and in tea-room on short leads. Water bowl and dog biscuits available.

Access: ♿🅿️ 🔈 🔊 🚻 🏚 House 🔊 🔊 🚹 Cider House 🔊 🔊 ⬆ Garden 🔊 🔊 ♿

Find out more: 01736 763194 or godolphin@nationaltrust.org.uk

Godolphin		M	T	W	T	F	S	S
Garden, outbuildings and tea-room								
1 Jan–31 Jan	10–4	M	T	W	T	F	S	S
1 Feb–1 Nov	10–5	M	T	W	T	F	S	S
2 Nov–31 Dec*	10–4	M	T	W	T	F	S	S
Estate								
Open all year	Dawn–dusk	M	T	W	T	F	S	S
House								
Limited opening**				·	·	·	·	·

*Closed 24 and 25 December. **House: open first Saturday to Thursday, February to December (except August) – please check before visiting.

Godrevy

near Hayle, Cornwall 1939

Long sandy beaches on St Ives Bay with wildlife-rich cliffs and walks. Godrevy café in dunes (concession) open most days. **Note**: unstable cliffs and incoming tides. Toilets open in top field. For satnav use TR27 5ED. Car-parking fields on headland open in summer, subject to weather and ground conditions.

Find out more: 01872 552412 or godrevy@nationaltrust.org.uk

Distinctive Carter's Rocks at Holywell

Gunwalloe

near Helston, Cornwall 1974

Two family-friendly beaches and reedbeds rich in wildlife. Between the two coves a medieval church shelters behind Castle Mound. **Note**: for satnav use TR12 7QE. Lifeguards patrol Church Cove (summer holidays). Dogs: council-enforced ban at Church Cove (Easter to 1 October). Seasonal beach kiosk.

Find out more: 01326 222170 or gunwalloe@nationaltrust.org.uk

Eat, shop, stay: seasonal refreshments on beach (concession). Pubs at Holywell and convenience store and café open all year at Cubert, 2 miles (none National Trust).

Things to see and do: surf schools. Beach has a stream running down one side and is great for building sandcastles. Wildlife-rich grasslands and coastline. **Dogs**: welcome everywhere, including the beach, but under close control (especially around livestock).

Access: ⓟ🚻

Find out more: 01208 863046 or holywell@nationaltrust.org.uk

Holywell

near Newquay, Cornwall

🏊‍♂️📶 1951

Satnav: use TR8 5PF. **Parking**: on site.

Classic north Cornish beach, with a sweep of golden sand and a towering dune system. There's lots of history to discover, including the remains of an Iron Age castle on Kelsey Head, a Bronze Age barrow on Cubert Common and the holy well in a cave on the beach.

Kynance Cove

on the Lizard peninsula, Cornwall 1935

It's a ⅓-mile walk through Lizard heathland down to this famous beach, with its serpentine stacks, islands and caves. **Note**: for satnav use TR12 7PJ. Car park extremely busy in summer. Seasonal beach dog ban (council-enforced). Café open seasonally. Steep, uneven beach path.

Find out more: 01326 222170 or kynancecove@nationaltrust.org.uk

Lanhydrock

Bodmin, Cornwall

🏠 ✝ ♣ ♿ 🛏 🍴 1953

Satnav: use PL30 4AB (1 Double Lodges).
Parking: 600 yards.

A tragic fire in 1881 meant that the Agar-Robartes family had to rebuild most of their 17th-century home. Out of the ashes came the country house you see today, presented as if time has stood still with the family having just popped out to tea. There are more than 50 rooms to discover – from the extensive kitchens, which reveal the servants' daily lives, to the elegant Victorian luxury of the family rooms. Outside is a garden, full of colour all year round and famed for its magnolias, and ancient woodlands with miles of footpaths to explore. The off-road cycle trails have different routes to suit all levels of experience, and you can even hire a bike when you get here.

Eat, shop, stay: the Park Café offers homemade dishes all year. At the house, there's the Stables tea-room, plus waitress service in the Victorian restaurant. Shop sells local food and gifts. Second-hand bookshop. A holiday cottage on the estate sleeps six.

Things to see and do: **Indoors** There's a remarkable early 17th-century ceiling in the gallery, which survived the fire and is the oldest room in the house. As you explore you will experience everyday life in both the upstairs and downstairs worlds. Free children's trail daily. At Christmas, there's a traditional Victorian atmosphere. **Outdoors** Guided tours (telephone for availability) help you discover one of the great Cornish gardens, as well as the more remote corners of the parkland and riverside woods. There are waymarked routes for exploring alone, as well as family-friendly cycle trails and a popular adventure playground. **Dogs**: dog-friendly walks throughout the estate (assistance dogs only in house and garden).

Lanhydrock offers woodland cycle trails, left, more than 50 historic rooms, right, and a large garden, below, to explore

Access:

Access icons row

House icons Grounds icons

Find out more: 01208 265950 or
lanhydrock@nationaltrust.org.uk
Bodmin, Cornwall PL30 5AD

Lanhydrock		M	T	W	T	F	S	S
House and garden								
1 Mar–1 Nov*	11–5:30**	M	T	W	T	F	S	S
5 Dec–31 Dec†	11–4	M	T	W	T	F	S	S
Estate and cycle trails								
Open all year	Dawn–dusk	M	T	W	T	F	S	S
Refreshments								
Open all year	9:30–5††	M	T	W	T	F	S	S

*Garden: opens 15 February. **House: March and October,
closes 5. †December opening for selected rooms only (until
3 January 2021). ††Refreshments: November to February,
close 4. Last house ticket available 45 minutes before closing.
Everything closed 25 and 26 December.

Lansallos

between Polperro and Polruan, Cornwall

🏛️🏖️♿🚻⛺ 1936

Satnav: use PL13 2PX for Lansallos.
Parking: at Lansallos.

East of the Fowey Estuary is a long stretch of unspoilt coast loved by walkers, with abundant wild flowers and birds. From Lansallos church, a path ambles down the valley to a west-facing sandy beach. A picnic and a nose for adventure are all you need for the perfect day.
Note: nearest toilets at Lantivet Bay car park.

Eat, shop, stay: Highertown Farm Campsite offers relaxed and unspoilt camping, or you could stay at Old and West House holiday cottages, with their far-reaching views over open countryside and the bay below.

Things to see and do: downloadable walking trails. Play trails alongside valley path. Kite-flying, paddling and bathing. Walking west along the coast path leads to Lantivet and Lantic bays. **Dogs**: welcome, under close control around livestock.

Find out more: 01726 870146 or lansallos@nationaltrust.org.uk

Lantic Bay

near Polruan, Cornwall 1959

Large shingly secluded beach on a beautiful bay, great spot for paddling and picnicking, well worth the climb back up. **Note**: sorry no toilet. Beach is down a very steep path with steps. Beware of rip tides. Nearest postcode for satnav is PL23 1NP.

Find out more: 01726 870146 or lanticbay@nationaltrust.org.uk

Lantivet Bay

between Polruan and Lansallos, Cornwall 1976

Great starting point for walks along this unspoilt sweep of coast, with its small rocky coves. Access to coast path. **Note**: toilets in car park. For satnav use PL23 1NP. National Trust holiday cottages at nearby Triggabrowne Farm, between Lantivet and Lantic bays.

Find out more: 01726 870146 or lantivetbay@nationaltrust.org.uk

Lawrence House

9 Castle Street, Launceston, Cornwall PL15 8BA 1964

This Georgian town house, now a museum, hosts special exhibitions. Large display of costumes and a children's toy room.
Note: leased to Launceston Town Council. Open 30 March to 30 October, Monday to Saturday, 10:30 to 4:30.

Find out more: 01566 773277 or lawrencehouse@nationaltrust.org.uk

Lansallos: abundant wild flowers and birds

Levant Mine and Beam Engine

on the Tin Coast, near Pendeen, St Just, Cornwall TR19 7SX

⊡ ⬚ ⬚ ⬚ ⬚ 1967

Levant Mine and Beam Engine sits high on the cliffs

Parking: 328 yards. Narrow road, please drive slowly and be considerate of our neighbours. Motorhomes and caravans should park at Geevor Tin Mine (½ mile via coastal path).

High on the cliffs of the Tin Coast is Levant, part of the Cornish Mining World Heritage Site. At its heart is an 1840s beam engine, run on steam. You can discover how Cornish miners, engineers and inventors risked everything in pursuit of mineral riches under the sea. **Note**: exposed clifftop location, uneven ground/mine ruins. Limited space in engine house and small staircases.

Eat, shop, stay: light refreshments, hot and cold drinks, pasties and ice cream. Picnic benches. Small shop selling books, minerals, souvenirs and postcards. Nearby Botallack Count House Cottage (sleeps two).

Things to see and do: **Indoors** Restored beam engine steams daily. **Outdoors** Walks to Botallack and Geevor. Free tours of mining landscape, archaeology and tunnel to man-engine shaft. Mineral panning. **Dogs**: welcome on short leads, but not in man-engine tunnel.

Access: ⬚ ⬚ ⬚ ⬚ ⬚ ⬚ **Reception** ⬚
Engine house ⬚ ⬚ **Grounds** ⬚ ⬚

Find out more: 01736 786156 or levant@nationaltrust.org.uk

Levant Mine		M	T	W	T	F	S	S
1 Mar–1 Nov	10:30–5	**M**	**T**	**W**	**T**	**F**	**S**	**S**

Access to man-engine tunnel by guided tour only. Winter opening available for arranged visits.

Lizard Point

on the Lizard peninsula, near Helston, Cornwall

⊡ ⬚ ⬚ ⬚ ⬚ 1935

Satnav: use TR12 7NT. **Parking**: at Lizard Point.

This is mainland Britain's most southerly point, infamous as a site of shipwrecks in the past and overlooking what is still one of the busiest shipping lanes in the world. The cliffs and farmland are incredibly rich in wildlife, and in early summer the wild flowers are at their best. From the Wildlife Watchpoint (below) you can spot seals and occasionally dolphins, as well as the iconic Cornish choughs that breed close by. At Bass Point, a short walk along the coast path, you'll find the tiny Lizard Wireless Station.

Lizard Point: the old lifeboat station, above, and enjoying the great views from Polpeor Café, below

Eat, shop, stay: highly rated Polpeor Café at Lizard Point (concession) open all year – weather-dependent – with outside seating and great views. Gifts on sale at information point (Easter to end October). One holiday cottage at Wireless Station, and more elsewhere on Lizard peninsula.

Things to see and do: take a walk along the coast path for superb coastal views, or try one of the inland routes to search for rare and unique plants. **Dogs**: welcome on leads (please note that livestock graze in some areas).

Access: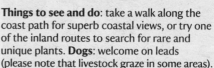

Find out more: 01326 222170 or lizard@nationaltrust.org.uk

Lizard Point			M	T	W	T	F	S	S
Wildlife Watchpoint*									
1 Apr–15 Sep	10–4		M	T	W	T	F	S	S

*Weather permitting.

Lizard Wireless Station

Bass Point, Lizard, near Helston, Cornwall 1996

The oldest surviving wireless station in the world – a tiny hut on the cliffs where Marconi conducted his world-changing experiments. **Note**: best access by foot from Lizard Point car park (TR12 7NT), 1 mile along coast path. Opening hours vary throughout year (please check before setting out).

Find out more: 01326 222170 or lizardwirelessstation@nationaltrust.org.uk

Morwenstow

near Bude, Cornwall 1956

Coastal realm of a great Victorian character – Parson Hawker. Hawker's Hut, driftwood-built, is on the cliff edge near his church.
Note: sorry no toilets. For satnav use EX23 9SR. Rectory Tea-rooms (tenant-run) open seasonally for cream teas and more.

Find out more: 01208 863046 or morwenstow@nationaltrust.org.uk

Mullion Cove

on the Lizard peninsula, near Helston, Cornwall 1945

Originally built in the 1890s, the picturesque harbour at Mullion Cove shelters a small fishing fleet from powerful westerly storms.
Note: toilets open seasonally. Dogs on leads welcome all year. Kayaking available (concession). For satnav use TR12 7ES. Parking 200 yards approximately, not National Trust (charge including members). National Trust campsite nearby at Teneriffe Farm.

Find out more: 01326 222170 or mullioncove@nationaltrust.org.uk

Northcott Mouth

near Bude, Cornwall 1981

Quiet and ruggedly beautiful, this small rocky beach opens up to expansive sand and rock pools as the tide drops. **Note**: sorry no toilets. Dogs welcome, under control. Lifeguards in high season. For satnav use EX23 9ED.

Find out more: 01208 863046 or northcottmouth@nationaltrust.org.uk

Penrose

near Helston and Porthleven, Cornwall

1974

Satnav: use TR13 0RA for Fairground car park and TR13 0RD for Penrose Hill car park.
Parking: several small car parks around Loe Pool, plus Fairground car park in Helston (not National Trust).

Home to Loe Pool (above), Cornwall's largest natural lake, Penrose is a mix of woods, farmland, parkland, cliffs and beaches: a great place to explore. There are 16 miles of bridleways and footpaths, including a trail around the pool and many coast-path links.
Note: to maintain the sense of peace, we don't allow watercraft on the pool. No fishing.

Eat, shop, stay: Stables Café (concession) with parkland views. Picnics welcome in the neighbouring walled garden. There are several holiday cottages around Penrose, some hidden away and others with sea or lake views.

Things to see and do: you can hire a bike at Helston, try the easy-access route from Helston to the café, or choose a downloadable trail to follow. **Dogs**: welcome under control, please note livestock graze in the fields.

Access: Stables Café 🏛 Helston Drive 🏛 ➡

Find out more: 01326 222170 or penroseestate@nationaltrust.org.uk

Penrose		M	T	W	T	F	S	S
Stables Café								
4 Jan–5 Apr	10–4						S	S
6 Apr–25 Oct	10–4	M	T	W	T	F	S	S
1 Nov–27 Dec	10–4						S	S

Pentire

near Wadebridge, Cornwall 1936

Carpeted with wild flowers, the farmed headlands of Pentire and the Rumps command views from Tintagel to Trevose Head. **Note**: for satnav use PL27 6QY for Pentireglaze and Pentire Farm; PL27 6QZ for Lundy Bay. Nearest toilets and shops at Polzeath (not National Trust).

Find out more: 01208 863046 or pentire@nationaltrust.org.uk

Poldhu Cove

near Mullion, Cornwall

[icons] 1984

Satnav: use TR12 7BU. **Parking**: on site, not National Trust (charge including members).

This unspoilt beach is popular with locals and visitors. The beach, dunes and reedbeds are designated as a Site of Special Scientific Interest for their rich wildlife. South of the cove the Marconi Monument and visitor centre celebrate Poldhu's role as the site of the first transatlantic wireless signal. **Note**: lifeguards on duty throughout summer. Car park and toilets not National Trust. Charge for parking (including members).

Two views of unspoilt Poldhu Cove, below and right

Eat, shop, stay: café at Poldhu Beach open all year (not National Trust). Trust campsite close by at Teneriffe Farm, near Mullion. Holiday cottages further away at Bass Point, Penrose and Cadgwith.

Things to see and do: popular surf school (not National Trust) offering lessons for all the family with ex-professional Dan Joel. **Dogs**: welcome on coast path. Council-enforced beach ban from Easter to 1 October.

Access: [P] Marconi Centre [icons]

Find out more: 01326 222170 or poldhucove@nationaltrust.org.uk

Port Quin

near Wadebridge, Cornwall 1936

Sheltered inlet on outstanding stretch of unspoilt coast. Nearby is Pentireglaze Haven and the headlands of Pentire and the Rumps. **Note**: for satnav use PL29 3SU. Nearest toilets in Polzeath, 3 miles (not National Trust). Holiday cottages here include the quirky Doyden Castle.

Find out more: 01208 863046 or portquin@nationaltrust.org.uk

Porth

on the Roseland peninsula,
near Portscatho, Cornwall 1958

The creekside and coastal footpaths are great
for walking and wildlife-spotting, or spend the
day on the beach at Towan. **Note**: for satnav
use TR2 5EX. The Thirstea Company
(concession) serves drinks, cakes, sandwiches
and ice cream. Toilets. Holiday cottages here
and nearby Bohortha.

Find out more: 01872 501062 or
porth@nationaltrust.org.uk

Porthcurno

near Penzance, Cornwall 1994

Popular sandy beach on a turquoise bay. Great
for watching birds and spotting marine wildlife
from the cliffs above. **Note**: for satnav use
TR19 6JU. Café, toilets and parking not
National Trust (charge including members).
Car park very busy in summer. Access to beach
via sandy slope or steep steps.

Find out more: 01736 761853 or
porthcurno@nationaltrust.org.uk

St Agnes Head

near St Agnes, Cornwall 1967

A patchwork of gorse and heather carpets
these clifftops high above the Atlantic Ocean,
overlooked by lofty St Agnes Beacon.
Note: car park height restriction 1.83 metres.
For satnav use TR5 0NU. Coast path walk
to Wheal Coates and café and toilets
at Chapel Porth.

Find out more: 01872 552412 or
stagneshead@nationaltrust.org.uk

St Anthony Head

on the Roseland peninsula,
near Portscatho, Cornwall

1959

St Anthony Head: strategically important for centuries

Satnav: use TR2 5HA. **Parking**: on site.

Standing guard on the eastern entrance to
Falmouth Harbour, this headland has been
strategically important for centuries. It
commands magnificent views up the Fal
Estuary and across Falmouth Bay towards
the Lizard, and you'll find plenty of historic
fortifications from various eras to explore.

Eat, shop, stay: you can stay in the old officers'
quarters (two adapted for disabled visitors),
or at Bohortha and Porth holiday cottages.
Many wonderful picnic spots. Seasonal café
(concession) at Porth.

Things to see and do: St Anthony Battery
tours (certain summer dates). Bird hide for
spotting peregrine falcons. Coast path to Porth
or Place. Molunan Beach. **Dogs**: welcome.

Access: 🚾 Battery and lookouts ♿

Find out more: 01872 501062 or
stanthonyhead@nationaltrust.org.uk

St Michael's Mount

Marazion, Cornwall TR17 0HS

🏚 ✝ 🏵 🎖 1954

Parking: numerous spaces in Marazion, opposite St Michael's Mount, not National Trust (charge including members).

This iconic rocky island, crowned by a medieval church and castle, is home to the St Aubyn family and a 30-strong community of islanders. Visiting the Mount, you are immersed in history, islanders' tales and legends, such as the famous 'Jack the Giant Killer'. There's a subtropical terraced garden to explore, and spectacular views of Mount's Bay and the Lizard from the castle battlements. If the tide is high, you can take an evocative boat trip to the island harbour; at low tide you walk across the ancient cobbled causeway from Marazion on the mainland, as pilgrims have done for centuries. **Note**: steep climb to the castle over uneven, cobbled, historic pathway. St Aubyn Estates/National Trust partnership. Members have to pay for car parking and boat trips to the Mount at high tide.

Eat, shop, stay: Island Café for pasties, sandwiches and ice cream. Sail Loft for Newlyn fish specials, homemade bread, cakes. Both serve local ales, cider, cream teas. Island and Courtyard shops sell emerging contemporary artists' ranges, local produce, jewellery, homewares. None National Trust.

Things to see and do: **Indoors** Children's castle quest. Find out more about the castle's history by asking our knowledgeable room guides. Sunday church services (Whitsun to September). **Outdoors** Storytelling and family activities during school holidays. **Dogs**: assistance dogs only in castle and garden.

Access: ♿🅿♿♿♿♿♿ Castle 🏞 Village 🏞♿

Find out more: 01736 710265 (information, tides and boats) or stmichaelsmount@nationaltrust.org.uk stmichaelsmount.co.uk Estate Office, King's Road, Marazion TR17 0EL

St Michael's Mount		M	T	W	T	F	S	S
Castle								
22 Mar–26 Jun	10:30–5	M	T	W	T	F	·	S
28 Jun–28 Aug	10–5:30	M	T	W	T	F	·	S
30 Aug–30 Oct	10:30–5	M	T	W	T	F	·	S
Garden								
13 Apr–26 Jun	10:30–5	M	T	W	T	F	·	·
2 Jul–28 Aug	10–5:30	·	·	·	T	F	·	·
3 Sep–25 Sep	10:30–5	·	·	·	T	F	·	·

Last admission one hour before castle closes (remember to allow enough time for travel from mainland). Telephone for details of November and December opening arrangements.

Three views of magical St Michael's Mount, which is reached by an ancient cobbled causeway from Marazion

Sandymouth

near Bude, Cornwall

 1978

Satnav: use EX23 9HW. **Parking**: on site.

A popular destination, yet Sandymouth remains unspoilt and breathtakingly beautiful. You'll find an extreme difference between the beach at low tide – when it is a huge sweep of sand and rocky outcrops – and at high tide, when it shrinks back to a pebbly cove, backed by twisted cliffs.

Eat, shop, stay: Sandymouth Café (concession) has outdoor and indoor seating and also sells beach goods. Pubs, shops and cafés in Kilkhampton and Bude (none National Trust).

Things to see and do: surf school. Fantastic rock-pooling and coastal walks. Look out for the waterfall and amazing geological formations backing the beach. Skylarks, song thrushes and stonechats. **Dogs**: welcome everywhere, including the beach, but under close control (especially around livestock).

Access:

Find out more: 01208 863046 or sandymouth@nationaltrust.org.uk

---

Sandymouth

Café at Sandymouth open daily April to October and Wednesday to Sunday during the winter, telephone 01288 354286 for opening times.

Catching a wave at Sandymouth

Tintagel Old Post Office

Fore Street, Tintagel, Cornwall PL34 0DB

1903

Parking: pay and display village car parks, not National Trust (charges including members). Nearest Trust parking at Glebe Cliff in Tintagel, ½ mile.

A medieval manor house in miniature, at more than 600 years old this is one of Cornwall's oldest domestic buildings. Used by a number of businesses throughout the Victorian period, its final function was as the village's letter-receiving office. The cottage garden hidden at the back offers a welcome retreat. **Note**: nearest toilet 54 yards in Trevena Square (not National Trust).

Eat, shop, stay: small souvenir shop in the Post Room selling craft items, gifts and books inspired by the Old Post Office's history and events. Picnics welcome in the cottage garden.

Things to see and do: **Indoors** Events all year, including traditional craft workshops, baking demonstrations and activities to provide entertainment during school holidays. **Outdoors** Family trail, games and dressing up. **Dogs**: assistance dogs only.

Access: Building Grounds

Find out more: 01840 770024 or tintageloldpo@nationaltrust.org.uk

Tintagel Old Post Office		M	T	W	T	F	S	S
15 Feb–23 Feb	11–4	M	T	W	T	F	S	S
14 Mar–27 Mar	11–4	M	T	W	T	F	S	S
28 Mar–27 Sep	10:30–5:30	M	T	W	T	F	S	S
28 Sep–1 Nov	11–4	M	T	W	T	F	S	S

Trelissick

Feock, near Truro, Cornwall TR3 6QL

1955

Parking: 80 yards.

Set on its own peninsula, Trelissick enjoys panoramic views over the Fal Estuary and the house provides the perfect setting to enjoy the ever-changing seascape and countryside. Visitors can explore meandering paths through the garden, leading to exotic planting and formal lawns with herbaceous borders bursting with colour. There are also longer walks to discover through the historic park and woodland, which sweep down towards the estuary, and along Lamouth Creek to the Iron Age promontory fort and 18th-century quay at Roundwood.

Trelissick's unrivalled position on its own peninsula, below, ensures the house, above, has spectacular views

There are many glorious walks to choose from within Trelissick's historic woods and parkland

Eat, shop, stay: Crofters Café and house kitchen open daily. The Barn and Courtyard Room both available for functions and private hire. Large shop with plant and garden centre. Second-hand bookshop. Cornish art and craft gallery. Six holiday cottages on the estate.

Things to see and do: **Indoors** Friendly family house. You're welcome to play the piano and sit in the East Library. House and garden Christmas events. **Outdoors** You can walk and run throughout the estate.
Dogs: welcome in the park and woodland walks. Assistance dogs only in garden.

Access: [icons] Reception [icons]
House [icons] Garden [icons]

Find out more: 01872 862090 or trelissick@nationaltrust.org.uk

Trelissick		M	T	W	T	F	S	S
Garden, café, shop, gallery and bookshop								
Open all year	10–5:30*	M	T	W	T	F	S	S
House								
1 Feb–15 Nov	11–5**	M	T	W	T	F	S	S
Parkland and walks								
Open all year		M	T	W	T	F	S	S

*1 January to 14 February and 2 November to 31 December: closes 4:30. Garden closes dusk if earlier. **1 to 14 February and 2 to 15 November: closes 4. Late-night openings and Christmas events in December. Everything closed 25 and 26 December.

Trengwainton Garden

Madron, near Penzance, Cornwall TR20 8RZ

⊕ ⊠ 1961

Parking: 150 yards.

Here in this sheltered garden you can follow in the footsteps of the 1920s plant hunters to see colourful species that were the first of their kind to flower in Britain. Award-winning magnolias and rhododendrons are still nurtured by those with a passion for plants, and subtropical varieties from around the world thrive in the shelter of the walled gardens, which contain a kitchen garden built to the dimensions of Noah's Ark. Winding wooded paths follow a half-mile incline offering sea views across Mount's Bay, and the descent via the drive is bordered by a stream garden and open meadows.

Eat, shop, stay: award-winning tea-room (tenant-run) with indoor and outdoor seating. Shop sells local gifts, food, souvenirs and Trengwainton-inspired plants. Second-hand bookshop and gallery in the former head gardener's cottage. Nearby, you can stay in an 18th-century former laundry house (sleeping nine).

Things to see and do: new this year, woodland wildlife area and bird hide. Seasonal family holiday activities all year, plus Christmas celebrations. 1940s garden plot with replica Anderson shelter and medicinal plant border. **Dogs**: welcome on leads in garden, shop, tea-room garden. Water, free biscuits and poo-bags available.

Access: 🅿️🐕♿🚻🎫🚪♿ Reception ♿♿
Tea-room ♿ **Garden** ♿➡️♿♿

Find out more: 01736 363148 or trengwainton@nationaltrust.org.uk

Trengwainton Garden		M	T	W	T	F	S	S
16 Feb–1 Nov	10:30–5	**M**	**T**	**W**	**T**		·	**S**

Open Good Friday. Tea-room opens at 10.

Trengwainton Garden is famed for its 100-year-old magnolia, above, and the sloping beds in its kitchen garden, below

Trerice

near Newquay, Cornwall

🏠 ✿ 🛏 🔔 ⊤ 1953

Satnav: enter Kestle Mill via A3058, not postcode. **Parking**: 300 yards. Electric vehicle charging point available.

Once the Cornish seat of the Arundell family, Trerice remains little changed since it was built in 1573, thanks to long periods under absentee owners. With golden stone, ornate gables and a magnificent hall window, Trerice is a grand Elizabethan house on a small scale. From the highest point of the garden, views stretch out over a landscape rich in history. Shouts of excitement ring out from the kayling lawn as the Cornish game of 'kayles' is played, bringing back some of the bustle and noise that must have typified Trerice's time as a working manor farm. **Note**: we occasionally need to close parts or all of Trerice for private functions.

Eat, shop, stay: barn restaurant serving light lunches, Cornish cream teas and hot and cold drinks. Shop selling local gifts, souvenirs, books and plants. Second-hand bookshop – books sold for a donation. The west wing of the house contains a holiday apartment (sleeping two).

With ornate gables and magnificent hall window, below, Trerice is a grand house on a small scale; 'kayles', above

Things to see and do: Indoors 16th-century plaster ceilings, introductory volunteer talks, brass rubbings and Tudor costume days on selected dates. **Outdoors** Family activities, traditional games, potager and knot garden. **Dogs**: welcome in car park. Assistance dogs only in house and garden.

Access: 🅿️🚻🏠♿🍴🐾 House ♿🚹♿ Barn ♿♿ Garden ♿♿➡️♿

Find out more: 01637 875404 or trerice@nationaltrust.org.uk
Kestle Mill, near Newquay, Cornwall TR8 4PG

Trerice		M	T	W	T	F	S	S
29 Feb–1 Nov	10:30–5*	**M**	**T**	**W**	**T**	**F**	**S**	**S**
7 Nov–6 Dec**	11–4	·	·	·	·	·	**S**	**S**
12 Dec–23 Dec**	11–4	**M**	**T**	**W**	**T**	**F**	**S**	**S**

*House opens 11. **Selected rooms, garden, shop and restaurant open.

Entry is still possible at most places up to 30 minutes before closing

Trevose Head

near Padstow, Cornwall

🏛 2016

Satnav: use PL28 8SL. **Parking**: on site. Open all year at scenic car park; summer car park for beaches open May to September.

Jutting into the Atlantic, Trevose Head commands views for miles along the coast. Exposed western cliffs contrast starkly with a gentler eastern coastline. Home of Trevose Lighthouse (owned by Trinity House) and Padstow Lifeboat Station, it's also famed for nesting corn buntings and skylarks, and rare plants like wild asparagus. **Note**: sorry no toilets. Be careful of the sheer-sided round hole and quarry near Dinas Head.

Eat, shop, stay: seasonal refreshments (concession). Convenience store and pub/café in St Merryn and Harlyn, 1 to 2 miles (none National Trust). Picnics welcome.

Wild on one side, below, and gentler on the other, above, Trevose Head juts out into the Atlantic Ocean

Things to see and do: coastal walks with chances to watch wildlife. Access to Booby's Bay Beach. Carnewas at Bedruthan, a few miles along the coast, is another spectacular spot. **Dogs**: welcome under control. Please be aware of ground-nesting birds and keep to signed footpaths.

Find out more: 01208 863046 or trevosehead@nationaltrust.org.uk

Wheal Coates

near St Agnes, Cornwall 1956

Dramatic mining ruins – an iconic Cornish sight – hugging the heather and gorse-carpeted clifftops. **Note**: for satnav use TR5 0NT. Follow the coast path for a steep, but lovely, walk down to Chapel Porth for beach, café and toilets.

Find out more: 01872 552412 or whealcoates@nationaltrust.org.uk

Additional coastal and countryside car parks in Cornwall

Strangles Beach	EX23 0LQ	Derrick Cove	TR14 0JG	Poltesco	TR12 7LR
Glebe Cliff, Tintagel	PL34 0DL	Fishing Cove	TR27 5EE	Nare Head	TR2 5PQ
Lundy Bay	PL27 6QZ	Trencrom	TR27 6NP	Lamledra (Vault Beach)	PL26 6JS
Park Head	PL27 7UU	Carn Galver	TR20 8YX	Coombe Farm	PL23 1HW
Treago Mill (Polly Joke)	TR8 5QS	Cot Valley	TR19 7NS	Hendersick	PL13 2HZ
St Agnes Beacon	TR5 0NU	Chyvarloe	TR12 7PY		
Reskajeage Downs	TR14 0JG	Predannack	TR12 7EZ		

'Being able to get out for a walk, some fresh air, a drink, some lunch; being able to get together for a moment or a whole day at the beach — looking back at all those times, it just would not have been the same without these special places.'

21-year-old Emily Martin loves spending time at National Trust places – so much so, she has recently fundraised for us, by taking on a marathon and two half-marathons

Devon and Dorset

Heathland near Heddon Valley. The North Devon coast is one of Emily's favourite places

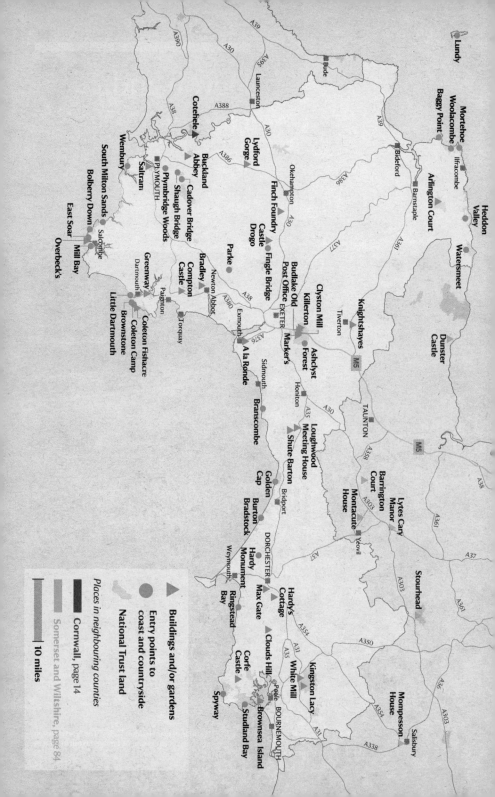

Lundy

Mortehoe
Woolacombe
Baggy Point

Ilfracombe

Heddon
Valley

Watersmeet

Arlington Court

Barnstaple

Bude

Bideford

Launceston

Cotehele

A388

A390

A30

A39

A3072

A39

A361

A386

A377

Dunster
Castle

M5

Knightshayes

Tiverton

Buckland
Abbey

Lydford
Gorge

Okehampton

Castle
Drogo

Finch Foundry

Cadover Bridge

Shaugh Bridge

Plymbridge Woods

PLYMOUTH

Saltram

Wembury

Bolberry Down

South Milton Sands

East Soar

Overbeck's

Mill Bay

Salcombe

Bradley

Compton
Castle

Greenway

Dartmouth

Paignton

Little Dartmouth

Brownstone

Coleton Camp

Coleton Fishacre

Torquay

Newton Abbot

Parke

Fingle Bridge

A386

A30

A382

A38

A380

A376

Exmouth

EXETER

Budlake Old
Post Office

Clyston Mill
Killerton

Marker's

Ashclyst
Forest

A la Ronde

Sidmouth

Branscombe

Honiton

A35

A30

Loughwood
Meeting House

Shute Barton

Golden
Cap

Burton
Bradstock

Bridport

TAUNTON

A358

M5

Barrington
Court

Montacute
House

Lytes Cary
Manor

Yeovil

A303

A37

A361

A38

Weymouth

DORCHESTER

Hardy
Monument

Max Gate

Hardy's
Cottage

Clouds Hill

Corfe
Castle

White Mill

Kingston Lacy

BOURNEMOUTH

Poole

Brownsea Island

Studland Bay

Spyway

Ringstead
Bay

A354

A31

A35

A350

A354

A338

A31

Mompesson
House

Salisbury

Stourhead

A303

A36

A37

A361

Places in neighbouring counties

Cornwall, page 14

Somerset and Wiltshire, page 84

▲ Buildings and/or gardens

● Entry points to
coast and countryside

National Trust land

10 miles

A la Ronde, Devon: eccentric and captivating inside and out

A la Ronde

Exmouth, Devon

🏠♿ 1991

Satnav: postcode unreliable, enter Summer Lane. **Parking**: on site.

Full of creativity and treasures from around the world, this amazing 16-sided house was the work of cousins Jane and Mary Parminter in the 1790s. Step inside and enter another world, one where their imaginations ran wild in design and ornamentation. They decorated walls with feathers, shells and pictures made of seaweed and sand, and every space contains mementoes from their travels. With the 360° touchscreen virtual tour, you can view the fragile shell gallery made with 25,000 shells. Outside, there's a sense of harmony around the orchard, hay meadow and colourful borders, and views over the Exe Estuary. **Note**: small and delicate rooms. Photography welcome without flash.

Eat, shop, stay: licensed café serving barista coffee, homemade scones, light lunches and seasonal specials. Indoor and outdoor seating with views of the Exe Estuary. Picnic areas. A range of high-quality and local products in the stables shop. Pre-loved book sales.

Things to see and do: Indoors Eclectic, artistic collection. Play the piano. **Outdoors** Family trail and activities. Short walk around hay meadow and orchard, with seating and views. Estate tours. Garden games, croquet and trails. **Dogs**: dogs on leads welcome everywhere (excluding house).

Access: 🅿️📶🚻📷🎦💻🛗🚫
House ♿♿🚻 **Grounds** ♿➡️

Find out more: 01395 265514 or alaronde@nationaltrust.org.uk
Summer Lane, Exmouth, Devon EX8 5BD

A la Ronde		M	T	W	T	F	S	S
1 Feb–8 Nov	10:30–5:30*	M	T	W	T	F	S	S
14 Nov–20 Dec	10:30–4:30**						S	S
27 Dec–31 Dec	10:30–4:30**M	T	W	T			S

*House: open 11 to 5 (last entry 4); **11 to 4 (last entry 3).

Arlington Court and the National Trust Carriage Museum

Arlington, near Barnstaple, Devon EX31 4LP

🏠✝🔥❄♿♿🛏 1949

Satnav: from South Molton, don't turn left into unmarked lane (deliveries only).
Parking: 150 yards.

Hidden in the lichen-draped landscape of North Devon, Arlington is a surprise and a delight. The starkly classical exterior of the house gives no clue to what lies inside – recently redisplayed to share the passions of the Chichester family who lived here. The stable block houses a nationally important display of more than 40 carriages, from grand state coaches to humble governess cars. The garden is restored to its colourful Victorian glory, and the conservatory's exotic plantings reveal the Chichesters' world travels.

Eat, shop, stay: Old Kitchen tea-room serving light lunches and Devonshire cream teas (reduced menu in winter). Two dog-friendly holiday cottages on edges of estate, sleeping two or three.

Things to see and do: Indoors Bat-cam for watching rare bats. Rooms in the cellar tell the servants' stories. Children's activities.
Outdoors Two woodland play areas. Bring your walking boots for exploring the large estate.
Dogs: welcome on leads in garden, Carriage Museum and wider estate.

Access: 🅿♿♿♿♿♿📷📹🖼♿👁🖌
House 🅿♿♿ Museum ♿🔼♿ Grounds ➡♿♿

Find out more: 01271 850296 or arlingtoncourt@nationaltrust.org.uk

Arlington Court		M	T	W	T	F	S	S
15 Feb–1 Nov	11–5*	M	T	W	T	F	S	S
6 Nov–20 Dec	11–4*	.	.	.	.	F	S	S
26 Dec–31 Dec†	11–4	M	T	W	T	.	S	S

*Garden, shop and tea-room open 10:30. Wider estate open all year, dawn to dusk. †House open by guided tour only; Carriage Museum closed.

Arlington Court and the National Trust Carriage Museum, Devon: opulent interiors contrast with the stark exterior

Baggy Point

near Croyde, Devon

⌂ 🏖 🎣 🐾 1939

Satnav: use EX33 1PA. **Parking**: in Moor Lane. Electric vehicle charging points available.

Baggy Point is the impressive headland at Croyde, once owned by the Hyde family and overlooking one of the best surfing beaches (above) in the South West. Huge coastal views out to Lundy Island, great walking and opportunities to climb, surf and coasteer make it a must-do destination for anyone visiting North Devon. Baggy Point also appeals to wildlife and nature lovers – keep a look out for seals and porpoises, as well as many bird species, including peregrine falcons, linnets and Dartford warblers. **Note**: toilets and outdoor shower in courtyard next to car park.

Eat, shop, stay: Sandleigh Tea-room, beside car park and near beach, serving drinks and meals (open-air and indoor seating overlooking garden). Car park kiosk offering drinks and snacks. You can stay at The Slipway holiday cottage, close to the beach with sea views.

Things to see and do: free family activity pack to borrow (or download). Walks leaflets in car park kiosk. Easy-access route to the Point. Woolacombe, Mortehoe and Arlington Court nearby. **Dogs**: welcome on leads (except for seasonal ban on Croyde Beach, May to September).

Access: 🅿️ 🏛 ➡️

Find out more: 01271 870555 or baggypoint@nationaltrust.org.uk

Baggy Point		M	T	W	T	F	S	S
Sandleigh Tea-room								
14 Feb–31 Oct	10–4*	M	T	W	T	F	S	S
1 Nov–27 Dec**	10–4	·	·	·	·	·	S	S

*1 April to 30 September: closes at 5.
**Also open 28 to 31 December.

Bolberry Down

between Salcombe and Hope Cove, near Malborough, Devon

🏖 🎣 1938

Satnav: use TQ7 3DY. **Parking**: at Bolberry Down or Hope Cove (not National Trust).

The starting point for a spectacular stretch of coast between Salcombe and Hope Cove, including the headlands of Bolt Head and Bolt Tail and the sandy beach at Soar Mill Cove. The majestic rugged cliffs have claimed countless ships over the centuries. There's an easy-access clifftop route (below).

Eat, shop, stay: Oceans Restaurant (not National Trust) serves refreshments and meals. Walkers' Hut café at East Soar Outdoor Experience (tenant-run) serves refreshments. Also at East Soar: catered camping and holiday cottage (tenant-run).

Things to see and do: level circular trail (just under a mile), accessible for most wheelchair users and pushchairs. **Dogs**: welcome (on leads where animals grazing).

Access: 🅿️ 🎵 🏛 ➡️

Find out more: 01752 346585 or bolberrydown@nationaltrust.org.uk

Bradley

Newton Abbot, Devon

🏠✝♿ 1938

Satnav: TQ12 1LX directs to gate lodge.
Parking: blue badge parking only on site
(please call 07745 236836). Car parks in town
centre not National Trust (charge including
members). Nearest public car park at
Wolborough Street (TQ12 1JW).

Surrounded by riverside meadows and
woodland, this unspoilt medieval manor house
(below) is still a relaxed family home. There are
original features to look out for, such as the
medieval cat hole and drip stones, as well as
the peaceful chapel that was licensed for
services in 1428. **Note**: sorry no toilet, and
card payments not accepted.

Eat, shop, stay: table-top shop selling
honey, souvenirs, gifts and postcards.
Picnics welcome in the meadows
surrounding the house and garden.

Things to see and do: free children's trail.
Open-air theatre performances in the garden.
Walks in Bradley meadow and woodland.
Dogs: welcome in meadows and woodland.
Assistance dogs only in garden and house.

Access: 🅿♿📷🎡👓📷 Building 🔦♿🚻
Grounds 🔦♿➡

Find out more: 01803 661907 or
bradley@nationaltrust.org.uk
Totnes Road, Newton Abbot, Devon TQ12 6BN

Bradley		M	T	W	T	F	S	S
1 Apr–29 Oct	11–5*	·	T	W	T	·	·	·

*27, 28 and 29 October: closes at 4.

Branscombe

on the Jurassic Coast, near Seaton, Devon

🏰🍴🏭🛏 1965

Satnav: use EX12 3DB. **Parking**: next to
Old Forge, limited spaces. Also village hall
and beach car parks (neither National Trust).

Nestling in a valley that reaches down to the sea
on East Devon's dramatic Jurassic Coast (above),
the village of Branscombe is surrounded by
picturesque countryside with miles of tranquil
walking through woodland, farmland and
beach. Charming thatched houses, forge
and restored watermill add to the timeless
magic of the place. **Note**: nearest toilets
(not National Trust) at information point,
village hall and beach car park.

Eat, shop, stay: Old Bakery tea-room serving
sandwiches, cakes and cream teas; Old Forge
selling quality ironwork (both tenant-run).
Forge Cottage holiday let in an ideal location
for exploring the village and coast.

Things to see and do: easy trail from beach
to village, passing Manor Mill, Old Bakery and
Old Forge. The beach is great for swimming
and picnics. **Dogs**: welcome on leads in the
Old Bakery garden, orchard, beach and
wider countryside.

Access: ♿ Tea-room ♿🚻 Mill ♿🚻 Grounds ♿

Find out more: 01752 346585 or
branscombe@nationaltrust.org.uk

Branscombe		M	T	W	T	F	S	S
Manor Mill								
29 Mar–27 Sep*	1–4	·	·	·	·	·	·	S
25 Oct–1 Nov	1–4	·	·	·	·	·	·	S
Old Forge								
Open all year	10–5**	M	T	W	T	F	S	S

*29 July to 26 August: also open Wednesdays. Last admission
to mill 3:45. **For forge opening times, call 01297 680481.
For Old Bakery tea-room openings, call 01297 680333.

Brownsea Island

Poole Harbour, Poole, Dorset

✝ 🏚 ♿ ⚓ ⛴ ⛺ 1962

Satnav: for Sandbanks Jetty use BH13 7QJ; for Poole Quay BH15 1HP. **Parking**: car parks near Sandbanks and Poole Quay, not National Trust (charge including members).

The perfect day's adventure, this island wildlife sanctuary is easy to get to but feels like a million miles away as soon as you step ashore. Wander through rich and varied habitats and spot wildlife, such as the rare red squirrel, or cosy up in a hide overlooking the lagoon to watch birds fly in from distant lands. The island has a surprising history too; as the birthplace of the Scouting movement you can experience your very own adventure and spend a night under the stars at the Outdoor Centre campsite. **Note**: half-hourly ferry service (not National Trust) from Poole and Sandbanks. *Seahorse* wheelchair ferry service available. Voluntary donation to enter the Dorset Wildlife Trust area (including members). No visitor or member access to castle.

Eat, shop, stay: Villano Café with harbour views and homemade food. Engine Gift Shop selling National Trust gifts and local products. Scout and Guide Trading Post sells memorabilia. Two quayside holiday cottages as well as the Outdoor Centre campsite and bunkhouse.

The wildlife sanctuary of Brownsea Island, Dorset, above and below, provides rich and varied habitats

The wheelchair ferry to Brownsea Island

Things to see and do: visitor centre and free family trails. Open-air theatre, early morning guided walks and bird boats. Campsite and bunkhouse. Relaxing picnic spots and fun natural play area. **Dogs**: assistance dogs only.

Access: 🏠🦽🧎🗺️♿🅿️ **Reception** ♿🦽
Visitor centre ♿🦽 **Grounds** ♿➡️♿

Find out more: 01202 707744 or brownseaisland@nationaltrust.org.uk

Brownsea Island		M	T	W	T	F	S	S
1 Feb–8 Mar	10–4*						S	S
17 Feb–21 Feb	10–4*	M	T	W	T	F		
14 Mar–1 Nov	10–5**	M	T	W	T	F	S	S
2 Nov–15 Nov	10–4*	M	T	W	T	F	S	S

*Hourly ferry service from Poole Quay and Sandbanks Jetty (last ferry at 4). **Half-hourly ferry service from Poole Quay and Sandbanks Jetty (last ferry at 5).

Brownstone

Brownstone Road, Kingswear, Devon TQ6 0EH 1981

Spectacular views on a coastal walk that leads to a rare Second World War gun battery at Froward Point. **Note**: naturally uneven coastal paths, steep in places – be aware of cliff edges and keep children and dogs supervised.

Find out more: 01803 752776 (rangers) or brownstone@nationaltrust.org.uk

Buckland Abbey

Yelverton, Devon

🏠✝️❀🦽🍴🍽️ 1948

Centuries-old Buckland Abbey in Devon, right, with its impressive Great Barn, above, lies in a tranquil valley

Satnav: follow brown signs, not satnav.
Parking: 150 yards.

Hundreds of years ago, Cistercian monks chose this tranquil valley as the perfect spot in which to worship, farm their estate and trade. The Abbey, later converted into a house, today combines furnished rooms with museum galleries, bringing to life the story of how seafaring adventurers Sir Richard Grenville and Sir Francis Drake changed the shape of Buckland Abbey and the fate of England. Outdoors you'll find the walled kitchen garden, Cider House garden and wild garden; the impressive medieval Great Barn; community growing areas; orchards and woodland walks with far-reaching views and late spring bluebells.

Eat, shop, stay: Ox Yard Restaurant serves freshly cooked local produce, often using ingredients grown in the kitchen garden. Picnics welcome in garden and grounds. Shop selling gifts and plants. Galleries and second-hand bookshop. Holiday cottage.

Things to see and do: **Indoors** Look for traces of the medieval Abbey and its Elizabethan conversion. **Outdoors** Higher Paddock natural play area and zip wire for younger visitors. Year-round events, estate walks and trails. **Dogs**: welcome on leads in farmland and on woodland walks. Assistance dogs only in garden.

Access: 🅿️🏢♿🛗🚹🚻♿ Abbey ♿🏢♿
Visitor Welcome ♿🏢♿ **Grounds** ♿🏢➡️♿♿

Find out more: 01822 853607 or bucklandabbey@nationaltrust.org.uk
Yelverton, Devon PL20 6EY

Buckland Abbey		M	T	W	T	F	S	S
11 Jan–9 Feb*	11–4	·	·	·	·	·	S	S
15 Feb–31 Dec	10–5**	M	T	W	T	F	S	S

*Garden, estate, restaurant and shop open; Abbey closed. **Abbey opens 11. From 25 October, everything closes at 4. Everything closed 25 and 26 December. Open 1 and 2 January 2021.

Burton Bradstock

on the Jurassic Coast, near Bridport, Dorset

🏖️🚗 1973

Satnav: use DT6 4RF for Burton Bradstock; DT6 4RL for Cogden. **Parking**: on site.

One of the main gateways to Dorset's Jurassic Coast. Here are spectacular sandstone cliffs (above) – Burton Cliff glows bright gold in sunlight – and miles of unspoilt beaches. Hive Beach is a popular family destination, nearby Cogden is quieter; both are part of Chesil Bank, the largest shingle ridge in the world.

Eat, shop, stay: tenant-run Hive Beach Café on Chesil Bank serving local seafood.

Things to see and do: paddling, swimming and outdoor activities. Circular and clifftop walks. **Dogs**: welcome. Dog-free zone on Hive Beach (1 June to 30 September).

Access: 🅿️

Find out more: 01297 489481 or burtonbradstock@nationaltrust.org.uk

Cadover Bridge

on Dartmoor, near Shaugh Prior, Devon 1960

Tranquil moorland by River Plym, with pools. Starting point for walks through ancient woodland or across open moors and tors. **Note**: for satnav use PL7 5EH.

Find out more: 01626 834748 or cadoverbridge@nationaltrust.org.uk

Castle Drogo

Drewsteignton, near Exeter, Devon EX6 6PB

🏠🏚✝♣♠ 1974

Parking: 400 yards from visitor centre.

High above the ancient woodlands of the Teign Gorge on the edge of Dartmoor stands Castle Drogo. Reminiscent of a medieval fortress, the castle was designed and built between 1910 and 1930 by the renowned architect Sir Edwin Lutyens for the self-made millionaire Julius Drewe. Inside the imposing granite walls, the ingenuity of Lutyens's design is revealed in grand show rooms, functional servants' spaces and comfortable family rooms, perfectly suited to the lifestyle of a modern 20th-century family. Outside, hidden behind immaculate yew hedges, the garden is a perfect partnership of colourful seasonal planting with Lutyens's formal architectural design. **Note**: major building restoration project almost completed. Access may change due to reinstatement.

Imposing Castle Drogo in Devon, below, and exploring one of the walks into the Teign Gorge, above

Eat, shop, stay: popular licensed café (outside seating) serving coffee, lunch, homemade cakes and scones for afternoon tea. Picnics welcome in orchard. Shop stocking a wide range of plants, books, cards and gifts. Holiday cottage nearby at Chagford.

Striking decorative tiles at Castle Drogo

Things to see and do: Indoors Programme of guided tours and family trails. **Outdoors** Garden with 273 yards of herbaceous borders. Games on lawn. Walks into the Teign Gorge, views across Dartmoor and riverside paths. **Dogs:** welcome on leads in grounds and wider estate. Assistance dogs only in formal garden.

Access: 🅿️♿♿♿♿♿♿📷📹♿🚷 Castle ♿♿♿ Grounds ♿♿♿➡️♿♿

Find out more: 01647 433306 or castledrogo@nationaltrust.org.uk

Castle Drogo		M	T	W	T	F	S	S
Castle								
16 Mar–1 Nov	11–5	M	T	W	T	F	S	S
28 Nov–23 Dec	11–4	M	T	W	T	F	S	S
Garden, visitor centre, café and shop								
1 Jan–15 Mar*	11–4	M	T	W	T	F	S	S
16 Mar–1 Nov	9:30–5**	M	T	W	T	F	S	S
2 Nov–31 Dec†	11–4	M	T	W	T	F	S	S
Estate								
Open all year	Dawn–dusk	M	T	W	T	F	S	S

*Closed 20 to 24 January. **Garden opens at 10; visitor centre toilets and garden close 5:30. †Closed 24 to 26 December.

Clouds Hill

Bovington, Dorset BH20 7NQ

🏠 1937

Parking: on site.

In this tiny woodsman's cottage you can discover the essentials and the luxuries chosen by T. E. Lawrence after he had abandoned the 'Lawrence of Arabia' persona and remodelled himself as a private in the army at Bovington Camp. Much of the furniture and fittings was designed by Lawrence himself.

Eat, shop, stay: self-service tea and coffee available. Small shop selling gifts, books and Lawrence memorabilia.

Things to see and do: you can visit the nearby homes of Thomas Hardy – Max Gate and Hardy's Cottage – along the very roads on which Lawrence himself rode.
Dogs: welcome on leads in grounds only.

Access: 📷 Building ♿🚻 Grounds ♿

Find out more: 01929 405616 or cloudshill@nationaltrust.org.uk

Clouds Hill		M	T	W	T	F	S	S
1 Mar–31 Oct*	11–5**	M	T	W	T	F	S	S

*Closed 3 March. **No electric light, so last admission at dusk if earlier.

Atmospheric Clouds Hill in Dorset

Coleton Camp

between Dart Estuary and Brixham,
Devon 1981

Great walks along the coast path to
Scabbacombe and Man Sands beaches on this
rugged stretch of coast. **Note**: naturally uneven
coastal paths, steep in places – be aware of cliff
edges and keep children and dogs supervised.
For satnav use TQ6 0EQ.

Find out more: 01803 753010 or
coletoncamp@nationaltrust.org.uk

Coleton Fishacre

Brownstone Road, Kingswear, Devon TQ6 0EQ

🏠🏵♿🚗👨‍👩‍👧🍴 1982

Parking: 20 yards from reception;
overflow parking 150 yards.

Art deco at Coleton Fishacre, Devon, above and left

This evocative 1920s Arts and Crafts-style
house, with its elegant art deco interiors,
perfectly encapsulates the spirit of the Jazz
Age. The former country home of the D'Oyly
Carte family, it has a light, joyful atmosphere
with touches of a bygone era. You can glimpse
life 'downstairs' in the servants' rooms. In the
RHS-accredited garden, paths weave through
glades and past tranquil ponds and rare tender
plants from New Zealand and South Africa;
many exotic plants thrive beneath the tree
canopy. You can walk down through the
valley garden to a coastal viewpoint with
inspiring sea views.

Eat, shop, stay: Café Coleton, with
dog-friendly covered outdoor seating,
serving light bites, lunches, cakes and bakes.
Shop selling souvenir guides, gifts, food, music
and plants. Why not stay in Chauffeur's Flat,
Coleton Barton Cottages or nearby Higher
Brownstone Farmhouse?

Things to see and do: family trails in the house
and garden. Daily guided garden walks from
Easter to October, led by a member of the
garden team. Events, including open-air
theatre. Wild play area. **Dogs**: welcome on
short leads in garden and Café Coleton.
Tethering rings by house.

Access: 🅿️🐕♿🚾🦽🔄📷📹📱♿
Building 🦽♿♿ Café Coleton ♿ Grounds ♿➡️♿

Find out more: 01803 842382 or
coletonfishacre@nationaltrust.org.uk

Coleton Fishacre		M	T	W	T	F	S	S
15 Feb–1 Nov	10:30–5	M	T	W	T	F	S	S
7 Nov–20 Dec	11–4	.	.	.	.	.	S	S
21 Dec–31 Dec	11–4	M	T	W	T	.	.	S

Compton Castle

Marldon, Paignton, Devon TQ3 1TA

 1951

 *(castle entrance photo)*

Parking: in Castle Barton's car park for cars and campervans, opposite entrance, 100 yards. Overflow parking on grass verges at castle entrance.

A rare survivor, this medieval fortified manor house has high curtain walls and portcullises. It was once the home of Sir Humphrey Gilbert, part-founder of the New World, and his descendants still live here today. Outside, you can discover roses climbing pergolas, knot and herb gardens and a picnic orchard. **Note**: hall, sub-solar, solar, study, kitchen, scullery, guard room, chapel open. Sorry, credit cards not accepted.

Eat, shop, stay: table-top shop selling guidebooks and gifts. Pop-up outdoors shop (summer holidays). Picnics welcome in lower orchard. Stay a little longer in the Watchtower. Castle Barton restaurant (not National Trust).

Things to see and do: family activities, including indoor and outdoor trails for children, medieval dressing up and garden games. You can join a 1½-mile circular walk opposite the castle. **Dogs**: welcome in the lower orchard on leads. Assistance dogs only in castle and garden.

Access: ⬚⬚⬚⬚ Building ⬚⬚ Grounds ⬚⬚

Find out more: 01803 661906 or comptoncastle@nationaltrust.org.uk

Compton Castle		M	T	W	T	F	S	S
1 Apr–29 Oct	10:30–4:30	·	**T**	**W**	**T**	·	·	·
Open Bank Holiday Mondays.								

Corfe Castle

near Wareham, Dorset

⬚⬚⬚⬚ 1982

Satnav: use BH20 5DR.
Parking: 800 yards uphill walk. Norden car park (½ mile) and West Street in village, neither National Trust (charge including members).

This fairy-tale fortress is an evocative survivor of the English Civil War, partially demolished by the Parliamentarians in 1646. It's a favourite haunt for adults and children alike – all ages are captivated by these romantic ruins with their breathtaking views. There are 1,000 years of the castle's history as a royal palace and fortress to be discovered here. Fallen walls and secret places tell tales of treachery and treason around every corner. Corfe Castle's brooding presence is a backdrop to some of Britain's most beautiful coast and countryside. Corfe Common and Hartland Moor are close by – you can explore them by walking or cycling, discovering rare wild flowers and masses of wildlife along the way. **Note**: steep, uneven slopes; steps; sudden drops throughout castle. All/parts of castle close in high winds.

Corfe Castle, Dorset: the ruins sit high on a steep hill, offering unbroken views for miles in every direction

Eat, shop, stay: 18th-century village tea-room and garden serving cream teas with a view of the castle. Locally made gifts available in the shop in the village square. Three National Trust holiday cottages in the village, and more in the wider Purbeck landscape.

Things to see and do: an action-packed programme of fun family history events runs from April until September, with something most weekends and school holidays. Highlights include Saxon and Viking re-enactments, wildlife events, open-air theatre and winter lights. Throughout the year, discover more about the castle's trebuchet and rich history. There's a children's activity trail and activities which run all year. Beyond the castle walls, you can explore a wildlife-rich landscape of hills and heathland on walks through Purbeck. **Dogs**: welcome on short leads.

East Soar

between Salcombe and Hope Cove, near Malborough, Devon

[icons] 1950

The coast path between East Soar and Salcombe, Devon

Satnav: use TQ7 3DR.
Parking: at East Soar car park.

This is a great starting point for exploring the isolated and rugged coast between Bolt Head and Bolt Tail. There's so much history to discover, including the remains of Bronze Age settlements, shipwrecks and 'orthostats' (ancient field boundary stones). There is a waymarked 1-mile route to Overbeck's, overlooking Salcombe.

Eat, shop, stay: quirky Walkers' Hut café (tenant-run) at East Soar Outdoor Experience, for hot drinks and cakes. Nearby Overbeck's offers crab sandwiches and cream teas. Catered camping and holiday cottage (also tenant-run).

Things to see and do: excellent for spotting wildlife – look out for cirl buntings, silver-studded blue butterflies and large flocks of swallows and house martins gathering for their autumn migration.

Access: [icon]

Find out more: 01752 346585. 01548 561904 (East Soar Outdoor Experience) or eastsoar@nationaltrust.org.uk

Within the ruins of the fairy-tale fortress of Corfe Castle, above, secret places tell tales of treachery and treason, making this a favourite haunt for adults and children alike, left

Access: [icons] Grounds [icon]

Find out more: 01929 477063 (ticket office). 01929 480921 (shop). 01929 481332 (tea-room) or corfecastle@nationaltrust.org.uk
Corfe, near Wareham, Dorset BH20 5EZ

Corfe Castle		M	T	W	T	F	S	S
1 Jan–14 Feb	10–4	M	T	W	T	F	S	S
15 Feb–3 Apr	10–5	M	T	W	T	F	S	S
4 Apr–6 Sep	10–6*	M	T	W	T	F	S	S
7 Sep–1 Nov	10–5	M	T	W	T	F	S	S
2 Nov–31 Dec	10–4	M	T	W	T	F	S	S

Castle, shop and tea-room: closed 5 March and 25 to 26 December. *Shop and tea-room: close 5:30.

Finch Foundry

Sticklepath, Okehampton, Devon EX20 2NW

[icons] 1994

Parking: on site (height/width restrictions).

The foundry was a 19th-century family-run business producing a range of tools for West Country industries, including farming and mining. The huge waterwheels and tilt hammer spring into action during regular demonstrations (above). Products of the business are displayed in the carpenters' workshop. Outside is a delightful cottage garden. **Note**: narrow entrance to car park, plus height restrictions.

Eat, shop, stay: cosy tea-room, with tables in the garden, offering cream teas, cakes, sandwiches, snacks, ice cream, hot and cold drinks. Shop selling accessories, plants, books, local food and drink.

Things to see and do: **Indoors** Talks and demonstrations on machinery and blacksmithing. St Clement's Day (patron saint of blacksmithing) in November. **Outdoors** Moorland walks starting point. Tom Pearse's summerhouse. **Dogs**: welcome in all areas (excluding tea-room).

Access: [icons] Foundry [icons] Grounds [icon]

Find out more: 01837 840046 or finchfoundry@nationaltrust.org.uk

Finch Foundry		M	T	W	T	F	S	S
15 Feb–23 Feb	11–3	M	T	W	T	F	S	S
7 Mar–1 Nov	11–5	M	T	W	T	F	S	S
7 Nov–20 Dec	11–3						S	S

Demonstrations of the working machinery throughout day. Conservation maintenance one day a month when the machinery may not be fully operational.

Fingle Bridge

near Drewsteignton, Devon 1990

Popular spot in Dartmoor's Teign Gorge. Walkers can explore the footpaths in nearby Fingle Woods, or climb towards Castle Drogo. **Note**: for satnav use EX6 6PW. Uneven terrain. Fingle Woods are being restored and managed in partnership with the Woodland Trust.

Find out more: 01647 433356 or finglebridge@nationaltrust.org.uk

Golden Cap

on the Jurassic Coast, near Bridport, Dorset

[icons] 1961

Satnav: for Stonebarrow use DT6 6RA; Langdon Hill DT6 6EP.
Parking: at Stonebarrow Hill and Langdon Hill.

Spectacular countryside estate on the Jurassic Coast – one of England's natural World Heritage Sites. The great rocky shoulder of Golden Cap is the south coast's highest point, with breathtaking views in all directions. Stonebarrow Hill is a good starting point for discovering the 25 miles of footpaths.

Eat, shop, stay: small volunteer-run shop and information centre (open Easter to October), with toilets and bunkhouse, in old radar station at Stonebarrow car park, Charmouth. Six holiday cottages.

Things to see and do: play trail on Langdon Hill. Smugglers' trail on Stonebarrow Hill. Family activities and events all year. Charmouth Beach for fossils. **Dogs**: welcome.

Access: [icon]

Find out more: 01297 489481 or goldencap@nationaltrust.org.uk

Golden Cap
Stonebarrow shop and information open Easter to October.

Greenway

Greenway Road, Galmpton, near Brixham, Devon TQ5 0ES

[symbols] 2000

Parking: spaces must be booked – same-day booking possible by telephone. No parking on Greenway Road or Galmpton.

Here you are given a glimpse into the lives of the famous author Agatha Christie and her family. Their holiday home is set in the 1950s, when Greenway overflowed with friends and family gathered together for holidays and Christmas. The family were great collectors: the house is brimming with their books, archaeology, Tunbridgeware, silver and porcelain. The informal woodland garden drifts down the hillside towards the Dart Estuary and the Boathouse, scene of the crime in *Dead Man's Folly*. Please consider 'green ways' to travel here: ferry (courtesy vehicle available from quay), steam train (½-mile woodland walk), cycling or walking. **Note**: booking essential for parking (01803 842382).

Eat, shop, stay: Barn Café (dog friendly) serving lunches and sweet treats. Tack-room open at peak times offering drinks, ice cream and snacks. Shop selling souvenir guides, Agatha Christie books and plants. Second-hand bookshop. Four holiday cottages, with after-hours access to the garden.

Things to see and do: family trails and pop-up talks. Guided garden tours daily until October. Events, such as open-air theatre and vintage fête. Family activities, outdoor trails and garden games, including croquet and tennis. **Dogs**: welcome on garden paths on short leads (tethering rings available in courtyard).

Access: [symbols]
Buildings [symbols] **Café** [symbol] **Garden** [symbols]

Find out more: 01803 842382 (car-park booking and infoline). 01803 882811 (ferry). 01803 555872 (Dartmouth Steam Railway and River Boat Company) or greenway@nationaltrust.org.uk

Greenway		M	T	W	T	F	S	S
15 Feb–1 Nov	10:30–5	M	T	W	T	F	S	S
7 Nov–20 Dec	11–4	·	·	·	·	·	S	S
21 Dec–31 Dec	11–4	M	T	W	T	·	·	·

Greenway in Devon: Agatha Christie's wonderfully warm and relaxed holiday home feels so welcoming

Hardy Monument

Black Down, near Portesham, Dorset 1938

Memorial to Vice-Admiral Hardy, Flag-Captain of HMS *Victory* at Trafalgar, designed to look like a spyglass. Views over the Channel.
Note: nearest postcode for satnav is DT2 9HY. Open Wednesday to Sunday and Bank Holiday Mondays, 1 April to 30 September, 11 to 4 (subject to weather).

Find out more: 01305 262538. 01297 489481 or hardymonument@nationaltrust.org.uk

Hardy's Cottage in Dorset, above and left, is truly 'far from the madding crowd'

Hardy's Cottage

Higher Bockhampton, near Dorchester, Dorset DT2 8QJ

1948

Parking: 700 yards (not National Trust, parking charge applies – free to members visiting Hardy's Cottage). Accessible parking available (speak to visitor centre staff on arrival). Bridlepath and woodland paths to cottage very uneven and steep in places.

You can find yourself 'far from the madding crowd', as you explore Hardy's rural childhood home and the birthplace of his literary land of 'Wessex'. Visitors are invited to make themselves at home, whether sitting next to the fire or wandering through the quintessential cottage garden.
Note: nearest toilet at visitor centre. Admission by timed tickets.

Eat, shop, stay: postcards, gifts and Thomas Hardy's books are on sale at the cottage, and at Hardy's Birthplace Visitor Centre near the car park. Café (not National Trust) at the visitor centre.

Things to see and do: Max Gate, Hardy's later home in Dorchester, and Clouds Hill, the retreat of Hardy's friend T. E. Lawrence, both nearby. For tramper call 01305 251228.
Dogs: welcome on leads in the garden and woods only.

Access: [icons] Building [icon] Grounds [icons]

Find out more: 01305 262366 or hardyscottage@nationaltrust.org.uk

Hardy's Cottage		M	T	W	T	F	S	S
1 Feb–29 Feb	11–4				T	F	S	S
1 Mar–31 Oct*	11–5	M	T	W	T	F	S	S
1 Nov–31 Dec**	11–4				T	F	S	S

Last admission one hour before closing (dusk if earlier). Admission by timed tickets, only available from visitor centre (590 yards from cottage); last ticket sold one hour before closing. Visitor centre: open daily, 10 to 4. Café: closing times vary with season (call 01305 251228 for details).
*Closed 3 March. **Closed 25 and 26 December.

Heddon Valley

on Exmoor, near Combe Martin, Devon

🗑🏚♿♨🛏🔔🍷 1963

Satnav: use EX31 4PY.
Parking: opposite Trust shop.

The dramatic West Exmoor coast, favourite landscape of the Romantic poets, offers not only the beautiful Heddon Valley to explore, but also Woody Bay and the Hangman Hills nearby. At the heart of the valley sits the historic Hunter's Inn, a good place to relax after discovering the spectacular coastal, moorland and woodland walks in the area. Nature highlights include one of the UK's last surviving colonies of high brown fritillary butterflies, which can be seen in June and July on the bracken-clad hillsides of Heddon Valley. Look out for the rich diversity of fungi in autumn.

Eat, shop, stay: shop selling walking equipment, gifts, books, Exmoor products and ice cream. Hunter's Inn offers accommodation, bar and locally sourced food, including meat from the National Trust's Kipscombe Farm. Heddon Orchard Bothy for more basic accommodation. Camping available during the summer.

Things to see and do: all-terrain children's buggies and all-terrain mobility scooter available to borrow (call 01598 763402 to book mobility scooter). **Dogs**: welcome.

Access: 🅿♿🚻♿🚶 Countryside ➡♿

Find out more: 01598 763402 or heddonvalley@nationaltrust.org.uk

Heddon Valley		M	T	W	T	F	S	S
Shop and kiosk								
15 Feb–31 Oct	10:30–4*	M	T	W	T	F	S	S
1 Nov–27 Dec**	10:30–4	.	.	.	.	.	S	S

*1 April to 30 September: close 5.
**Also open 28 to 31 December.

Heddon Valley in Devon, above and below, offers walkers dramatic scenery to enjoy and rare wildlife to spot

Killerton

Broadclyst, Exeter, Devon EX5 3LE

🏠✝🏛🎗♿🅿 1944

Satnav: on arrival, follow brown signs to main car park. **Parking**: main car park 280 yards. Additional smaller car parks, including Ashclyst Forest Gate, Ellerhayes Bridge, Danes Wood.

Would you give away your family home for your political beliefs? Sir Richard Acland did just that with his Killerton Estate in the heart of Devon, when he gave it to the Trust in 1944. Today you'll find a welcoming Georgian house set in 2,600 hectares (6,400 acres) of working farmland, woods, parkland, cottages and orchards. There's plenty of calm space in the glorious garden, beautiful year-round with rhododendrons, magnolias, champion trees and formal lawns. You can explore winding paths, climb an extinct volcano, discover an Iron Age hill fort and take in distant views towards Dartmoor. More family home than grand mansion, the relaxed house holds the National Trust's largest fashion collection, with selected items exhibited annually.

Killerton in Devon, this page and opposite: Georgian grace, a glorious garden and so much to explore on the estate

Eat, shop, stay: table service in the highly rated Killerton Kitchen. Snacks and cake in the Stables Coffeeshop or Dairy Café. Picnics welcome. Plant centre, bookshop and shop selling gifts and award-winning estate produce. Five holiday cottages on the estate.

Things to see and do: **Indoors** Interactive, family-friendly house. You're welcome to play the piano, read library books and sit on chairs. Daily family trail. **Outdoors** You can walk, run and cycle throughout the estate, which is made up of parkland, woods, orchards and rolling Devon countryside. Winding garden paths to the Bear's Hut, ice house and chapel. There are giant redwoods, rhododendrons and far-reaching views to discover. Many seasonal events and trails, including Easter trails, apple festival and Christmas at Killerton. **Dogs**: welcome in the parkland and estate. Assistance dogs only in garden and chapel grounds.

Having fun in the woods at Killerton

Access: 🚼♿🏛️🅿️🐕🚻📷💻🎵🔊♿
House ♿🏛️♿ **Grounds** ♿➡️♿

Find out more: 01392 881345 or
killerton@nationaltrust.org.uk

Killerton		M	T	W	T	F	S	S
House and Killerton Kitchen restaurant								
15 Feb–27 Mar	11–4	M	T	W	T	F	S	S
28 Mar–1 Nov	11–5	M	T	W	T	F	S	S
21 Nov–31 Dec*	11–4	M	T	W	T	F	S	S
Chapel, garden, Stables Coffeeshop, shop, plant centre**								
1 Jan–14 Feb	11–4	M	T	W	T	F	S	S
15 Feb–31 Dec*	10–5:30	M	T	W	T	F	S	S
Parkland								
Open all year	8–7	M	T	W	T	F	S	S

House: entry by timed tickets at peak times.
Fashion collection exhibition open with house,
15 February to 1 November. *Special Christmas opening
to 5 January 2021: closes at 3 on 24 December;
park only open 25 December; house closed 26 December.
**Open 9 on Saturdays. Park: open daily to 7
(or dusk if earlier). Dairy Café: open at peak times.

Killerton Estate: Budlake Old Post Office

Broadclyst, Exeter, Devon EX5 3LW [1944]

Visiting this old village post office with its
cottage garden and outbuildings is like
stepping back into the 1950s. **Note**: parking
and toilets at Killerton. Open Monday, Tuesday,
Wednesday, weekends, April to October, 1 to 5.

Find out more: 01392 881345 or
budlakepostoffice@nationaltrust.org.uk

Killerton Estate: Clyston Mill

Broadclyst, Exeter, Devon EX5 3EW [1944]

A historic working water-powered corn mill
in a picturesque setting by the River Clyst.
Note: nearest parking and toilets in Broadclyst
village. Open Monday, Tuesday, Wednesday
and weekends, 1 April to 30 October, 1 to 5.

Find out more: 01392 462425 or
clystonmill@nationaltrust.org.uk

Killerton Estate: Ashclyst Forest

near Broadclyst, Exeter, Devon [1944]

One of the largest woods in East Devon,
with waymarked trails for exploring.
A haven for butterflies, bluebells and birds.
Note: for satnav use EX5 3DT, follow signs
to Ashclyst. Nearest toilets, café and shop
at main Killerton car park.

Find out more: 01392 881345 or
ashclystforest@nationaltrust.org.uk

Killerton Estate: Marker's

Broadclyst, Exeter, Devon EX5 3HS [1944]

A medieval hall-house with a thatched roof,
smoke-blackened timbers, a rare painted
screen, garden and cob summerhouse.
Note: nearest parking and toilets in Broadclyst
village. Open Monday, Tuesday, Wednesday
and weekends, April to October, 1 to 5.

Find out more: 01392 461546 or
markers@nationaltrust.org.uk

Kingston Lacy

Wimborne Minster, Dorset

🏢🏛️♿👫🚻🅰️🍽️ 1982

Satnav: unreliable, follow B3082 to main entrance. Use BH21 4EL for Eye Bridge; BH21 4EE for Pamphill Green; DT11 9JL for Badbury Rings. **Parking:** on site or at Eye Bridge, Pamphill Green and Badbury Rings. Members pay for parking at Badbury Rings on point-to-point race days.

Kingston Lacy: an Italian palace in the heart of Dorset

Home to the Bankes family for over 300 years, Kingston Lacy is a monument to the family's exceptional taste and desire to surround themselves with beauty. After the family lost their Corfe Castle stronghold to the Parliamentarians in the Civil War, they moved here and gradually created an astonishing Italian palace in the heart of rural Dorset. Today you can discover an internationally acclaimed art collection, including paintings by Rubens, Velázquez and Titian, exquisite carvings and lavish interiors. There's even more to explore outside, with sweeping lawns, a Japanese Garden, kitchen garden, woodland and parkland walks – look out for the award-winning herd of Red Ruby Devon cattle – and a huge 3,500-hectare (8,500-acre) countryside estate to enjoy.

For information about getting to National Trust places, please see page 8

Note: timed house tickets only. Some rooms may close at short notice. Low light levels.

Eat, shop, stay: hot meals at lunchtime, light bites, cream teas, ice cream and cakes in the Stables Café. The old kitchen shop stocks local food, plants, gifts and souvenirs. Second-hand bookshop. Holiday cottage.

Things to see and do: **Indoors** Lavish interiors, world-class art collection, sculptures and wood carvings (levels of light are kept low to protect these treasures). **Outdoors** The garden changes with the seasons from snowdrops, blossom and bluebells to summer flowers and autumn colour. There are deckchairs for relaxing on the lawn, or why not explore the kitchen garden? Activities all year, including guided walks, family trails and evening events. Longer walks across the estate, including a riverside route past Eye Bridge or the Iron Age hill fort of Badbury Rings, home to 14 varieties of orchid. **Dogs**: welcome on leads in parkland, woodlands and wider estate. Indoors and outdoors in café.

Access: 🅿️🏛️♿🚽🛗🦽🖼️📷🚶‍♂️👀🅰️
Building 🔧 Grounds ♿➡️🔧♿

Find out more: 01202 883402 or
kingstonlacy@nationaltrust.org.uk
Wimborne Minster, Dorset BH21 4EA

The lavish Saloon, opposite, Japanese Garden, below, and cycle route, above, at Kingston Lacy

Kingston Lacy		M	T	W	T	F	S	S
House								
2 Mar–1 Nov	11–5	M	T	W	T	F	S	S
Part of house: for exhibition or seasonal experience only								
1 Jan–1 Mar	11–4	M	T	W	T	F	S	S
2 Nov–22 Nov	11–4	M	T	W	T	F	S	S
27 Nov–31 Dec	11–4*	M	T	W	T	F	S	S
Garden, park, shop and café								
Open all year	10–4**	M	T	W	T	F	S	S

House: last admission one hour before closing; open by timed-entry tickets only, bookable online up to 24 hours in advance (limited places available on day); some rooms/areas may close at short notice (please check before visiting). *Christmas experience: from 2 December, Wednesday to Sunday, house open to 6 and garden (with light displays) to 7. Everything closed 15 January and 25 December. **2 March to 1 November: close at 6.

Knightshayes

near Tiverton, Devon

🏠 ♿ ❋ 👶 🍽 1972

Satnav: do not use, follow brown signs on nearing Tiverton/Bolham. **Parking**: on site.

With one of the finest gardens in the South West, Knightshayes is a masterpiece of architectural planting, home to one of the most outstanding botanical collections in the country. Among champion trees, including first introductions to this country, there are hidden glades and pathways to discover far-reaching views. The Gothic Revival house is a rare example of the genius of William Burges, whose opulent designs have inspired extremes of opinion, even among the family who commissioned them. The walled garden combines full productivity with aesthetic appeal and is an excellent example of a restored Victorian kitchen garden.
Note: access to the house and garden is restricted during spring and winter.

Gothic Revival Knightshayes in Devon, above and left: is a rare example of the genius of William Burges

Eat, shop, stay: Stables Café serves cooked breakfasts and hot lunches, made using ingredients from the kitchen garden, also soup, sandwiches, cakes and drinks. Conservatory tea-room (seasonal opening) selling cakes, ice cream and drinks. Well-stocked shop, kitchen garden shop and plant centre.

Things to see and do: **Indoors** Spotter trails around the house. Gothic Halloween decorations and traditional family Christmas. **Outdoors** Two play areas, trails and events, including summer maze festival, Christmas fairs and winter garden illuminations. **Dogs**: welcome on leads in parkland and woods; in formal garden, November to February only.

Access: 🅿♿🚽👶🛗🎧📷⊙🚌 ⠿ 🅰
House 🅰🅰🍴🅰 Stables 🅰🅰🅰
Gardens 🅰🅰🅰➡🅰

Find out more: 01884 254665 or knightshayes@nationaltrust.org.uk
Bolham, near Tiverton, Devon EX16 7RQ

Knightshayes		M	T	W	T	F	S	S
1 Jan–29 Feb	10–4	M	T	W	T	F	S	S
1 Mar–1 Nov	10–5	M	T	W	T	F	S	S
2 Nov–31 Dec	10–4	M	T	W	T	F	S	S

House: opens 11; upstairs open to 3:30 only (closed November and December). Selected rooms open January and February. Parkland and woods: open 7:30 to 6:30 (5:30 winter). Garden, café and shop: open to 5:30 in July and August. Everything closed 24, 25 and 26 December.

Little Dartmouth

near Dartmouth, Devon 1970

A gentle coastal landscape west of Dartmouth, with wonderful views, wild flowers and the remains of a Civil War encampment. **Note**: for satnav use TQ6 0JP. Toilets at Dartmouth Castle (not National Trust). Compass Cottage holiday let – ideal base for exploring Dartmouth and the coast.

Find out more: 01752 346585 or littledartmouth@nationaltrust.org.uk

Loughwood Meeting House

Dalwood, Axminster, Devon EX13 7DU 1969

Atmospheric 17th-century thatched Baptist meeting house dug into the hillside. **Note**: sorry no toilet. Open daily, 10 to 5. Services held twice yearly (details at Meeting House).

Find out more: 01752 346585 or loughwood@nationaltrust.org.uk

Lundy

Bristol Channel, Devon

1969

Satnav: use EX34 9EQ for Ilfracombe; EX39 2EY for Bideford. **Parking**: at Bideford and Ilfracombe, not National Trust (charge including members).

Lundy is a remarkable island in the Bristol Channel, a place of solitude, stark beauty and abundant wildlife, much loved by its regular visitors and residents. A day trip on the MS *Oldenburg* allows time to explore the rugged clifftops, discover seabirds and visit the church, castle and welcoming tavern. **Note**: Lundy is owned by the National Trust, and run by the Landmark Trust. The *Oldenburg* runs from Bideford or Ilfracombe, and National Trust members pay fares (discounts available).

Eat, shop, stay: Marisco Tavern serves hot and cold food and drinks. General store sells groceries, souvenirs, Lundy stamps, snacks and ice cream. Stay in one of the Landmark Trust's 23 holiday cottages.

Things to see and do: coastal walking, letterboxing, photography, bird- and wildlife-watching. **Dogs**: assistance dogs only.

Access: ⬚⬚⬚⬚⬚ Tavern ⬚

Find out more: 01271 863636 or lundy@nationaltrust.org.uk lundyisland.co.uk The Lundy Shore Office, The Quay, Bideford, Devon EX39 2LY

Lundy

MS *Oldenburg* sails from Bideford or Ilfracombe up to four times a week from the end of March until the end of October carrying both day and staying passengers. A helicopter service operates from Hartland Point from November to mid-March, Mondays and Fridays only, for staying visitors.

Lundy, off the Devon coast, offers solitude and stark beauty

Lydford Gorge

Lydford, near Tavistock, Devon

📷 1947

Satnav: EX20 4BH (Devil's Cauldron entrance); EX20 4BL (waterfall entrance).
Parking: on site.

This steep-sided river gorge carved into the western edge of Dartmoor has been drawing visitors in search of the picturesque since Victorian times. It is a truly breathtaking experience. Around every corner the River Lyd plunges, tumbles, swirls and gently meanders as it travels through the steep-sided, oak-wooded valley, which is abundant with wildlife. Walking through the gorge (the deepest in the South West) is a challenging but rewarding adventure. There is a range of trails to suit different abilities and timescales. **Note**: sturdy footwear – rugged terrain, vertical drops. Booking required for Tramper (sorry no personal mobility vehicles).

Eat, shop, stay: two tea-rooms (dog-friendly), one at each entrance, serving cream teas, cakes, light lunches and ice cream. Takeaway available. Shop selling outdoor clothing, footwear and accessories, plants, books, local food and drink. Picnic areas.

Things to see and do: the Whitelady Waterfall, and the Devil's Cauldron (viewed from a platform over the water). Nature-themed and bushcraft activities, spotter sheets, bird hide, children's play area. Torchlit evening walks, pixie door-making. **Dogs**: welcome on leads.

Access: 🅿️ 🚻 ♿ 🚼 📷 🐕 ♿
Buildings ♿ Gorge 🥾

Find out more: 01822 820320 or lydfordgorge@nationaltrust.org.uk

Lydford Gorge		M	T	W	T	F	S	S
Gorge trails, shop and tea-rooms								
29 Feb–1 Nov	10–5*	M	T	W	T	F	S	S
Waterfall trails, shop and tea-room								
15 Feb–23 Feb	10–3:30	M	T	W	T	F	S	S
6 Nov–20 Dec	10–3:30					F	S	S

*Waterfall tea-room: opens 10:30, closing dependent on weather. October: last admission to Gorge 3:30; shop and tea-room close 4.

Lydford Gorge, Devon: steep slopes, a rushing river and abundant wildlife make for exhilarating walks

Max Gate

Dorchester, Dorset

🏠 ✣ 1940

Satnav: enter Max Gate not postcode.
Parking: on roadside in front of the house (50 yards, limited spaces, not National Trust).

Max Gate, home to Dorset's most famous author and poet, Thomas Hardy, was designed by the writer himself in 1885. This atmospheric Victorian house is where Hardy wrote some of his most famous novels, including *Tess of the d'Urbervilles* and *Jude the Obscure*, as well as most of his poetry.

Find out more: 01305 262538 or maxgate@nationaltrust.org.uk
Alington Avenue, Dorchester, Dorset DT1 2FN

Max Gate		M	T	W	T	F	S	S
2 Jan–29 Feb	11–4				T	F	S	S
1 Mar–31 Oct*	11–5	M	T	W	T	F	S	S
1 Nov–31 Dec**	11–4				T	F	S	S

Closes dusk if earlier. *Closed 3 March.
**Closed 25 and 26 December.

Thomas Hardy designed Max Gate in Dorset, above and right, before writing some of his most famous novels there

Eat, shop, stay: Thomas Hardy's books, souvenirs and small gifts on sale.
Tea, coffee, cakes and ice cream available.

Things to see and do: Hardy's Cottage, where the writer was born and grew up, and Clouds Hill, the retreat of Hardy's friend T. E. Lawrence ('Lawrence of Arabia') nearby.
Dogs: welcome on leads in garden only.

Access: 🅿️♿ Building 🔅🚻 Garden 🔅

Mill Bay

East Portlemouth, near Salcombe, Devon 1991

There are sandy beaches at Mill Bay, Sunny Cove and Seacombe Sands, with rugged walking past coastguard lookouts towards Prawle. **Note**: for satnav use TQ8 8PU. Toilets and Mill Bay Beach not National Trust.

Find out more: 01752 346585 or millbay@nationaltrust.org.uk

Mortehoe

near Ilfracombe, Devon 1909

Gateway to a wild, remote coast with a rich history of wrecking and smuggling. Amazing walking, wildlife and sunbathing seals.
Note: use EX34 7DT for village car park and toilets, not National Trust (charge including members). Town Farmhouse (tenant-run) offers cream teas in summer.

Find out more: 01271 870555 or mortehoe@nationaltrust.org.uk

Overbeck's

Sharpitor, Salcombe, Devon TQ8 8LW

🏠 ✿ ♿ 🏛 1937

Satnav: follow brown signs through Salcombe.
Parking: small car park at top of drive and on approach lane. Additional parking at East Soar (1½ miles along coast path).

Carved into the cliff-side high above the sea, Overbeck's garden overlooks the Salcombe Estuary. It is a hidden gem set within 5 miles of unspoilt coastline. Its extraordinary position not only provides breathtaking views but also allows tender plants to flourish, a factor that previous owners were well aware of as they quite literally sowed the seeds of the exotic and subtropical. The garden hosts a collection of botanically unusual and unexpected plants from across the globe. The Edwardian villa is the perfect vantage point to view the garden and provides a glimpse of life in a bygone era. **Note**: entrance path and grounds are very steep in places.

Overbeck's in Devon, above and below: a hidden gem

Eat, shop, stay: licensed tea-room serving light lunches (crab sandwiches a speciality), cream teas and afternoon tea. Terrace seating with sea views. Shop selling the unique 'First Flight' statuette inspired by the bronze sculpture in the garden. Local prints, plants and coast-inspired gifts.

Things to see and do: **Indoors** Generations of children return to hunt for Fred the ghost. Choose from the selection of games to play from a bygone age. **Outdoors** Children's garden trail. Wednesday garden tour.
Dogs: assistance dogs only.

Access: Building Grounds

Find out more: 01548 842893 or overbecks@nationaltrust.org.uk

Overbeck's		M	T	W	T	F	S	S
8 Feb–1 Nov	11–5	M	T	W	T	F	S	S

House closes at 4:30. Tea-room closes at 4:45.

Parke

near Bovey Tracey, Devon

1974

Satnav: use TQ13 9JQ.
Parking: on site (limited).

On the south-eastern edge of Dartmoor sits this historic parkland, rich in wildlife. The Wray Valley cycle trail runs along the old railway line, and paths follow the course of the River Bovey meandering through woodlands and meadows. Look out for the medieval weir, walled garden and historic orchard.

Eat, shop, stay: Home Farm Café (not National Trust) – freshly cooked food from the seasonal menu board, coffee, teas and homemade cakes. Parke Lodge holiday cottage at the entrance to Parke.

Things to see and do: orienteering trails to follow. Apple Day in autumn. Self-guided woodland trails leaflets available in courtyard and membership van. Dartmoor Pony Heritage Trust (not National Trust).
Dogs: welcome under close control.

Access: Countryside

Find out more: 01626 834748 or parke@nationaltrust.org.uk

Parke	
Open every day all year	Dawn–dusk

Home Farm Café (not National Trust) open 10 to 5 daily (10 to 4, November to March), plus Thursday, Friday and Saturday evenings (booking essential).

The River Bovey meanders through Parke, Devon

Plymbridge Woods

near Plymouth, Devon

🏛🚻 1968

Satnav: use PL7 4SR for Plymbridge.
Parking: at Plymbridge.

The wooded valley of the River Plym creates a link from the edge of Plymouth to the heights of Dartmoor. Footpaths lead through woodlands and alongside industrial ruins. There's also a family-friendly cycle path (NCN27) along an old railway line, a wooded mountain-bike trail and a variety of running routes.

Eat, shop, stay: seasonal refreshment van in car park (concession). Riverside picnic spots. Saltram is a short cycle ride away, with its popular Park Café and Chapel Tea-room.

Things to see and do: perfect for walkers, runners, cyclists and birdwatchers. Peregrine falcons can be spotted from Cann Viaduct viewpoint in spring. Downloadable walks, cycling and orienteering trails. **Dogs**: welcome under close control.

Access: 🅿♿

Find out more: 01752 341377 or plymbridgewoods@nationaltrust.org.uk

Exploring industrial ruins in Plymbridge Woods, Devon

Ringstead Bay

on the Jurassic Coast, near Weymouth, Dorset

🚻🚗 1949

Unspoilt Ringstead Bay on Dorset's Jurassic Coast

Satnav: use DT2 8NQ for Southdown.
Parking: on the clifftop farmland at Southdown Farm and beach car park (not National Trust).

This quiet, unspoilt stretch of the Jurassic Coast in West Dorset is like the seaside of childhood memories: a perfect sweep of shingle beach with rock pools inviting you to explore, backed by farmland and cliffs covered with flowers and butterflies. The seawater is incredibly clear and safe for bathing.

Eat, shop, stay: picnics welcome at Trust car park at top of hill – views of the Jurassic Coast World Heritage Site. Shop and café at the beach car park (not National Trust).

Things to see and do: spectacular views of the bay and across to the Isle of Portland to enjoy. Why not walk out to the chalk headland of White Nothe? **Dogs**: welcome, including on the South West Coast Path.

Find out more: 01297 489481 or ringsteadbay@nationaltrust.org.uk

Saltram

near Plymouth, Devon

🏛️ ♿ 👥 1957

Satnav: enter Romilly Gardens, not postcode (look for Saltram sign). **Parking**: 50 yards.

High above the River Plym, with magnificent views across the estuary, Saltram's rolling landscape parkland now provides wooded walks and open space for rest and play on Plymouth's outskirts. Saltram was home to the Parker family from 1743 and the house reflects their increasingly prominent lifestyle during the Georgian period. The magnificent decoration and original contents include Robert Adam's Neo-classical Saloon, original Chinese wallpapers, 18th-century oriental, European and English ceramics and a superb country-house library. Outside, the garden's planting offers something of interest all year, and there are also an 18th-century orangery and follies to explore. After wandering along scented pathways and the magnificent lime avenue, why not treat yourself to afternoon tea in the Chapel Tea-room?

Magnificent Saltram in Devon, below, and its Saloon, above

Eat, shop, stay: Park Café serving meals, drinks, snacks and ice cream. The Chapel Tea-room in the garden offers light lunches and afternoon tea with waitress service. Shop selling seasonal gifts, local food, books and plants.

Saltram's superb country-house library, above, and fun on the lawn, left. The garden, woods and park provide precious green space on the outskirts of Plymouth

Access: 🅿️ ♿ 👶 🏢 📷 🎵
House ♿♿ Grounds ♿➡️♿

Find out more: 01752 333500 or
saltram@nationaltrust.org.uk
Plympton, near Plymouth, Devon PL7 1UH

Things to see and do: Indoors Dressing up, guided tours, themed family trails, conservation in action. Visit at Christmas to see the house decorated. **Outdoors** Seasonal spectacles of winter snowdrops, spring daffodils, summer blooms and autumn colour in the garden. At Christmas the garden is illuminated in the evening. Activities, trails, '50 things to do before you're 11¾', guided walks and tours all year. The park is ideal for anyone wanting a stroll, to walk the dog, run, cycle or simply to feed the ducks. **Dogs:** welcome in the park (identified on- and off-lead areas).

Saltram		M	T	W	T	F	S	S
House								
20 Jan–29 Feb*	11–3:30	M	T	W	T	F	S	S
1 Mar–31 Oct	12–4:30**	M	T	W	T	F	S	S
Garden, Park Café, Chapel Tea-room and shop								
Open all year	10–5†	M	T	W	T	F	S	S
Park								
Open all year	Dawn–dusk	M	T	W	T	F	S	S
Enchanted Saltram								
20 Nov–31 Dec	12–8††	M	T	W	T	F	S	S

*Winter route. **House: 11 to 12, entry by guided tour only.
Last admission 45 minutes before closing. †January, February and November, closes 4. Chapel Tea-room: last orders one hour before closing; winter opening may vary.
††24 and 31 December: everything closes 4; everything closed 25 and 26 December.

Shaugh Bridge

on Dartmoor, near Shaugh Prior, Devon 1960

Ancient oakwoods and mossy boulders cloak the Plym Valley; riverside walks pass the atmospheric Dewerstone Rocks and industrial ruins. **Note**: for satnav use PL7 5HD. Watch out for climbers on the Dewerstone Rocks.

Find out more: 01626 834748 or shaughbridge@nationaltrust.org.uk

Shute Barton

Shute, near Axminster, Devon EX13 7PT 1959

Medieval manor house, with later Tudor gatehouse and battlemented turrets – now a holiday cottage. **Note**: very limited parking. Open Weekends, 16/17 May, 20/21 June, 17/18 October and 14/15 November, 10:30 to 3:45 by guided tour only (no need to book).

Find out more: 01752 346585 or shute@nationaltrust.org.uk

South Milton Sands

Thurlestone, near Kingsbridge, Devon

🏊 📶 1980

Satnav: use TQ7 3JY. **Parking**: car park behind beach very busy in summer. Narrow lane from South Milton village (limited passing places).

This popular beach – a long sweep of golden sand and rock pools – edges a sheltered bay of crystal-clear water and looks out to the iconic Thurlestone Rock offshore. The nearby wetland is home to many bird species and is an ideal place to spot rare migratory visitors.

Eat, shop, stay: beach café (tenant-run) inspired by its seaside location serving freshly prepared food (to eat in or take away).

A young visitor gets busy on South Milton Sands, Devon

Things to see and do: great for swimming and watersports. Wetsuits, as well as windsurf and paddle boards, for hire (seasonal). The South West Coast Path offers great walks.
Dogs: welcome on coast path and beach.

Access: 🅿️ 📶 Café and toilets 🔽 Beach ♿

Find out more: 01752 346585 or southmiltonsands@nationaltrust.org.uk

South Milton Sands
Beachhouse café seasonal opening, telephone 01548 561144.

Spyway

on the Purbeck coast, Langton Matravers, near Swanage, Dorset 1982

Gateway to a dramatic coast of grassy clifftops teeming with wildlife, and Dancing Ledge. Fabulous walking – some steep slopes. **Note**: for satnav use BH19 3HG. Sorry no toilet.

Find out more: 01929 450002 or spyway@nationaltrust.org.uk

Studland Bay

Studland, near Swanage, Dorset

🏖️ ♿ 🚻 🅿️ 1982

Satnav: use BH19 3AQ for Knoll Beach.
Parking: at Shell Bay (7 to 9); South Beach
(9 to 11); Knoll Beach and Middle Beach
(9 to 8, or dusk if earlier).

This glorious slice of Purbeck coastline is
famed for its 4-mile stretch of golden sand,
gently shelving bathing waters and views of Old
Harry Rocks and the Isle of Wight. With four
beaches to choose from, Studland is loved by
young families and watersports fans of all ages,
and it includes the most popular naturist beach
in Britain. The vast swathe of heathland behind
the beach is a haven for native wildlife and
features all six British reptiles. Footpaths and
bridleways through sand dunes, woods and
wild open landscape encourage you to explore.
Wildlife to spot includes deer, insects and
birds, as well as numerous wild flowers.
Studland was the inspiration for Toytown in
Enid Blyton's *Noddy*. **Note**: toilets at Shell Bay,
Knoll Beach and Middle Beach; also South
Beach (not National Trust).

Family fun at Studland Bay, Dorset, above and below

Listen to stories about Trust places – nationaltrust.org.uk/podcasts

Eat, shop, stay: Knoll Beach Café on the beach with spectacular views of Old Harry Rocks; indoor and open-air seating. Log burner in winter. Wood-fired pizza oven in summer. Beach goods and seaside gifts for sale. Thirteen holiday cottages in the area.

Things to see and do: year-round events programme, family trails and multitude of watersports and beach sports – geocaching, slacklining, orienteering, beach volleyball, snorkelling, swimming, beach table tennis, paddle-boarding, sea kayaking and sailing. And don't forget sandcastles and rock-pooling. You can hire bikes or go horse-riding to explore inland. You can also hire a beach hut for the day or longer. Signposted trails, including one of the most popular coastal walks to Old Harry Rocks. Second World War remains tell of Studland's role in the build-up to D-Day. Five bird hides overlook Poole Harbour and Little Sea. Discovery Centre for private hire.
Dogs: welcome on short leads 1 May to 30 September. Under control in winter.

Access: 🅿️ ♿ 🚻 🏠 **Grounds** ♿ ♿

Find out more: 01929 450500 or studlandbay@nationaltrust.org.uk

Studland Bay	
Shop and café	
Open every day all year	9:30–5*

*29 March to 24 October: open to 6 at weekends. July and August open daily, 9 to 6. Reduced hours in winter, 10 to 4. Shop and café: closed 4 and 5 March and 25 December.

One of the cycle trails at Studland Bay

Watersmeet

on Exmoor, near Lynmouth, Devon

🏠🏚♿🗺️🛏️☕ 1955

Satnav: use EX35 6NT. **Parking**: pay and display (not National Trust) on Watersmeet Road; steep walk down to house. Trust car parks nearby at Combe Park and Countisbury. Please call to book accessible parking.

This area, where the lush valleys of the East Lyn and Hoar Oak Water meet the high open moorland of Kipscombe, is a haven for wildlife and offers excellent walking. At the heart sits Watersmeet House, a 19th-century fishing lodge, which is now a tea garden, shop and information point. **Note**: deep gorge with steep walk down to house.

Eat, shop, stay: tea garden serving hot and cold food and drinks in magnificent wooded setting. Shop selling Exmoor produce and gifts, walking gear and maps. Holiday cottages nearby.

Things to see and do: Exmoor Spotter chart for families and 'Exmoor Coast of Devon' walks leaflet available. **Dogs**: welcome on leads in tea garden.

The fishing lodge, now tea garden, at Watersmeet in Devon, below, and an inviting woodland path, right

Access: 🅿️♿ Building 🔍 Grounds ♿

Find out more: 01598 752648 or watersmeet@nationaltrust.org.uk

Watersmeet		M	T	W	T	F	S	S
Tea-room and tea garden								
15 Feb–31 Oct	10:30–5*	M	T	W		F	S	S
1 Nov–20 Dec**	10:30–4	·	·	·	·	·	S	S

*February, March and October: close 4.
**Also open 26 to 31 December, 10 to 4.

Wembury

near Plymouth, Devon

🏠♿🗺️🛏️ 1939

Satnav: use PL9 0HP.
Parking: just above beach.

A great beach, and more: some of the best rock pools in the country, good surfing, masses of wildlife and views of a distinctive island – the Great Mewstone. Starting point for lovely coastal walks to Wembury Point and the Yealm Estuary. **Note**: toilet (not National Trust).

Eat, shop, stay: Old Mill Café (tenant-run) serves coffees, homemade cakes, soups, pasties and ice cream. Beach shop (tenant-run). Mill Cottage adjoining the café is an idyllic holiday let right on the shore.

Things to see and do: Marine Centre full of information. Rock-pooling, surfing and snorkelling. **Dogs**: welcome on coast path all year; on beach 1 October to 30 April.

Access: 🅿️♿ Café 🏖️ Marine Centre 🏖️ Beach 🏖️

Find out more: 01752 346585. 01752 862538 (Marine Centre) or wembury@nationaltrust.org.uk

Wembury
For details of the Old Mill Café seasonal opening, telephone 01752 863280.

White Mill

Sturminster Marshall, near Wimborne Minster, Dorset BH21 4BX 1982

This 18th-century corn mill with original wooden machinery is built on a Domesday Book site in a peaceful riverside setting. **Note**: open weekends 4 April to 1 November and Bank Holiday Mondays, 12 to 5. Guided tours available, last tour at 4.

Find out more: 01258 858051 or whitemill@nationaltrust.org.uk

Woolacombe

near Ilfracombe, Devon 1935

A golden beach and huge dunes, amazing surfing, perfect coves for rock-pooling and numerous headland walks with views of Lundy. **Note**: for satnav use EX34 7BG. The Porthole café (tenant-run) is located on Marine Drive, accessible toilets and outdoor showers provided. Car park not National Trust (charge including members).

Find out more: 01271 870555 or woolacombe@nationaltrust.org.uk

A fascinating rock pool at Wembury in Devon, with distinctive Great Mewstone island beyond

Additional coastal and countryside car parks in Devon and Dorset

Devon				Danes Wood	EX5 3LH
Countisbury	EX35 6NE	Ringmore	TQ7 4HR	Ellerhayes	EX5 4PY
Combe Park	EX35 6LF	Snapes Point	TQ8 8NQ	**Dorset**	
Woody Bay	EX31 4QU	Prawle Point	TQ7 2BX	Cogden	DT6 4RJ
Trentishoe Down	EX34 0PF	Scabbacombe	TQ6 0EF	Lambert's Castle	DT6 5QJ
Torrs Walk, Ilfracombe	EX34 8BA	Man Sands	TQ6 0EF	Acton	BH19 3JN
Hartland: Brownsham	EX39 6AN	Salcombe Hill	EX10 0NY	Dean Hill Viewpoint	BH19 3AA
Exmansworthy	EX39 6AR	Dunsland	EX22 7AA		
East Titchberry	EX39 6AU	Steps Bridge	EX6 7EQ		
Stoke	PL8 1JG	Hembury Woods	TQ11 0HW		
		Holne Woods	TQ13 7ST		

Borders in bloom at
Montacute House, Somerset

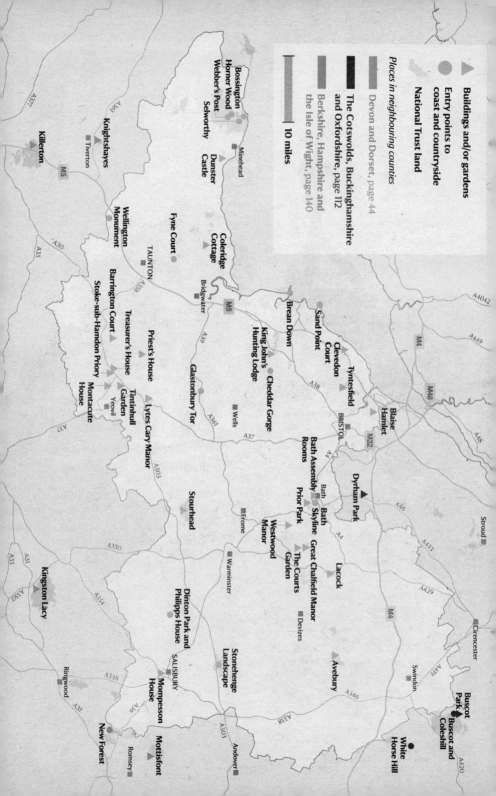

National Trust land

Entry points to
coast and countryside

Buildings and/or gardens

Places in neighbouring counties

Devon and Dorset, page 44

The Cotswolds, Buckinghamshire
and Oxfordshire, page 112

Berkshire, Hampshire and
the Isle of Wight, page 140

10 miles

Killerton

Knightshayes

Tiverton

A361

A377

A35

A30

M5

Bossington
Homer Wood
Webber's Post
Selworthy

Minehead

Dunster Castle

Wellington
Monument

Fyne Court

Coleridge
Cottage

TAUNTON

A358

Bridgwater

A38

M5

Barrington Court

Stoke-sub-Hamdon Priory

Treasurer's House

Priest's House

Montacute
House

Yeovil

A37

A303

Tintinhull
Garden

Lytes Cary Manor

Glastonbury Tor

A361

Wells

A37

King John's
Hunting Lodge

Cheddar Gorge

Brean Down

Sand Point

Clevedon
Court

Tyntesfield

BRISTOL

A38

A4

Blaise
Hamlet

M32

M48

A48

Bath Assembly
Rooms

Prior Park

Bath
Skyline

Westwood
Manor

The Courts
Garden

Great Chalfield Manor

Lacock

Dyrham Park

A46

A4

Stroud

A433

Cirencester

A419

A417

M4

A4042

A449

A429

Swindon

M4

Buscot Park

Buscot and
Coleshill

White
Horse Hill

A420

Stourhead

Frome

A350

Warminster

Devizes

Kingston Lacy

A31

A350

A354

Dinton Park and
Philipps House

SALISBURY

A338

Ringwood

A31

A36

Mompesson
House

Mottisfont

New Forest

Romsey

A303

Andover

A346

Avebury

Stonehenge
Landscape

A36

A338

Avebury

near Marlborough, Wiltshire

🏚️✝️🍴🏛️❀♿🛏️ 1943

Satnav: use SN8 1RD. **Parking**: 300 yards.
Please do not park on village streets.

At Avebury you'll find the largest stone circle in the world, which partially encompasses a pretty village. Avebury forms part of the Stonehenge and Avebury World Heritage Site. The renowned archaeologist Alexander Keiller excavated here in the 1930s, and Avebury's museum bears his name. The museum is divided into two galleries displaying local archaeological finds and telling the story of this ancient landscape. Visiting Keiller's home, the 15th-century Avebury Manor with its lovely garden, is a hands-on experience celebrating and reflecting the lives of the people who once lived here. In Avebury chapel you can learn more about the outdoors, with displays about local wildlife and current conservation work, plus information on walks around Avebury and the wider Wiltshire landscape. **Note**: the National Trust owns and manages Avebury Stone Circle (under guardianship of English Heritage).

Eat, shop, stay: Circles Café; Avebury Manor Tea-room serving afternoon tea (seasonal); Coach House Café (seasonal). National Trust shop selling products with locally inspired designs. Cobblestones second-hand bookshop. Holiday cottage within the stone circle available all year.

Things to see and do: **Indoors** Specialist talks. Seasonal family activities and children's events during the holidays. **Outdoors** Guided tours of the stone circles, archaeological landscape walks. Family activities in the Old Farmyard and manor garden during the holidays. **Dogs**: welcome on leads. Assistance dogs only in the manor, garden and cafés.

Access: 🅿️♿🚻🚌♿🖼️🏛️🚪♿
Museum ♿♿ **Manor** ♿♿🚹♿ **Grounds** ➡️♿

The prehistoric stone circle, below, and the manor's Tudor Parlour, above, at Avebury in Wiltshire

Avebury Manor offers exciting hands-on experiences, below, as well as a colourful garden to explore, above

Find out more: 01672 539250 or avebury@nationaltrust.org.uk
National Trust Estate Office, High Street, Avebury, Wiltshire SN8 1RD

Avebury		M	T	W	T	F	S	S
Stone circle								
Open all year	Dawn–dusk	M	T	W	T	F	S	S
Manor and garden								
15 Feb–28 Mar	11–4	M	T	W	T	F	S	S
29 Mar–24 Oct*	11–5	M	T	W	T	F	S	S
25 Oct–22 Nov	11–4	M	T	W	T	F	S	S
28 Nov–31 Dec	11–4	M	T	W	T	F	S	S
Museum								
1 Jan–28 Mar	10–4	M	T	W	T	F	S	S
29 Mar–24 Oct	10–6	M	T	W	T	F	S	S
25 Oct–31 Dec	10–4	M	T	W	T	F	S	S

*20 to 22 June: manor and garden closed. Entry to manor by timed ticket only, last entry one hour before closing. 24 to 26 December: stone circle only open. Shop and café open daily. In winter, parts of garden, manor and museum may be closed.

Barrington Court

near Ilminster, Somerset

🏠🌀🏊🛏️ 1907

Satnav: misdirects visitors to rear entrance – follow brown signs from Barrington village. **Parking**: 200 yards.

Colonel Lyle, whose family firm became part of Tate & Lyle, rescued the partially derelict 16th-century Court House in the 1920s, surrounding it with a productive estate. A keen collector of architectural salvage, Colonel Lyle filled the house with his collection of panelling, fireplaces and staircases. Now without furniture, the light, empty spaces provide atmospheric opportunities to explore their stories freely. The walled White Garden, Rose and Iris Garden and Lily Garden were influenced by Gertrude Jekyll, with playing fountains, vibrant colours and intoxicating scents. The original kitchen garden supplies the restaurant and continues the Lyle family's vision of self-sufficiency. **Note**: independently run artisan workshops (opening times vary).

Eat, shop, stay: Strode dining and tea-rooms offering tea, homemade cakes and meals with ingredients often grown in the kitchen garden. Children's menu available. Shop selling gifts, plants and award-winning cider and apple juice. Second-hand bookshop. Artisan workshops. Holiday lets in Strode House.

Things to see and do: Indoors House tours and children's trail, seasonal events. Activities in artisan workshops.
Outdoors Trails and tours. Seasonal events, including Easter and Christmas activities.
Dogs: assistance dogs only in formal garden.

Access: 🅿️♿🚻👶🦽📷🚪🎧♿
Building 🦽 **Grounds** ♿➡️♿

Find out more: 01460 241938 or barringtoncourt@nationaltrust.org.uk
Barrington, near Ilminster, Somerset TA19 0NQ

Barrington Court		M	T	W	T	F	S	S
3 Jan–9 Feb	10:30–3					**F**	**S**	**S**
10 Feb–1 Nov	10:30–5	**M**	**T**	**W**	**T**	**F**	**S**	**S**
2 Nov–31 Dec*	10:30–3	**M**	**T**	**W**	**T**	**F**	**S**	**S**

*Closed 24 and 25 December.

The 16th-century Court House, right of picture, and Strode House, left, at Barrington Court in Somerset

Bath Assembly Rooms

Bennett Street, Bath, Somerset BA1 2QH 1931

The Assembly Rooms were at the heart of Georgian society. **Note**: run by Bath and North East Somerset Council. Charge for the Fashion Museum on lower ground floor (including members). Open daily 10:30 to 6 (closes at 5 November to February). Closed 25 and 26 December. Last entry one hour before closing.

Find out more: 01225 477789 or bathassemblyrooms@nationaltrust.org.uk

Bath Skyline

Bath, Somerset

1959

Parking: none on site, nearest city centre, not National Trust (charge including members).

One of Bath's unique features, leading to its World Heritage Site designation, is its 'green setting' – encircling meadows and wooded hillsides where you can walk and relax with grandstand views over the historic cityscape. Six-mile Bath Skyline waymarked walk, and shorter routes from city centre. **Note**: no toilet.

Eat, shop, stay: picnics welcome. Cafés in Widcombe and local museums (none National Trust, some entry fees).

Things to see and do: 'Walk to the view' is a 3-mile self-led circular route from Bath Abbey. Geocaching trail and other family activities. Bath parkrun every Saturday. Guided walks. **Dogs**: welcome under control (on leads in some areas). Cattle grazing April to November.

Access: 🦽➡️

Find out more: 01225 833977 or bathskyline@nationaltrust.org.uk

Blaise Hamlet

Henbury, Bristol BS10 7QY 1943

Delightful hamlet of nine picturesque cottages, designed by John Nash in 1809 for Blaise Estate pensioners. **Note**: access to green only; cottages not open. Sorry no toilet.

Find out more: 01275 461900 or blaisehamlet@nationaltrust.org.uk

Bossington

on Exmoor, near Minehead, Somerset

🏠🛎️🚾🛏️ 1944

Satnav: use TA24 8HF. **Parking**: on site.

Part of the Holnicote Estate, Bossington is a peaceful coastal hamlet with distinctive thatched cottages. You can race sticks from the footbridge in the woods, look for water voles or wander down to the pebble beach. There's wildlife to spot and far-reaching views to Wales and along the Exmoor coastline. **Note**: accessible facilities in the car park.

Eat, shop, stay: barbecue pits in picnic field by car park. Kitnors tea-room open year round for cream teas and light lunches (not National Trust). Picturesque Lower House holiday cottage sleeps 10.

Things to see and do: you can discover limekilns on the beach, or take the South West Coast Path to Hurlstone Point's coastguard lookout – a top spot for porpoise sightings. **Dogs**: welcome on leads.

Access: 🚾

Find out more: 01643 862452 or bossington@nationaltrust.org.uk

Brean Down

near Weston-super-Mare, North Somerset

🏠🏚🐕🖼️🚻🛏️ 1954

Satnav: use TA8 2RS. **Parking**: on site.

One of Somerset's most striking coastal landmarks: a dramatic limestone peninsula jutting out into the Bristol Channel. You can relax on the beach at the foot of the down or take a walk along this spectacular 'natural pier' to the fort, which provides a unique insight into Brean's military past.
Note: steep climbs and cliffs; please stay on main paths. Tide comes in quickly.

Eat, shop, stay: with winter woodburner or summer courtyard and picnic benches, Brean Down café serves breakfast, lunch, tea and cakes. Shop selling ice cream, beach games and souvenirs. Holiday apartment sleeping four.

Things to see and do: historic fort to discover and many birds, feral goats and wild flowers to spot. Downloadable circular walk. Events all year. **Dogs**: welcome on leads, but please note that stock may be grazing on the down.

Access: 🅿️ Building 🔼♿

Find out more: 01278 751874 or breandown@nationaltrust.org.uk

Brean Down		M	T	W	T	F	S	S
Café and shop								
1 Jan–29 Feb	10–4	M	T	W	T	F	S	S
1 Mar–31 Oct	9–5	M	T	W	T	F	S	S
1 Nov–31 Dec*	10–4	M	T	W	T	F	S	S

*Closed 25 December.

The sun sets over the fort at Brean Down, Somerset

Cheddar Gorge

in the Mendips, near Wells, Somerset

🐕🚻 1910

Dramatic sheer drop at Cheddar Gorge in Somerset

Satnav: use BS27 3QE.
Parking: car parks on both sides of gorge, not National Trust (charge including members).

At almost 400 feet deep and 3 miles long, Cheddar is Britain's largest gorge. It was formed during successive ice ages, when glacial meltwater carved into the limestone, creating steep cliffs. The gorge is a haven for wildlife and contains many rare plants and flowers, including the Cheddar pink. **Note**: terrain is steep away from the road. Caves and car parks privately owned (charge including members).

Eat, shop, stay: seasonal shop and information centre providing leaflets, information on National Trust membership and walks, gifts and souvenirs. Free Wi-Fi and computer tablets available to plan days out.

Things to see and do: 4-mile circular gorge walk (details from shop and information centre) and Strawberry Line (NCN26) cycle route to Cheddar. Top of the Gorge festival in June. **Dogs**: welcome on leads in shop and gorge.

Find out more: 01934 744689 or cheddargorge@nationaltrust.org.uk

Cheddar Gorge		M	T	W	T	F	S	S
Shop and information centre								
15 Feb–1 Nov	10–5	M	T	W	T	F	S	S
7 Nov–20 Dec	11–4						S	S

Clevedon Court

Tickenham Road, Clevedon,
North Somerset BS21 6QU

🏠✣ 1961

Parking: 50 yards (unsuitable for trailer or motor caravans). Alternative parking 100 yards east of entrance in cul-de-sac.

Home to Clevedon's lords of the manor for centuries, Clevedon Court features rare domestic architecture from the medieval period and a beautiful terraced garden. The house was bought by Abraham Elton in 1709 and is still the well-loved family home of the Eltons today. **Note**: sorry no debit or credit card facilities.

Eat, shop, stay: kiosk serving refreshments.

Things to see and do: an extensive collection of Elton Ware pottery, Nailsea glass and prints of industrial archaeology. Family guide and children's trail. **Dogs**: assistance dogs only.

Access: 🅿♿🚶🏛🎫♿🅿
House ♿🏛 Garden ♿

Find out more: 01275 872257 or clevedoncourt@nationaltrust.org.uk

Clevedon Court		M	T	W	T	F	S	S
1 Apr–30 Sep	2–5			W	T			S

Tea kiosk and car park open 1:15. House entry by timed ticket (not bookable). Open Bank Holiday Mondays.

Clevedon Court, North Somerset: much-loved family home

Coleridge Cottage

35 Lime Street, Nether Stowey, Bridgwater,
Somerset TA5 1NQ

🏠✣ 1909

Simple but inspiring Coleridge Cottage in Somerset

Parking: in pub car park (not National Trust).

Home to Samuel Taylor Coleridge for three years, this simple house, where he wrote his best-known poems, was the birthplace of literary Romanticism. You can immerse yourself in 18th-century sights and sounds, and Coleridge's poetry comes to life in the cottage and wildflower garden. New exhibition in the Garden Room.

Eat, shop, stay: tea-room serving light refreshments. Shop selling gifts reflecting Coleridge's life and work.

Things to see and do: **Indoors** Write with a quill or dress up in Georgian costumes. Family trails. **Outdoors** Poetry in the garden. Draw water from the well.

Access: 🎫🚶♿ Building ♿🏛 Garden ♿➡

Find out more: 01278 732662 or coleridgecottage@nationaltrust.org.uk

Coleridge Cottage		M	T	W	T	F	S	S
29 Feb–1 Nov	11–5	M	T	W	T	F	S	S
5 Dec–20 Dec	11–4						S	S

Private tours/educational visits by arrangement.

The Courts Garden

Holt, near Bradford on Avon,
Wiltshire BA14 6RR

❖ 1943

Parking: 80 yards in village hall car park
(not National Trust). Follow signs for overflow
parking. Please avoid parking on village streets.

This curious English country garden is a hidden
gem. Garden rooms of different styles, shaped
by the vision of past owners and gardeners,
reveal themselves at every turn. You'll find
herbaceous borders, topiary, a peaceful water
garden, statuary, an arboretum, kitchen
garden, naturally planted spring bulbs and
a sunken garden.

Eat, shop, stay: kitchen garden produce for
sale. Small selection of gifts and guidebooks.
Second-hand bookshop (sales support
conservation work). Rose Garden tea-room
(concession) serving lunch and afternoon tea.
Picnics welcome in arboretum.

The apple tunnel, left, and graceful bridge,
above, in The Courts Garden in Wiltshire

Things to see and do: trails and wildlife garden
for young explorers. Friendly team happy to
offer gardening tips. Garden history in the
Orchard Room. **Dogs**: assistance dogs only.

Access: 🔲🔲🔲🔲🔲🔲🔲 **Garden** 🔲🔲

Find out more: 01225 782875 or
courtsgarden@nationaltrust.org.uk

The Courts Garden		M	T	W	T	F	S	S
1 Feb–23 Feb	11–5:30	·	·	·	·	·	**S**	**S**
24 Feb–1 Nov	11–5:30	**M**	**T**		**T**	**F**	**S**	**S**

Tea-room: last orders 45 minutes before closing.

Dinton Park and Philipps House

Dinton, Salisbury, Wiltshire SP3 5HH 1943

Tranquil rolling parkland, perfect for walks
and picnics, surrounds a neo-Grecian house
designed by Jeffry Wyatville in 1820.
Note: the house is closed this year.
The park is open daily all year. Sorry no toilet.
Parking next to St Mary's Church.

Find out more: 01672 539920 or
dintonpark@nationaltrust.org.uk

Dunster Castle and Watermill

Dunster, near Minehead, Somerset TA24 6SL

🏠 ♿ 👥 🔔 🍴 1976

Parking: castle 300 yards, watermill 800 yards (main car park – enter from A39). No separate parking at watermill.

Dramatically sited on top of a wooded hill, a castle has existed here since at least Norman times. Its impressive medieval gatehouse and ruined Bastion Tower are a reminder of its turbulent history. The castle that you see today, home to the Luttrell family for over 600 years, became an elegant country home during the 19th century and features ornate plaster ceilings and rare 17th-century leather hangings. The terraced garden displays varieties of Mediterranean and subtropical plants, while the tranquil riverside wooded garden below, with its natural play area, leads to the surviving 18th-century working watermill. There are panoramic views from the castle and grounds of the surrounding Exmoor countryside and over the Bristol Channel towards Wales.

Eat, shop, stay: riverside tea-room and garden serving light lunches and afternoon teas. Light refreshments at the Camellia House. Stables gift shop with home-grown plants. Watermill gift and produce shop, selling wholemeal flours ground on site. Second-hand bookshop. Holiday cottage near village gate.

Things to see and do: Indoors 'Chapters' and conservation story interpretation in the Castle. Guided tours of Victorian kitchens, hidden attics and 'behind the scenes' all year. Flour milling on the first Wednesday of every month and selected Saturdays all year. Underground Victorian reservoir experience. Discover Dunster's ghosts and bats in the Crypt. 17th–century stables and Tenants' Hall exhibitions. **Outdoors** You can walk around four different micro-climates in the garden and learn more in the garden exhibition at the keep. New compost zone. Parterre 'Dream Garden' (open May to October). Events, including living history, open-air theatre and year-round family garden trail. **Dogs**: welcome on short leads everywhere, except Castle and tea-room.

Access: 🅿️♿🚶🔵📷🎦🎧🔆 ⓘ
Castle 🔵🔆🏛♿ Stables ♿ Grounds ♿➡️♿

Find out more: 01643 823004 (Infoline). 01643 821314 or dunstercastle@nationaltrust.org.uk

Dunster Castle and Watermill		M	T	W	T	F	S	S
Castle								
1 Jan–5 Jan	11–4			W	T	F	S	S
6 Jan–14 Feb	Tour	M	T	W	T	F	S	S
15 Feb–1 Nov	11–5	M	T	W	T	F	S	S
2 Nov–18 Dec	*	M	T	W	T	F	S	S
19 Dec–31 Dec**	11–4	M	T	W	T	F	S	S
Watermill, garden, park, shop and tea-room								
Open all year**	10–5†	M	T	W	T	F	S	S

*Entry by tour only in November and weekdays in December; from 6 December freeflow at weekends (11 to 4) – except for 'Dunster by Candlelight', 4 and 5 December, when castle is open 4 to 9. When entry is by tour only, places are limited.
**Everything closed 24 and 25 December. †Close dusk if earlier. Last entry to castle 45 minutes before closing.

Three views of impressive yet welcoming Dunster Castle in Somerset, this page and opposite

Somerset and Wiltshire

Fyne Court

near Bridgwater, Somerset

⌂ ✿ ♨ ✈ 1967

Satnav: use TA5 2EQ. **Parking**: on site.

This is a hidden gem in the Quantock Hills (above). While the house (former home of amateur scientist Andrew Crosse) no longer stands, the site remains simply beautiful within its woods and meadows. A great place for gentle walks, splashing in streams, building dens and discovering ruins. Information available in courtyard.

Eat, shop, stay: courtyard tea-room serving light lunches, cream teas and cakes. You're welcome to picnic in the walled garden. Fyne Court Cottage is a holiday let (sleeps six).

Things to see and do: three walking trails (one accessible). Natural play and den-building areas. Year-round events. The Skyglade is a great spot for observing the heavens. **Dogs**: welcome on leads.

Access: ⬚ ⬚ ⬚ Grounds ⬚ ⬚ ⬚

Find out more: 01823 451587 or fynecourt@nationaltrust.org.uk

Fyne Court		M	T	W	T	F	S	S
Estate								
Open all year		M	T	W	T	F	S	S
Tea-room								
1 Jan–29 Feb	10–3	M	T	W	T	F	S	S
1 Mar–31 Oct	10–4	M	T	W	T	F	S	S
1 Nov–31 Dec*	10–3	M	T	W	T	F	S	S

*Closed 25 December. Opening varies according to weather conditions.

Glastonbury Tor

near Glastonbury, Somerset 1933

Iconic tor topped by a 15th-century tower, with spectacular views over the Somerset Levels, Dorset and Wiltshire. **Note**: for satnav use BA6 8DB for nearest parking – Somerset Rural Life Museum, not National Trust (charge including members). Sorry no toilet.

Find out more: 01278 751874 or glastonburytor@nationaltrust.org.uk

Great Chalfield Manor and Garden

near Melksham, Wiltshire SN12 8NH

⌂ ✝ ✿ ♨ 1943

Great Chalfield Manor and Garden in Wiltshire

Parking: 100 yards, on grass verge outside manor gates.

A monkey, soldiers and griffins adorn the rooftops of this moated medieval manor, looking over the terraces of the romantic garden with topiary houses, rose garden and spring-fed fishpond. All is lovingly looked after by the Floyd family. The manor has featured in several television dramas, including *Wolf Hall*. **Note**: home to the donor family tenants, who manage it for the National Trust. Charges apply for events outside normal opening times (including members).

Eat, shop, stay: guidebooks, postcards and plants for sale. Picnics welcome in the Motor House. Self-service tea, coffee and biscuits also available, with honesty box cash payment only (not National Trust).

Things to see and do: Indoors Guided tours (limited). **Outdoors** Beautiful garden with year-round interest. Map for cross-country walk to The Courts Garden available. **Dogs**: assistance dogs only.

Access: 🅿️ ♿ 🏛️ 🏠 ⛴️ 📷
Manor 🔎 🏛️ Garden 🏛️ ➡️

Find out more: 01225 782239 or greatchalfieldmanor@nationaltrust.org.uk

Great Chalfield Manor		M	T	W	T	F	S	S
Manor								
1 Apr–29 Oct	Tour*			T	W	T		S
Garden								
1 Apr–29 Oct	11–5			T	W	T		
5 Apr–25 Oct	1–5							S

*Manor: admission by 45-minute guided tour (places limited, not bookable) Tuesday, Wednesday and Thursday at 11, 12, 2, 3 and 4; Sunday at 2, 3 and 4. Group visits welcome Friday and Monday (not Bank Holidays); please contact the tenant on 01225 782239 (charges apply, including members).

Horner Wood

on Exmoor, near Minehead, Somerset

🏛️ ♿ 🐾 1944

Satnav: use TA24 8HY. **Parking**: on site.

One of the largest and most beautiful ancient oak woods in Britain, Horner Wood (above) is part of the Holnicote Estate. 324 hectares (800 acres) of woodland clothe the lower slopes of surrounding moorland, following river and stream valleys.

Beautiful and ancient Horner Wood in Somerset

This National Nature Reserve is home to a rich variety of wildlife. **Note**: toilets in car park.

Eat, shop, stay: cream teas at Horner Tea Garden or Horner Vale Tea-room (neither National Trust). Pizzas at Horner Farm (tenant-run). Four holiday cottages on the Holnicote Estate.

Things to see and do: 17th-century packhorse bridge and a Tudor iron-smelting site, plus some of Britain's rarest lichens, mosses and bats, and The General, a 500-year-old oak tree. **Dogs**: welcome under close control, so as not to disturb wildlife and grazing animals.

Find out more: 01643 862452 or hornerwood@nationaltrust.org.uk

King John's Hunting Lodge

The Square, Axbridge, Somerset BS26 2AP 1968

This early Tudor timber-framed wool merchant's house (dating from around 1500) provides a fascinating insight into local history. **Note**: run as a local history museum by Axbridge and District Museum Trust. Open daily, 1 April to 31 October, 1 to 4.

Find out more: 01934 732012 or kingjohns@nationaltrust.org.uk

Lacock

near Chippenham, Wiltshire

🏠✝🍷♻♿🚲 1944

Satnav: may direct down closed road. Set to Hither Way, Lacock, for car park. **Parking**: 220 yards. No visitor parking on village streets.

You can see why Ela of Salisbury chose this spot for her abbey in 1232: nestled alongside the River Avon in a rolling Wiltshire landscape, Lacock invites you to stay. The abbey reveals evidence of a legacy of almost 800 years of past owners with sophisticated taste, who sensitively turned it from a nunnery into an unusual family home, furnished with well-loved mementoes and furniture. Seasonal colour can be discovered in the wooded grounds, Botanic Garden, greenhouse and orchard. The Fox Talbot Museum celebrates William Henry Fox Talbot, who created the first photographic negative and established this as a birthplace of photography. Lacock has a homely feel and the village, with its timber-framed cottages, remains a bustling community.

Note: please check abbey opening arrangements in winter, as access is limited.

Eat, shop, stay: there are many places to eat and drink in Lacock village, including the Stables café and Courtyard tea-room at the abbey. Two National Trust shops, independent village businesses and a beautiful holiday cottage make Lacock a great place to stay.

Things to see and do: Indoors The abbey offers two distinct experiences: a peaceful ground-floor monastic cloister, and first-floor furnished rooms. The Fox Talbot Museum gives an insight into the history of photography and includes changing exhibitions.

Outdoors The level grounds are great for picnics and walks. There is a range of events and exhibitions, seasonally changing family trails in the abbey grounds, open-air theatre, and a play area in the village. Lacock is a famous filming location and its appearances include *Harry Potter*, *Wolf Hall* and *Pride and Prejudice*. **Dogs**: 1 November to 31 March – welcome on short leads in abbey grounds.

At Lacock in Wiltshire, the abbey, opposite and above, and village, below, are inextricably linked to the origins of photography and to contemporary film-making

Access: 🅿️ ♿ 🦽 🪑 🔍 📷 🖥️ 📺 🔲 👓 📷
Abbey 🔲 ♿ Museum ♿ ⬇️ ♿
Grounds ♿ ♿ ➡️ ♿ .

Find out more: 01249 730459 or lacock@nationaltrust.org.uk
Lacock, near Chippenham, Wiltshire SN15 2LG

Lacock		M	T	W	T	F	S	S
2 Jan–14 Feb*	11–4	M	T	W	T	F	S	S
15 Feb–1 Nov	10:30–5**	M	T	W	T	F	S	S
2 Nov–31 Dec*	11–4	M	T	W	T	F	S	S

Abbey: first-floor rooms open 30 minutes later; last admission 45 minutes before closing. Last orders in tea-rooms 15 minutes before closing. Closed 25, 26 December and 1 January 2021. *Cloister only, plus Great Hall at weekends (to 3:30). **Stables café and High Street shop open from 10.

Lytes Cary Manor

near Somerton, Somerset TA11 7HU

🏠➕✥♿🖼 1949

Parking: 40 yards.

This intimate medieval manor house was originally home to the Lyte family, who lived here for several generations until the 18th century. After years of neglect, Lytes Cary was lovingly restored in the early 20th century by Sir Walter Jenner and his wife Lady Flora, and is arranged as it was in their time. A stroll around the Arts and Crafts-inspired garden beside the house reveals garden rooms, divided by high yew hedges, collections of topiary, sensuous herbaceous borders, orchards and manicured lawns. The Manor is surrounded by fertile farmland, wild meadows, woodland and flood plains. **Note**: access to parts of the garden may be restricted to preserve the grass.

Eat, shop, stay: small tea-room offering cakes and drinks. Picnic tables in the courtyard. Shop selling gifts, garden accessories and plants. Second-hand books. The west wing of the house is available as a holiday let, as is a Victorian cottage on the estate.

Things to see and do: tranquil walks on the wider estate and children's outdoor natural play area in woodland, with trails which can be enjoyed all year. Allotments bursting with creative and colourful designs. **Dogs**: welcome on leads in the courtyard and on estate walks.

Access: 🅿️🏛️♿🛗📷📱🔊🅿️ **Building** ♿🚻♿
Tea-room ♿🅿️♿ **Grounds** ♿♿

Find out more: 01458 224471 or lytescarymanor@nationaltrust.org.uk

Lytes Cary Manor		M	T	W	T	F	S	S
4 Jan–23 Feb*	10–2	·	·	·	·	·	S	S
29 Feb–1 Nov	10:30–5**	M	T	W	T	F	S	S
7 Nov–27 Dec*	10–2	·	·	·	·	·	S	S

*Garden (limited viewing), tea-room and shop only (not house). **House opens 11 to 4:30 (timed tickets at peak times); tea-room closes 4:45. Estate walks open dawn to dusk.

Lytes Cary Manor in Somerset, above and below, is surrounded by an uplifting Arts and Crafts-inspired garden

Mompesson House

The Close, Salisbury, Wiltshire SP1 2EL

🏠 ❄ 1952

Parking: 260 yards in city centre, not National Trust (charge including members).

Visiting Salisbury's Cathedral Close, you step back into a past world. As you enter Mompesson House, featured in the film *Sense and Sensibility*, the feeling of leaving the modern world behind deepens. The tranquil atmosphere is enhanced by the magnificent plasterwork, graceful oak staircase and fine period furniture, which are the main features of this perfectly proportioned Queen Anne town house. Mompesson House has one of the finest displays of English 18th-century drinking glasses and a collection of stumpwork, a fascinating example of raised embroidery. The garden, with traditional herbaceous borders and pergola, is an oasis of calm in Salisbury.

Gracious Mompesson House in Wiltshire, above, has elegant rooms, left, and a tranquil garden, below

Eat, shop, stay: the garden tea-room has indoor and outdoor seating and serves tea, coffee, light bites and cakes. The Studio shop in the courtyard offers a range of gifts for you and your home.

Things to see and do: Indoors Special exhibition: 'Inspired? Mompesson House and the Creative Arts'. Family trail. **Outdoors** Family trail and toys and games on the lawn in summer. Events, including music in the garden. **Dogs**: assistance dogs only.

Access: 🐕♿🚻🎫📷🚪👶📖 🅿 Building 🔲🔳 Grounds 🔲🔳

Find out more: 01722 335659 or mompessonhouse@nationaltrust.org.uk

Mompesson House		M	T	W	T	F	S	S
7 Mar–1 Nov	11–5*	M	T	W	T	F	S	S
25 Nov–20 Dec**	11–3:30			W	T	F	S	S

*Closes at 4 from 25 October.
**Ground floor rooms decorated for Christmas.

Montacute House

Montacute, Somerset TA15 6XP

🏛️ ❖ ❦ ⬚ 1931

Parking: on site.

This architecturally daring Elizabethan mansion was built to flaunt both wealth and power. Today its glittering façade shelters nationally important collections of furniture and textiles: 500-year-old tapestries exquisitely worked with heroes, saints, fishes and flowers; samplers touchingly stitched by little fingers; and more than 50 portraits on loan from the National Portrait Gallery. Outside, you can walk in Elizabethan footsteps through a formal garden, broken by cloud-pruned hedges and Victorian floral profusion. Wide lawns create open spaces, while avenues of trees lead you out into parkland, bluebell woods and a former motte-and-bailey castle now topped by an 18th-century folly. **Note**: this year conservation work may be undertaken on the staircases – please check before visiting.

Eat, shop, stay: café serving freshly made seasonal lunches and tempting cakes; dogs welcome in outside courtyard. Gift shop, plant sales and second-hand bookshop. Farmers' markets. Two historic holiday cottages on the estate.

Built to impress, Montacute House in Somerset, above and left, epitomises Elizabethan pomp and style

Things to see and do: **Indoors** Family trails and activities. **Outdoors** Regular 'Welcome' tours, seasonal events, family trails and open-air theatre. **Dogs**: welcome in garden and café courtyard (on short leads). Elsewhere, assistance dogs only.

Access:
Building 🏠🏠🏠 Grounds 🏠➡️🏠

Find out more: 01935 823289 or montacute@nationaltrust.org.uk

Montacute House		M	T	W	T	F	S	S
House								
1 Jan–1 Mar	11–3	M	T	W	T	F	S	S
2 Mar–1 Nov	11–4:30	M	T	W	T	F	S	S
2 Nov–31 Dec	11–3*	M	T	W	T	F	S	S
Garden, parkland, café and shop								
1 Jan–1 Mar	10–4	M	T	W	T	F	S	S
2 Mar–1 Nov	10–5	M	T	W	T	F	S	S
2 Nov–31 Dec	10–4*	M	T	W	T	F	S	S

House: visitor routes vary depending on essential conservation work. *19 to 31 December: house open 12 to 5; everything open 10 to 6. Closed 24 and 25 December.

Priest's House, Muchelney

Muchelney, Langport, Somerset TA10 0DQ 1911

Medieval hall-house, built in 1308.
Note: private home. Sorry no toilet or parking. For satnav use TA10 0DQ. Open Sunday and Monday, 5 April to 28 September, 2 to 5.

Find out more: 01935 823289 or priestshouse@nationaltrust.org.uk

Prior Park Landscape Garden

Ralph Allen Drive, Bath, Somerset BA2 5AH

⚜ 1993

Parking: on site for disabled visitors only (may not be available Monday to Friday during project, please telephone for information). Car parks in city centre, 1 mile (steep, uphill walk), not National Trust (charge including members). Frequent bus services from bus station or City Sightseeing bus (Skyline route) from city centre.

Perched on a hillside overlooking Bath, this elevated spot was chosen by Ralph Allen to show off his estate to the city. The magical landscape garden that he created captures a moment in time: 1764, the year of Allen's death.

There is a lot to discover, including winding paths leading to hidden retreats, dramatic views over Bath and a rare Palladian Bridge. This year sees the continuation of our major restoration project to repair the 18th-century dams. Access to the lakes may be restricted, but you'll have a once-in-a-lifetime opportunity to see the work in progress. **Note**: no parking on site. Steep slopes, steps, uneven paths. House not accessible (not National Trust).

Eat, shop, stay: Tea Shed serving light snacks, cakes and refreshments (outdoor seating only). Small shop next to visitor reception offering a selection of National Trust products.

Things to see and do: events and activities all year. Free 'Discover the Dams' tours. Natural play area and seasonal trails. The Bath Skyline 6-mile circular walk is just minutes from the garden. **Dogs**: welcome on short leads.

Restoration of the 18th-century dams continues at magical Prior Park Landscape Garden in Bath, Somerset

Creative activities at Prior Park Landscape Garden

Access: 🖼️ 🔁

Find out more: 01225 833977 or
priorpark@nationaltrust.org.uk

Prior Park		M	T	W	T	F	S	S
4 Jan–26 Jan*	10–4	.	.	.	.	.	S	S
1 Feb–1 Nov	10–5:30**	M	T	W	T	F	S	S
7 Nov–27 Dec	10–4	.	.	.	.	.	S	S

Last admission one hour before closing. *Also open 1 January.
**Closes dusk if earlier. Tea Shed opening times vary.

Sand Point

near Kewstoke, North Somerset 1964

A natural pier into the Bristol Channel,
north of Weston-super-Mare and Brean Down.
Perfect for picnics; views across Sand Bay.
Note: for satnav use BS22 9UD. Steep climbs
and cliffs – please stay on main paths.
Tide comes in quickly. Sorry, no toilets.

Find out more: 01278 751874 or
sandpoint@nationaltrust.org.uk

Selworthy

on Exmoor, near Minehead, Somerset

✠ 🏚 🛏️ 🔁 1944

Satnav: use TA24 8TP. **Parking**: on site.

Selworthy is a good place to start discovering
the wonderfully varied Exmoor landscapes
within the 4,856-hectare (12,500-acre)
Holnicote Estate. This is a timeless rural
landscape of thatched cottages, a medieval
church, woodland walks and sweeping
views across the vale to Dunkery Beacon,
Exmoor's highest point.

Selworthy in Somerset, with its thatched cottages and fine
church, is an excellent starting point for exploring Exmoor

Eat, shop, stay: Periwinkle Cottage Tea-room
and Clematis Cottage shop (tenant/National
Trust partnership) are top spots for treats and
trinkets. Or stay a little longer in romantic,
thatched Ivy's Cottage (sleeps two).

Things to see and do: a walk through
the woods leads to Bury Castle, an
Iron Age hill fort. The whitewashed church
of All Saints looks out over the vale.
Dogs: welcome on leads.

Find out more: 01643 862452 or
selworthy@nationaltrust.org.uk

Stoke-sub-Hamdon Priory

North Street, Stoke-sub-Hamdon,
Somerset TA14 6QP 1946

Fascinating small complex of buildings,
formerly the home of priests serving the
Chapel of St Nicholas (now destroyed).
Note: sorry no toilet or parking. Please respect
the privacy of tenants in the main house.
Conservation work on the roofs may affect
your visit – please check before setting out.
Open Sunday and Monday, 5 April to
28 September, 2 to 5.

Find out more: 01935 823289 or
stokehamdonpriory@nationaltrust.org.uk

Stonehenge Landscape in Wiltshire, above and left,
has miles of walks and a wealth of ancient monuments

Stonehenge Landscape

near Amesbury, Wiltshire

🏛 ♿ 1927

Satnav: use SP3 4DX.
Parking: at visitor centre (English Heritage),
free to Trust members displaying Trust sticker.
Booking is recommended to guarantee a space.
Limited parking at Woodhenge.

You can wander freely through thousands of
acres of downland within the Stonehenge and
Avebury World Heritage Site. The landscape
around the famous stones is studded with
ancient monuments, such as the Avenue and
Cursus, and abounds with wildlife. The visitor
centre shuttle stops at Fargo woodland on
request. **Note**: English Heritage manages stone
circle, visitor centre/car park. Bookings via
english-heritage.org.uk. Pay and display car
park free to Trust members (booking essential).
Trust members enter free (excluding
International National Trust or affiliate
membership organisation members).

Eat, shop, stay: café and shop at visitor centre
(not National Trust).

Things to see and do: guided walks
and family activities throughout the year.
Dogs: assistance dogs only.

Access: 🅿♿🐕

Find out more: 0370 333 1181 (English
Heritage). 01672 539920 (National Trust) or
stonehenge@nationaltrust.org.uk

Stourhead

near Mere, Wiltshire BA12 6QF

🏠✝🍴🏛♿♿🛋🔔🍽 1946

Parking: 400 yards. King Alfred's Tower, 100 yards.

'A living work of art' is how Stourhead was described when it first opened nearly 300 years ago. The world-famous landscape garden surrounds a glistening lake. There are towering trees, exotic rhododendrons, classical temples and a magical grotto to explore. The house at Stourhead was one of the first in the country to showcase Palladian architecture. With a unique Regency library, Chippendale furniture and inspirational paintings, this was a grand family home, shaped by generations of the Hoare family. Outside, views stretch across the countryside, and the lawns are perfect for picnics. Great for walking and wildlife spotting, with 1,072 hectares (2,650 acres) of chalk downs, ancient woods, Iron Age hill forts and farmland to explore.

Eat, shop, stay: restaurant, shop with garden and plant selection and a second-hand bookshop. Spread Eagle Inn, ice-cream parlour, Red Lion pub, farm shop and art gallery (all concessions). Picnics welcome. Holiday cottage by garden entrance, CL site for Caravan Club members.

Things to see and do: **Indoors** Before exploring the collection, you can discover a potted history of Stourhead in the house basement. Learn how the Hoare family rose from yeoman farmers to landed gentry, and how they created the Stourhead we know and love today. **Outdoors** Stourhead has offered refreshment for the mind, body and spirit for generations. Today families can enjoy fun activities, from holiday trails to summer workshops, activity packs and creating special Christmas memories. Guided walks and talks explore seasonal highlights throughout the year. Hidden gems such as King Alfred's Tower await you on the wider estate. **Dogs**: in garden on short fixed leads – March to November, after 3; December to February, all day.

Stourhead, Wiltshire, this page and opposite: a mirror-like lake surrounded by follies, is set against steep wooded slopes. The house has a unique Regency library, below right

Access: 🅿️🚌♿🚻🛗📷🎡👓🐕🔈🚫🐕

House 🛗📷♿ **Landscape garden** ➡️♿

Find out more: 01747 841152 or
stourhead@nationaltrust.org.uk

Stourhead		M	T	W	T	F	S	S
Garden								
Open all year	9–5*	M	T	W	T	F	S	S
House								
7 Mar–8 Nov	11–4:30**	M	T	W	T	F	S	S
21 Nov–23 Dec†	11–3:30	M	T	W	T	F	S	S
King Alfred's Tower								
7 Mar–25 Oct	12–4						S	S

*Closes at 6 in main season (30 March to 25 October),
3 during 'Christmas at Stourhead' (27 November to
31 December), or dusk if earlier. **Closes at 3:30 after
25 October. †Selected show rooms only, decorated
for Christmas. Everything closed 25 December.
King Alfred's Tower is open more often at popular times,
including Bank Holidays (check before setting out).

Tintinhull Garden

Farm Street, Tintinhull, Yeovil,
Somerset BA22 8PZ

⚜ ⛵ 1953

Parking: 150 yards.

The vision of Phyllis Reiss, amateur gardener,
lives on in this small yet perfectly formed
garden, with 'living rooms' of colour and
scent. Created in the last century around a
17th-century manor house, it's one of the most
harmonious small gardens in Britain, featuring
secluded lawns, pools and imaginative borders.

Eat, shop, stay: tea-room serving cakes
and cream teas. Small shop and plant sales.
You can stay for longer in the holiday cottage
that forms part of Tintinhull House.

Colour, scent, graceful pools and imaginative
borders characterise harmonious Tintinhull Garden
in Somerset, right and below

Things to see and do: arboretum and
orchard producing apple juice sold
on site. Why not combine with a visit to
Montacute House or Lytes Cary Manor?
Dogs: welcome in courtyard only.

Access: 🚐🖑♿👓🅿◨ Garden 🚐🏠♿

Find out more: 01458 224471 or
tintinhull@nationaltrust.org.uk

Tintinhull Garden			M	T	W	T	F	S	S
28 Mar–27 Sep	11–5		**M**	**T**	**W**	**T**	**F**	**S**	**S**
Tea-room closes at 4:45.									

Treasurer's House, Martock

Martock, Somerset TA12 6JL 1971

Completed in 1293, this medieval house
includes a Great Hall, 15th-century kitchen and
an unusual wall-painting. **Note**: private home.
Sorry no toilets or parking. Open Sunday and
Monday, 5 April to 28 September, 2 to 5.

Find out more: 01935 823289 or
treasurersmartock@nationaltrust.org.uk

Tyntesfield

Wraxall, Bristol, North Somerset BS48 1NX

🏠✝🧷♿👜☕ 2002

Parking: 550 yards.

Cocooned in the Somerset countryside, Tyntesfield is a rare survivor – a near-complete Victorian Gothic country house and estate. It was created for the Gibbs family to celebrate their achievements, raise their children and share their passions for family and faith. The richly decorated house contains over 60,000 of the family's possessions, some collected by William Gibbs as he traded in the Hispanic world. Born in Madrid, William's story is one of long struggles with sacred debts, of young love, loss, a close-knit family and the making of a vast fortune. Today you're welcomed into this cherished place with its ornate private chapel, flower-filled terraces, towering trees, abundant kitchen garden and views across the working estate to the Somerset hills. **Note**: entry to the house is by timed ticket only (booking online in advance is advised).

Eat, shop, stay: restaurant at Home Farm visitor centre and café in grounds serving dishes inspired by Tyntesfield's history, using ingredients grown on the estate. Shop offering plant sales, gifts and local artisan products. Second-hand bookshop. Three holiday cottages on the estate.

Things to see and do: **Indoors**: Knowledgeable house guides share the story of the Gibbs family life. You can follow family trails and play at dressing up. Regular opportunities to witness conservation in action and guided tours at certain times of year. A Very Victorian Christmas (November to January).

Tyntesfield, North Somerset: the spectacular Victorian Gothic house, below, and garden, above

Tyntesfield's terrace, above. There's plenty for all ages to enjoy in three play areas, below

Outdoors: Free daily guided walks on the history of the Tyntesfield Estate (check times on arrival). Extensive parkland, formal garden and seasonal kitchen garden, growing flowers for house arrangements and produce for the restaurant and café. Three play areas, including a woodland adventure trail and den-building village. Changing events and things to do throughout the season.
Dogs: welcome on short leads in specified areas (map available from ticket office).

Access: ⬚⬚⬚⬚⬚⬚⬚⬚⬚⬚⬚⬚
House ⬚⬚⬚⬚⬚ Grounds ⬚⬚⬚⬚⬚

Find out more: 0344 800 4966 (Infoline). 01275 461900 or tyntesfield@nationaltrust.org.uk

Tyntesfield		M	T	W	T	F	S	S
House								
1 Jan–15 Mar	11–3†	M	T	W	T	F	S	S
16 Mar–1 Nov	11–5	M	T	W	T	F	S	S
2 Nov–27 Nov	11–3†	M	T	W	T	F	S	S
28 Nov–31 Dec	*	M	T	W	T	F	S	S
Estate and garden								
Open all year	10–5**	M	T	W	T	F	S	S

†Tours only on weekdays, freeflow visits on weekends. Timed tickets to house, limited availability. *For Christmas opening, including regular late nights, please see website for details. 24 and 31 December house closes at 2, estate closes at 3. Everything closed 25 December. **Close at 6 in main season. Shop and restaurant close 30 minutes before estate and garden. Last entry one hour before closing.

Webber's Post

on Exmoor, near Minehead, Somerset 1944

Great spot for views over Horner Wood, short strolls, cycling, picnics and walking up to Dunkery Beacon, Exmoor's highest point. **Note**: for satnav use TA24 8TB and follow signs to Webber's Post. Sorry no toilets.

Find out more: 01643 862452 or webberspost@nationaltrust.org.uk

Places may occasionally close for events or bad weather, check at nationaltrust.org.uk

Wellington Monument

near Wellington, Somerset

🏛 1934

Satnav: use TA21 9PB.
Parking: small car park, ⅓ mile.

Standing in an informal rural setting on the edge of the Blackdown Hills, Wellington Monument (above) is undergoing major repairs. The Trust is still raising vital funds towards these, and welcomes donations and involvement in the campaign. **Note**: essential repairs all year (under scaffolding). Sorry no toilet.

Things to see and do: see conservation in action on a tour.

Find out more: 01823 451587 or wellingtonmonument@nationaltrust.org.uk

Westwood Manor

Westwood, near Bradford on Avon, Wiltshire BA15 2AF

🏛 ✚ ❋ 1960

Parking: 90 yards.

Over the centuries, the residents of this small late medieval, Tudor and Jacobean house have modified the building to their own tastes, each leaving a permanent mark. The interiors are rich with decorative plasterwork, fine furniture and beautiful tapestries. Highlights are two rare keyboard instruments: a spinet and a virginal. **Note**: Westwood Manor is a family home, administered by the tenants.

Eat, shop, stay: fascinating guidebook, postcards and CD of Elizabethan music recorded on the virginal and spinet. Tea and cake (and toilets) available in parish room next door (not National Trust).

Things to see and do: children's quizzes (house suitable for over fives). Close to Lacock, The Courts Garden at Holt and Great Chalfield Manor and Garden.

Access: 📖 ⠿ ⌖ Manor ♿ ♿ Garden ♿

Find out more: 01225 863374 or westwoodmanor@nationaltrust.org.uk

Westwood Manor		M	T	W	T	F	S	S
1 Apr–30 Sep	2–5		T	W				S

Groups (eight people plus): please contact tenant on 01225 863374 to arrange private tour.

Westwood Manor in Wiltshire is still a family home today

Additional coastal and countryside car parks in Somerset and Wiltshire

Somerset

Sand Point	BS22 9UD
Staple Plain, Quantock Hills	TA4 4DQ
Holford	TA5 1SE
Quarts Moor	EX15 3UZ
King's Wood, Mendip Hills	BS25 1DH
Ivy Thorn, Polden Hills	BA16 0TZ
Walton Hill, Polden Hills	BA16 9RD

Wiltshire

Whitesheet Hill	BA12 6RP
Win Green Hill	SP5 5AW
Overton Hill	SN8 1QG
Pepperbox Hill	SP5 3QL
Cley Hill	BA12 7QU

'There is such a sense of freedom at Dyrham and children can explore and have fun. It has a perfect mix of wild open fields, wildlife, beautiful gardens and flowers, as well as the house itself. It's definitely one of our happy places.'

Nell Mallia on how Dyrham Park feels like a home away from home for her and her family

The Cotswolds, Buckinghamshire and Oxfordshire

Enjoying a new perspective at Dyrham Park, South Gloucestershire. Competition entry from Nell Mallia

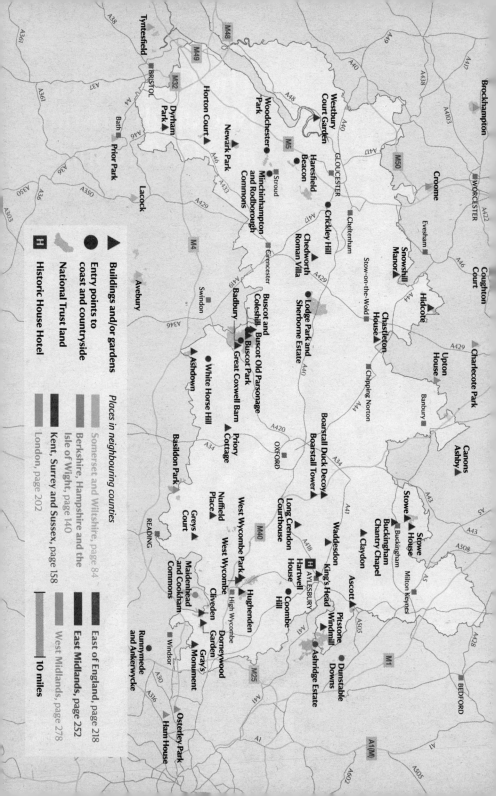

H   Historic House Hotel

National Trust land

Buildings and/or gardens

Entry points to
coast and countryside

Places in neighbouring counties

Somerset and Wiltshire, page 84

Berkshire, Hampshire and the
Isle of Wight, page 140

Kent, Surrey and Sussex, page 158

London, page 202

East of England, page 218

East Midlands, page 252

West Midlands, page 278

10 miles

Ascott

Wing, near Leighton Buzzard,
Buckinghamshire LU7 0PP

🏠✹♿ 1949

Parking: on site (218 yards).

Ascott House (above), an 'Old English'
half-timbered manor, dates back to the 16th
century. It was transformed by the Rothschilds
towards the end of the 19th century and
houses several exceptional collections. The
extensive gardens are an attractive mix of
formal and natural, with specimen trees,
shrubs and beautiful herbaceous borders.
Note: Ascott is a family home, administered
by the de Rothschild family.

Eat, shop, stay: tea-room offering light
lunches, afternoon tea, ice cream and hot and
cold drinks. Shop and takeaway selling food
and drinks, souvenirs, guidebooks, plants,
flowers and kitchen garden produce in season.

Things to see and do: Dutch Masters and
Stubbs, Gainsborough and Reynolds paintings.
Fine furniture and amazing collection
of oriental porcelain. Relaxing cricket
matches most summer weekends.
Dogs: assistance dogs only.

Access: 🅿️🅳♿🎟️🖐️♿
Building 🔆♿♿ Grounds 🔆♿♿

Find out more: 01296 688242 or
ascott@nationaltrust.org.uk

Ascott		M	T	W	T	F	S	S
House and garden								
17 Mar–20 Sep*	12–6**			T	W	T	F	S	S

*Open Bank Holiday Mondays. **House: open 2 to 5 (entrance
by timed ticket only); tea-room open 12 to 5:30. **National
Gardens Scheme: 25 May and 31 August (£6 charge,
including members); house closed. Grounds: last entry at 5.

Ashdown

Lambourn, Newbury, Oxfordshire RG17 8RE

🏠🏛️✹♿ 1956

Satnav: from B4000 follow local brown signs.
Parking: in main estate car park, 437 yards.

Unique 17th-century chalk-block hunting
lodge, with doll's-house appearance, built for
the Queen of Bohemia by the Earl of Craven,
set in a historic woodland. The guided tour,
which reveals an intriguing family history, leads
up the staircase hung with fine 17th-century
paintings. Outstanding rooftop views across
three counties. **Note**: access to roof via
100-step staircase. Admission by guided tour
only (tickets available on arrival).

Things to see and do: guided staircase tour.
White Horse Hill nearby. **Dogs**: welcome on
leads in woodland only.

Access: ♿🖐️🖥️ Building 🔆 Grounds ♿

Find out more: 01793 762209 or
ashdown@nationaltrust.org.uk

Ashdown		M	T	W	T	F	S	S
House								
1 Apr–31 Oct	Tour*			W			S	
Woodland								
Open all year	Dawn–dusk	M	T	W	T	F	S	S

*House: open 2 to 5; admission by guided tour only,
2:15, 3:15 and 4:15.

Ashdown in Oxfordshire: looking across
three counties from Ashdown House

Badbury

Coleshill, near Swindon

⌖ 2011

Satnav: use SN7 7NJ (does not take you directly to car park).
Parking: at countryside car park.

This former plantation woodland is criss-crossed with easy circular walks, offering stunning views over the Upper Thames Valley. A spread of snowdrops heralds spring, followed by a carpet of bluebells. A copse of military-straight beech trees defines the Iron Age hill fort. **Note**: sorry no toilets.

Eat, shop, stay: three holiday cottages on the Buscot and Coleshill Estates.

Things to see and do: perfect woodland for family adventures and den-building. Natural woodland wild play area. Great Coxwell Barn nearby. **Dogs**: welcome under close control.

Find out more: 01793 762209 or badbury@nationaltrust.org.uk

There are wonderful circular walks and stunning views to be enjoyed at Badbury, near Swindon

Boarstall Duck Decoy

Boarstall, near Bicester,
Buckinghamshire HP18 9UX 1980

One of the last remaining decoys in the country, a fascinating insight into rural life. Natural play area for children.
Note: open Mondays and weekends, 7 March to 1 November, 11 to 5.
Also open Good Friday.

Find out more: 01280 817156 or boarstalldecoy@nationaltrust.org.uk

Boarstall Tower

Boarstall, near Bicester,
Buckinghamshire HP18 9UX 1943

Charming 14th-century moated gatehouse set in beautiful gardens, retaining original fortified appearance. Grade I listed.
Note: access to upper levels is via a spiral staircase. Approach paths not suitable for wheelchairs. Open on selected days between 1 April and 31 October, call for details.

Find out more: 01280 817156 or boarstalltower@nationaltrust.org.uk

Buckingham Chantry Chapel

Market Hill, Buckingham,
Buckinghamshire MK18 1JX 1912

Atmospheric 15th-century chapel, restored by Sir Gilbert Scott in 1875. Today it is a thriving coffee shop and second-hand bookshop.
Note: open Tuesday, Wednesday, Friday and Saturday, 3 January to 19 December, 10 to 3 (to 4 on Saturday).

Find out more: 01280 817156 or buckinghamchantry@nationaltrust.org.uk

The Buscot and Coleshill Estates

Coleshill, near Swindon

✠ 🏛 🍴 ♿ 🛏 1956

The Buscot and Coleshill Estates, near Swindon

Satnav: use SN6 7PT.
Parking: at Buscot car park, Coleshill Old Carpenters Yard and by Coleshill Estate office.

These countryside estates on the western border of Oxfordshire include the attractive, unspoilt villages of Buscot and Coleshill, each with a thriving tea-room. There are circular walks of differing lengths and a series of footpaths criss-crossing the estates, with breathtaking countryside and wildlife at Buscot Lock and Badbury Hill. **Note:** toilets at the Old Carpenters Yard in Coleshill, outside the estate office and in Buscot.

Eat, shop, stay: Coleshill Carpenters Canteen café, Buscot tea-room and The Radnor Arms (none National Trust). Three holiday cottages.

Things to see and do: guided walks all year, including tours of the Second World War bunker. Restored watermill in action. Replica operational bunker (special open afternoons). **Dogs:** welcome on leads near livestock and under close control at all times.

Find out more: 01793 762209 or buscotandcoleshill@nationaltrust.org.uk

Buscot and Coleshill		
Coleshill watermill and replica operational bunker open second Sunday of the month: April to October, 2 to 5. Countryside and footpaths open dawn to dusk.		

Buscot Old Parsonage

Buscot, Faringdon, Oxfordshire SN7 8DQ 1949

Early 18th-century house with small walled garden, on the banks of the Thames.
Note: no toilets. Open Wednesdays, 1 April to 28 October, 2 to 6 (admission by email).

Find out more: 01793 762209 or buscot@nationaltrust.org.uk

Buscot Park

Faringdon, Oxfordshire SN7 8BU

🏛 ✿ ♿ 1949

Parking: on site.

Lord Faringdon's family live in the house, maintain the interior, manage the grounds, gardens and tea-room, and are responsible for the public display of the contents owned by The Faringdon Collection Trust. This unusual arrangement with the National Trust breathes life into the property and gives it an individualistic air.

Eat, shop, stay: tea-room (not National Trust), serving cream teas, cakes and ice cream. Local goods and garden produce. Ice cream. Picnics.

Things to see and do: occasional events in grounds and theatre (available for hire).
Dogs: in paddock (overflow car park) only.

Access: 🅿️ 🚻 ⬆️ 🔔 📷 🎵 ⠿ House 🛗 🚶
Grounds 🚶 🏛 ♿ ➡️ 🐑 ♿

Find out more: 01367 240932 (Infoline). 01367 240786 or buscotpark.com buscotpark@nationaltrust.org.uk

Buscot Park		M	T	W	T	F	S	S
House, grounds and tea-room								
1 Apr–30 Sep*	2–6	·	·	W	T	F	·	·
Grounds only								
6 Apr–29 Sep	2–6	M	T	·	·	·	·	·

*Occasional weekend openings. House: last admission one hour before closing. Open Bank Holiday Mondays.

Chastleton House

near Moreton-in-Marsh, Oxfordshire

🏠 ❀ 1991

Satnav: use GL56 0SP to the Greedy Goose pub, then follow brown signs.
Parking: on site at visitor centre. Limited accessible parking available by request only by visitor centre. No roadside parking.

Within the warm, weathered Cotswold stone walls of this ancient country house (above), lie faded elegant interiors full of myths and memories – a compelling time capsule of 400 years of family life. Discover the secrets they hide, then explore the garden, a sleeping beauty preserved in graceful decline.
Note: entry by timed ticket, available at visitor centre. House is challenging for the less able.

Eat, shop, stay: local ice cream, honey from Chastleton's hives, plants and garden produce available. Old Garage second-hand bookshop. Light refreshments available most days in church (not National Trust). Picnics welcome in garden.

Things to see and do: Indoors Experience the romantic decline of a country manor. The Old Garage second-hand bookshop. Introductory film. Family explorer packs. **Outdoors** Croquet on the lawn. **Dogs**: assistance dogs only.

Access: 🅿️♿🏷️🏛️🎫🔈 Building 🏠 Garden 🏠

Find out more: 01494 755560 (Infoline). 01608 674355 or chastleton@nationaltrust.org.uk Chastleton, near Moreton-in-Marsh, Oxfordshire GL56 0SU

Chastleton House		M	T	W	T	F	S	S
4 Mar–1 Nov	1–5*			W	T	F	S	S

*House: last entry one hour before closing.

Chedworth Roman Villa

Yanworth, near Cheltenham, Gloucestershire GL54 3LJ

🏛️ 1924

Parking: on lane at entrance, plus woodland overflow (March to October).

Cradled in a beautiful wooded valley and fed by a natural spring, this high-status Roman villa saw imperial fashions and local spirits living side by side. Nature took over and hid the magnificent mosaics, intricate hypocaust systems, bathhouses and ancient water-shrine for more than 1,500 years until Victorian gamekeepers rediscovered the site. The National Trust has, in turn, looked after Chedworth's Roman treasures and Victorian legacy for nearly a century, providing its modern villa guests with new facilities, as well as astonishing archaeology, to enjoy. It remains a hidden place of natural beauty and continual discovery.

Stone pillars for the underfloor heating system at Chedworth Roman Villa, Gloucestershire, above, and playing with pieces of mosaic, opposite

Eat, shop, stay: café serving sandwiches, soup, jacket potatoes, cakes, snacks, hot and cold drinks and ice cream. Roman-themed souvenirs, books and games, seasonal plants and National Trust gifts available in the shop.

Things to see and do: **Indoors** Guidebooks, audio guides and free guided tours. Activities, including Roman dressing up. Costumed interpreters and living history events. **Outdoors** Family activities and trails (Bank Holiday weekends and school holidays). **Dogs**: assistance dogs only.

Access: 🅿️🔄♿🔊🔆🎬📷🖼️♿ Reception ♿♿
West Range ♿♿♿ Grounds ♿♿➡️♿

Find out more: 01242 890256 or chedworth@nationaltrust.org.uk

Chedworth Roman Villa		M	T	W	T	F	S	S
8 Feb–28 Mar	10–4	M	T	W	T	F	S	S
29 Mar–24 Oct	10–5	M	T	W	T	F	S	S
25 Oct–22 Nov	10–4	M	T	W	T	F	S	S

Claydon

Middle Claydon, near Buckingham, Buckinghamshire MK18 2EY

🏠➕❄️♿🔔🍽️ 1956

Parking: on site, limited hard-standing parking.

Nestled in peaceful parkland, the simple Georgian exterior hides a lavish interior (below) showcasing every 18th-century style imaginable, from Palladian and Neo-classical to Chinoiserie and Gothick fantasy, with exceptional Rococo carvings. Florence Nightingale had her own rooms at Claydon, spending many summers looking out over the lakes and medieval church. **Note**: garden entry charges apply (including members).

Eat, shop, stay: shop and second-hand bookshop. Independent courtyard shops, galleries and tea-room (not National Trust). Formal grass terrace and spacious lawn area, ideal for picnics. All Saints Parish Church open.

Things to see and do: Florence Nightingale's bicentenary year: special events, children's trails and dressing up. **Dogs**: welcome on leads in the courtyard and parkland. Assistance dogs only in the gardens.

Access: 🅿️🔄♿🔊🔆🎬📷🖼️♿
House ♿♿♿ Grounds ♿♿➡️♿

Find out more: 01296 730349 or claydon@nationaltrust.org.uk

Claydon		M	T	W	T	F	S	S
House and grounds*								
7 Mar–1 Nov**	11–4	M	T	W	·	·	S	S

*House: opens 12 to 4. **Open Fridays, 24 July to 28 August. Open Bank Holidays. Phoenix Kitchens (not National Trust): open 10 to 4.

Cliveden

near Maidenhead, Buckinghamshire

🏠 ❄ 🐾 🚻 1942

Satnav: for gardens use Cliveden Road and SL1 8NS; for woodlands use SL6 0HJ. **Parking**: on site.

A majestic vision set high above the Thames, Cliveden is a proud celebration of status and splendour, where the charms of art and nature join. Six powerful families have embellished and enhanced Cliveden's history over the course of 350 years. Each family added their own extravagant touch, creating a series of distinctive and delightful gardens. You can discover vibrant floral displays at the grand Parterre, satisfying symmetry in the Long Garden, the tranquil intimacy of the Rose Garden and rich autumn colour within the oriental Water Garden. The tree-lined avenue of the Green Drive is the spine of the estate, acting as a gateway to the miles of footpaths that meander through the majestic woodlands and along the riverbank. **Note**: overnight mooring available on Cliveden Reach, does not include entry.

Eat, shop, stay: Conservatory Café serving lunch and snacks. Outdoor kiosk (dog-friendly) serving light refreshments. Doll's House seasonal 'grab and go' beside play area, designed for families. Shop and plant centre. Second-hand bookshop. Picnic areas.

Things to see and do: **Indoors** Guided tours of the house (now a hotel) on certain days.

The elaborate Parterre at Cliveden in Buckinghamshire, which is set high above the Thames

Springtime daffodils at Cliveden

Outdoors More than 70,000 bedding plants create striking displays in spring, summer and early autumn. In March and April you can experience 'Gilded Gardens' where you can see hundreds of daffodils in the formal gardens. The fragrant Rose Garden blooms from June until September. Highlights for families include the storybook-themed play area, yew-tree maze, woodland play trail and den-building area. Events include open-air theatre, seasonal trails, guided walks and workshops. Boat trips on the Thames (April to October, additional charge including members).
Dogs: welcome under close control in woodlands; other locations on a short lead.

Access: ⬚⬚⬚⬚⬚⬚⬚⬚ House (hotel) ⬚⬚ Chapel ⬚ Garden ⬚⬚⬚⬚⬚

Find out more: 01628 605069 or cliveden@nationaltrust.org.uk
Cliveden Road, Taplow, Maidenhead, Buckinghamshire SL1 8NS

Cliveden	
Garden, shop, café and woodland	
Open every day all year	10–5*

House and chapel: limited opening April to October (call for details). House: admission by timed ticket only (available from Information Centre). *1 January to 14 February and 2 November to 31 December: estate closes 4. Everything closed 24 and 25 December.

Coombe Hill

Butler's Cross, near Wendover, Buckinghamshire 1918

Nationally important chalk grassland site and the highest viewpoint in the Chilterns with stunning views over the Aylesbury Vale.
Note: for satnav use HP17 0UR. Picnic area and play trail. Sorry no toilet.

Find out more: 01494 755573 or coombehill@nationaltrust.org.uk

Crickley Hill

Birdlip, Gloucestershire GL4 8JY 1935

Sitting high on the Cotswold escarpment with views towards the Welsh hills, Crickley Hill overlooks Gloucester and Cheltenham.
Note: car park, café, toilets and visitor centre not National Trust. For satnav use GL4 8JY. Parking charges (including members).

Find out more: 01452 814213 or crickleyhill@nationaltrust.org.uk

Dorneywood Garden

Dorneywood, Dorney Wood Road, Burnham, Buckinghamshire SL1 8PY 1942

Ministerial residence since 1954 with country garden. Teas. Open selected afternoons (dates may change at short notice).
Note: no photography. Visitor details recorded for security reasons. House and garden: open daily, 5 to 15 July, 2 to 4:30. Garden: open Wednesday and Thursday, 13 May to 13 August and 2 September to 24 September, 2 to 4. Booking essential via email. May be closed at short notice, please check before travelling.

Find out more: dorneywood@nationaltrust.org.uk

Dyrham Park

Dyrham, near Bath,
South Gloucestershire SN14 8HY

🏛🕇✚♿ 1961

Satnav: enter via A46.
Parking: on site (just over ½ mile from house).

This year we are in the middle of a £10-million project to restore, revitalise and reimagine Dyrham Park, including the house, park, garden and facilities. The aim is to keep a section of the 17th-century house open throughout the project, so that visitors will be able to keep up with the works, see a selection of items from the collection and get a taste of the conservation work being carried out. Parkland adventurers can savour far-reaching views towards the Welsh hills or encounter the majestic herd of fallow deer. For inspiration and tranquillity, you can wander round the ever-changing garden. Sumptuous planting in the Pool Garden contrasts with the formality of The Avenue set against the peaceful wooded terraces. **Note**: please check the website before visiting to find out what you can expect to see.

Eat, shop, stay: tea-room (indoor seating) and tea garden (outdoor seating) serving lunch, cakes and refreshments. Courtyard kiosk offering drinks, ice cream and snacks on busy days. Picnics are welcome in certain areas. Shop selling plants, books, local products and gifts. Second-hand bookshop.

Things to see and do: **Indoors** As the house project develops, access will vary so please check ahead for the latest tours and up-to-date information online. You'll be able to get a taste of the 17th century with a collection of ceramics and art dating from house builder William Blathwayt's time in Holland. **Outdoors** Access to certain areas may also be affected but there will be year-round events and activities, guided tours of the park and garden, self-led trails and walks. For families there's a natural play area, where younger children can explore the allotment and wooden climbing area. New play activities coming this year.

Parking is free for members, but don't forget to scan your card in the car park when you visit

Dogs: assistance dogs only.

Access: ⓟ♿🚻♿🚾♿📷♿

House ♿♿♿ Grounds ♿➡️

Find out more: 0117 937 2501 or
dyrhampark@nationaltrust.org.uk

Dyrham Park		M	T	W	T	F	S	S
Park, garden, shop and tea-room								
Open all year*	10–4	M	T	W	T	F	S	S
House								
6 Jan–14 Feb	Tour†	M	T	W	T	F	S	S
15 Feb–24 Oct	11–5	M	T	W	T	F	S	S
25 Oct–31 Dec**	Tour†	M	T	W	T	F	S	S

Last admission one hour before closing. *15 February to
24 October: park, garden, shop and tea-room open until 5.
Everything closed until 1 on 9, 16, 23, 30 September; 4, 11, 18,
25 November; 2, 9 December. **Everything closed 24 and
25 December. †During busy periods, the house may open
as freeflow instead of tours.

**Dyrham Park in South Gloucestershire, this page and
opposite, is being restored, revitalised and reimagined**

Gray's Monument

Stoke Poges, Buckinghamshire SL2 4NZ [1925]

This 5-metre-high monument, surrounded by expansive parkland views, captures the poet Thomas Gray's long association with the village. **Note**: gate open from dawn to dusk. Limited parking. Sorry no toilet or tea-room.

Find out more: 01628 605069 (Cliveden) or graysmonument@nationaltrust.org.uk

Great Coxwell Barn

Great Coxwell, Faringdon, Oxfordshire SN7 7LZ [1956]

Former 13th-century monastic barn, a favourite of William Morris, who would regularly bring his guests to wonder at its structure.
Note: sorry no toilet; narrow access lanes leading to property.

Find out more: 01793 762209 or greatcoxwellbarn@nationaltrust.org.uk

Greys Court

Rotherfield Greys, Henley-on-Thames, Oxfordshire RG9 4PG

[icons] [1969]

Parking: 220 yards.

Set in the rolling hills of the Chilterns, Greys Court is a picturesque Tudor manor house surrounded by layers of history, intimate walled gardens and glorious wooded parkland. The house is warm and welcoming, unfurling the memories of the Brunner family through the rooms of their comfortable home. Across the perfect lawn, a medieval tower and patchwork of mellow brick buildings conceal an English country garden. Through an ancient arch, seasonal blooms are revealed, from bright bulbs through clematis and wisteria to glorious peonies and roses in the summer. Winter walks in the woodland are a must.

Eat, shop, stay: tea-room serving morning coffee, afternoon tea, lunches and snacks. Shop selling books, gifts, souvenirs and plants. Seasonal organic produce and plants from the gardens (when available).

Things to see and do: **Indoors** Enjoy the Brunner's comfortable family rooms. Learn about the wider history in the Cromwellian Building. **Outdoors** Discover 'rooms' in the walled gardens and explore the rambling woodland walks. **Dogs**: welcome on leads (excluding house and walled gardens).

Access: [icons]
House [icon] Tea-room [icon] Grounds [icons]

Find out more: 01491 628529 or greyscourt@nationaltrust.org.uk

Greys Court in Oxfordshire, opposite and above, is set in the rolling hills of the Chilterns

Haresfield Beacon in Gloucestershire

Greys Court		M	T	W	T	F	S	S
Garden, tea-room and shop								
Open all year	10–5*	M	T	W	T	F	S	S
House								
1 Jan–1 Mar	11–3	M	T	W	T	F	S	S
2 Mar–1 Nov	1–5**	M	T	W	T	F	S	S
2 Nov–31 Dec	11–3	M	T	W	T	F	S	S

*1 January to 1 March and 2 November to 31 December: closes at 4. **House tours at 11 and 12, tickets available from reception (places limited). 6 September: everything opens at 12 for village fête. Closed 24 and 25 December.

Haresfield Beacon

near Stroud, Gloucestershire

🏛️♿ 1931

Satnav: use GL6 6PP for Shortwood car park.
Parking: at Shortwood.

High on three spurs of the Cotswold escarpment with views towards the Brecon Beacons. Abundant wildlife and a wealth of archaeological features to discover, including long and round barrows, a hill fort and cross dyke.

Eat, shop, stay: pubs in Randwick and Haresfield (not National Trust). Occasional ice-cream vendor (not Trust). Picnics welcome.

Things to see and do: bluebells and butterflies to spot and woods to explore. Superb veteran beech trees. Fly kites or watch buzzards and kestrels.
Dogs: welcome (on leads near livestock).

Find out more: 01452 814213 or haresfieldbeacon@nationaltrust.org.uk

Hartwell House Hotel, Restaurant and Spa

Oxford Road, near Aylesbury, Buckinghamshire HP17 8NR

🏠♿🅿️📶🔔📅 2008

Elegant Grade I-listed stately home, with both Jacobean and Georgian façades, magnificent Great Hall, with exceptional ceiling, and elegant drawing rooms. Set in beautifully landscaped grounds, including ruined Gothick church, lake, bridge and 36 hectares (90 acres) of parkland. One hour from central London.
Note: access is for hotel guests only, including for luncheon, afternoon tea and dinner. Children over six welcome. Held on a long lease from the Ernest Cook Trust.

Find out more: 01296 747444 or info@hartwell-house.com hartwell-house.com

Hidcote

near Chipping Campden, Gloucestershire

❋ 🔔 ⊤ 1948

Satnav: do not use, instead follow signs to
Mickleton and then brown signs.
Parking: 100 yards.

This world-famous Arts and Crafts-inspired
garden nestles in a north Cotswolds hamlet.
Created by the talented horticulturist Major
Lawrence Johnston, Hidcote's colourful and
intricately designed outdoor spaces are full of
surprises, which change in harmony with the
seasons. Many of the unusual plants found
growing in the garden were collected from
Johnston's plant-hunting trips around the
world. Wandering along the narrow pathways,
you come across secret gardens, unexpected
views and plants that burst with colour.

Eat, shop, stay: Winthrop's Café serving hot
food until 2:30. 'Grab and go' Barn Café
serving lighter snacks. The National Trust's
largest plant centre. Shop selling exclusive
Hidcote-inspired gifts. Second-hand
bookshop. Picnics welcome in the picnic area,
close to the car park.

**Colourful borders and unusual plants are just a few of the
surprises at Hidcote in Gloucestershire, above and below**

Things to see and do: **Indoors** Exhibitions in
the chapel and manor house. **Outdoors**
Seasonal spectaculars throughout the garden.
Croquet on the lawn, or tennis using period
wooden racquets (activities are weather
dependent). **Dogs**: assistance dogs only.

Access: 🅿️ 🈂️ 🍽️ 🛗 🖼️ 🏞️ 🖼️ 🔘 🅿️
Reception 🛗 **Grounds** 🛗 🔜 🔛 🛗

Find out more: 01386 438333 or
hidcote@nationaltrust.org.uk
Hidcote Bartrim, near Chipping Campden,
Gloucestershire GL55 6LR

Hidcote		M	T	W	T	F	S	S
Garden, shop and Winthrop's Café								
4 Jan–16 Feb	11–4						S	S
17 Feb–29 Mar	11–4	M	T	W	T	F	S	S
30 Mar–27 Sep	10–6	M	T	W	T	F	S	S
28 Sep–1 Nov	11–4	M	T	W	T	F	S	S
7 Nov–20 Dec	11–4						S	S

Garden: last admission one hour before closing. In bad
weather, Barn Café, plant centre and shop may close
early. Barn Café: closed January, February, November and
December. Shop: closed January (plant centre open).

Horton Court

Horton, near Chipping Sodbury,
South Gloucestershire BS37 6QR 1949

Atmospheric manor house, with Norman hall
and Tudor loggia, on the edge of the rolling
Cotswolds countryside – now a holiday
cottage. **Note**: open 12 to 15 June, 12 to
20 September and 7 to 9 November. Advanced
booking may be required (check before visiting
for opening details/booking).

Find out more: 01453 842644 (Newark Park)
or hortoncourt@nationaltrust.org.uk

Hughenden

High Wycombe, Buckinghamshire HP14 4LA

🏠✝❀🗝️ 1947

Parking: on site.

It's hardly surprising that the unconventional Victorian Prime Minister Benjamin Disraeli so loved Hughenden. His handsome home, set in an unspoiled Chiltern valley with views of ancient woods and rolling hills, is full of fascinating personal memorabilia of this charismatic colourful statesman. Disraeli's country retreat later became the headquarters for a top-secret Second World War operation codenamed 'Hillside' and put Hughenden high on Hitler's target list. The Hillside exhibition and ice-house bunker bring wartime Britain to life. The estate also offers a variety of walks in the parkland and wider countryside, rewarding visitors with views of the Chiltern Hills.

Eat, shop, stay: Stableyard café serving hot meals, sandwiches, cakes and drinks. Dizzy's tea-room open weekends and holidays serving sandwiches, cakes and drinks. The shop stocks local produce, as well as Disraeli and 'Hillside' memorabilia. Second-hand bookshop, plants and estate produce available.

Handsome Hughenden in Buckinghamshire, above and below, is full of fascinating memorabilia

Things to see and do: **Indoors** Historical introductory talks throughout the day. **Outdoors** Woodland walks. Children's trails and events in the school holidays. **Dogs**: welcome on short leads in orchard and gardens. Assistance dogs only in manor.

Access: 🅿️♿🏢🪜🔧🏛️📷📱🎧📹♿
Manor 🪜♿🏛️♿ Grounds 🪜♿➡️♿

Find out more: 01494 755565 (Infoline). 01494 755573 or hughenden@nationaltrust.org.uk

Hughenden		M	T	W	T	F	S	S
House*								
1 Jan–14 Feb	11–3	M	T	W	T	F	S	S
15 Feb–1 Nov	11–5	M	T	W	T	F	S	S
2 Nov–31 Dec	11–3	M	T	W	T	F	S	S
Gardens, shop, café and kiosk								
Open all year	10–5**	M	T	W	T	F	S	S

*House: admission by timed ticket at certain peak times; show rooms closed 6 to 24 January for conservation work, but Hillside exhibition open. **1 January to 14 February and 2 November to 31 December close at 4. Everything closed 24 and 25 December.

King's Head

King's Head Passage, Market Square, Aylesbury, Buckinghamshire HP20 2RW 1925

Historic public house dating back to 1455, with a pleasant family atmosphere. This is one of England's best-preserved coaching inns. **Note**: Farmers' Bar leased by Chiltern Brewery. Open all year (apart from 25 December), Monday to Saturday, 11 to 11, including Bank Holiday Mondays and other public holidays (please check before visiting).

Find out more: 01296 718812 (Farmers' Bar). 01280 817156 (National Trust) or kingshead@nationaltrust.org.uk

Lodge Park and Sherborne Park Estate

near Cheltenham, Gloucestershire

1987

Satnav: for Lodge Park use GL54 3PP; for Sherborne Estate use GL54 3DT (Ewe Pen Barn) or GL54 3DL (Water Meadows). **Parking**: on site for Lodge Park. For Sherborne Estate use either Ewe Pen Barn or Water Meadows car parks.

Lodge Park is England's only 17th-century deer-coursing grandstand. Set within a landscape designed by Charles Bridgeman and part of the Sherborne Park Estate, the grandstand was built in 1634 to satisfy John 'Crump' Dutton's love of gambling and entertaining. There are lovely walks through the Bridgeman landscape and wider estate. **Note**: toilets at Lodge Park only.

Eat, shop, stay: drinks, cakes, ice cream, retail, plants and second-hand books at Lodge Park. Tea-room and shop in Sherborne village (not National Trust). Holiday cottages at Lodge Park, Sherborne and Bibury.

Things to see and do: nature activities and talks, living history and games. Historic shepherd's hut and walks in Bridgeman landscape at Lodge Park. Wider estate walks, including guided walks. **Dogs**: welcome on leads in Lodge Park grounds/near livestock. Under close control at all times.

Lodge Park, on the Sherborne Park Estate, Gloucestershire

Access: 🅿️ 👦 🏛️ 🚽 🚻 🖼️ Lodge Park 🔼 🏛️ 🔽

Find out more: 01451 844130 (Lodge Park) or lodgepark@nationaltrust.org.uk Aldsworth, near Cheltenham, Gloucestershire GL54 3PP

Lodge Park and Sherborne Park		M	T	W	T	F	S	S
Lodge Park								
2 Mar–31 Oct*	11–4		M				F	S	S
Sherborne Park Estate								
Open all year	Dawn–dusk	M	T	W	T	F	S	S

*Open every day in August. Lodge Park occasionally closes for private functions (call to check).

Long Crendon Courthouse

Long Crendon, Aylesbury, Buckinghamshire HP18 9AN 1900

Superb example of a 14th-century courthouse with a wealth of local history – the second building acquired by the National Trust. **Note**: extremely steep stairs. Sorry no toilet. Village exhibition on display. Limited parking in village. Open Wednesday and weekends, 7 March to 1 November, 11 to 5. Open all public and Bank Holidays.

Find out more: 01280 817156 or longcrendon@nationaltrust.org.uk

Minchinhampton and Rodborough Commons

near Stroud, Gloucestershire

🏛♿ 1913

Satnav: use GL5 5BJ for Minchinhampton; GL5 5BP for Rodborough (postcodes may be approximate). **Parking**: at Reservoir car park on Minchinhampton Common; Rodborough Fort car park on Rodborough Common.

These historic Cotswold commons, traditionally grazed, are famed for rare flowers and butterflies, prehistoric remains and far-reaching views. Minchinhampton Common contains a nationally important complex of Neolithic and Bronze Age burial mounds, while Rodborough Common's limestone grasslands (above) have abundant wild flowers, including rare pasqueflowers and many varieties of orchid.

Eat, shop, stay: picnics welcome. Historic Winstones ice-cream factory is on Rodborough Common; there are usually ice-cream vans in Reservoir car park (summer). Several pubs nearby (none National Trust). Two holiday cottages.

Things to see and do: the commons are great places to walk or spot rare butterflies and moths, such as the wood tiger moth. Downloadable Rodborough Common butterfly walk available. **Dogs**: welcome everywhere (under close control near livestock). Dog bins in car parks.

Find out more: 01452 814213 or minchinhampton@nationaltrust.org.uk

Newark Park

Ozleworth, Wotton-under-Edge, Gloucestershire GL12 7PZ

🏛🏛♿♿👜 1949

Satnav: only works when approaching from north; if approaching from south follow brown signs from Wotton-under-Edge and A46. **Parking**: 100 yards from house.

With splendid views from the Cotswold escarpment, Newark Park is a secluded estate with a historic country home at its heart. From Tudor beginnings to dramatic rescue by a 20th-century Texan, the house has many stories to tell. The informal garden and estate provide space to play, explore and contemplate. **Note**: toilets in car park (additional toilets in Newark House).

Eat, shop, stay: gift shop (first floor) and plant sales (next to reception). Tea pavilion in garden serving light lunches, cakes, drinks and ice cream. Outdoor and indoor seating. Holiday cottage.

Splendid views from Newark Park in Gloucestershire

Things to see and do: Indoors Exhibitions in house. **Outdoors** Waymarked walks, geocaching and play garden. Open-air theatre and croquet. Seasonal garden specials, including snowdrops, cyclamen and wild garlic. **Dogs**: welcome on leads in garden and estate (please mind peacocks and grazing livestock).

Access: 🅿️🐕♿🧑‍🦯📷📹ℹ️∴📷
Building ♿🔷♿ Grounds 🔷

Find out more: 01453 842644 or newarkpark@nationaltrust.org.uk

Newark Park		M	T	W	T	F	S	S
1 Feb–1 Nov	10–5*	**M**	**T**	**W**	**T**	**F**	**S**	**S**
6 Nov–13 Dec	10–4	·	·	·	·	**F**	**S**	**S**

House: opens 11. *Everything closes at 4 before 2 March and after 24 October.

Things to see and do: Indoors Wonderful stories of Lord and Lady Nuffield. **Outdoors** Arts and Crafts-style garden with colourful herbaceous borders, kitchen garden and croquet lawn. Why not visit Greys Court nearby? **Dogs**: welcome on leads in the gardens and woodlands.

Access: 🅿️ House, shop and grounds 🔷

Find out more: 01491 641224 or nuffieldplace@nationaltrust.org.uk

Nuffield Place		M	T	W	T	F	S	S
2 Mar–8 Nov*	10–5**	**M**	**T**	**W**	**T**	**F**	**S**	**S**

*Closed 26 April, 28 June, 14 July. **House: access from 11; timed tickets may be used on busy days (available from visitor reception, places limited).

Nuffield Place

Huntercombe, near Henley-on-Thames, Oxfordshire RG9 5RY

🏠♿ 2011

The tool cupboard at Nuffield Place in Oxfordshire

Parking: on site.

Nuffield Place reveals the surprisingly down-to-earth lives of Lord Nuffield, founder of the Morris Motor Company, and his wife. Their home and personal possessions are just as they left them, the décor and furnishings intact. This intimate home exudes the tastes and interests of its remarkable owner.

Eat, shop, stay: tea-room serving light lunches and afternoon tea. Shop selling unique Nuffield Place mementoes, gifts, books and postcards.

Pitstone Windmill

Ivinghoe, Buckinghamshire LU7 9EJ 1937

Believed to be the oldest postmill in England. Stunning views of the Chilterns. **Note**: access to windmill 262 yards via a grassy field track. Steep steps. Sorry no facilities. Limited parking. Open Sundays, 3 May to 30 August, 10 to 4 (also open Friday 8 May, plus Monday 25 May and 31 August).

Find out more: 01442 851227 or pitstonemill@nationaltrust.org.uk

Priory Cottage

1 Mill Street, Steventon, Abingdon, Oxfordshire OX13 6SP 1939

Now converted into two houses, these former monastic buildings were gifted to the National Trust by the famous Ferguson's Gang. **Note**: administered by tenant. Sorry no toilet. Open Tuesdays, 7 April to 29 September, 2 to 6 (Great Hall only open). Admission by email request.

Find out more: 01793 762209 or priorycottages@nationaltrust.org.uk

Snowshill Manor and Garden

Snowshill, near Broadway,
Gloucestershire WR12 7JU

🏚️ ❄️ ♿ 1951

Satnav: follow signs from centre of village.
Parking: 500 yards.

Charles Wade was an artist and architect who collected curious and interesting objects that were for him a celebration of colour, craftsmanship and design. With a sense of fun and theatre, he took great pleasure in turning his home into a stage for these varied and sometimes unusual finds. Next to the manor house is the small cottage where Charles Wade lived. Both the manor house and cottage are surrounded by an intimate Arts and Crafts terraced garden where he created 'different courts for different moods'.

A colourful corner of the Arts and Crafts garden at Snowshill Manor, Gloucestershire

Eat, shop, stay: café serving hot meals, sandwiches, cakes and drinks using home-grown produce where possible. Shop selling gifts, plants and local produce. Second-hand bookshop. Picnics welcome. Why not stay a while longer at one of four picturesque holiday cottages in the village?

Things to see and do: Indoors Family trail, handling collection and, through regular demonstrations, a chance to see how we care for the collection. **Outdoors** Family trail, natural play area and introductory talks. **Dogs**: assistance dogs only.

Access: 🅿️ 🚍 ♿ 🏠 🔄 📷 📺 🔆 🎨
Manor 🔄 🚶 Priest's House 🔄 Garden 🔄 ♿

Find out more: 01386 852410 or snowshillmanor@nationaltrust.org.uk

Snowshill Manor		M	T	W	T	F	S	S
Manor								
16 Mar–1 Nov	11:30–4:30	M	T	W	T	F	S	S
7 Nov–29 Nov	11–2:30	·	·	·	·	·	S	S
Garden, shop and café								
16 Mar–1 Nov	11–5:30	M	T	W	T	F	S	S
7 Nov–29 Nov	10:30–3:30	·	·	·	·	·	S	S

Manor: entry by timed ticket (including members); places limited. Last admission one hour before closing. Charles Wade's cottage opens at 11.

Stowe

Buckingham, Buckinghamshire MK18 5EQ

🏠 ❄ 🐾 🔔 🍵 1989

Parking: 545 yards.

The beauty of Stowe has attracted visitors since 1717. Picture-perfect views, lakeside walks and temples create a monumental landscape that changes with the seasons. Full of hidden meaning and classical references, the garden remains an earthly paradise. Follow in the footsteps of 18th-century tourists by beginning your visit at the New Inn visitor centre. From here it is a short walk or buggy-ride to the garden, where another world awaits. Our restoration programme continues to return Stowe to its former glory. The sheer size and scale are perfect for a steady stroll or vigorous ramble but will leave you overwhelmed by the garden's awe-inspiring splendour. Boost your wellbeing on the new Grecian Valley tours and 'world of water' art installation.

Eat, shop, stay: New Inn café serving light lunches, cakes, soups and scones. Courtyard café and covered porch welcomes dogs. Shop selling local products inspired by Stowe, as well as gifts and plants. A second-hand bookshop is a must for bookworms. Picnics welcome.

Things to see and do: **Indoors** 18th-century parlour rooms in the New Inn. Visitor centre at New Inn provides details about visiting Stowe House state rooms (not National Trust). House visitor centre includes exhibitions and family-friendly activities. St Mary's Church open for visits. **Outdoors** Crisp winter walks, blooming spring displays, lazy summer days and vivid autumn colour – Stowe is forever changing. Fun family activities and outdoor event programme. We're restoring paths, returning replica statues and opening new garden areas all year, so there will be more to explore however many times you visit. **Dogs**: welcome on leads (downloadable dog trail available). Tie-up points and water provided. Monthly walk.

Access: 🅿️♿🚻♿♿📷🅿️
Visitor centre ♿⬆ **Grounds** ♿➡♿

There are temples, lakeside walks and perfect views at magnificent Stowe in Buckinghamshire, above and below

Find out more: 01280 817156 or stowe@nationaltrust.org.uk

Stowe	
Open every day all year*	10–5**

*Gardens: closed 23 May (New Inn, parkland, café and shop open); recommended last entry 90 minutes before closing.
**1 January to 2 February and 2 November to 31 December: closes 4. Closed 24 and 25 December.

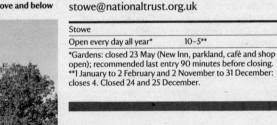

Stowe House

Buckingham, Buckinghamshire MK18 5EH

Stunning 18th-century house in the heart of Stowe's gardens. You can tour the restored state rooms and discover fascinating history. **Note**: operated by the Stowe House Preservation Trust. For satnav use MK18 5EQ. Parking at Stowe car park, ¾ mile. Discount on admission price for members. Open daily, March to October, 11 to 4:30 and November, 11 to 3:30; weekends only December to February, 11 to 3:30. Opening subject to change (please check before visiting).

Find out more: 01280 818186 or stowehouse@nationaltrust.org.uk

Waddesdon

Waddesdon, near Aylesbury,
Buckinghamshire HP18 0JH

🏰 ♟ ✤ ♨ 🔔 🍷 1957

Parking: ¾ mile (frequent free shuttle service).
Electric vehicle charging points in main car park.

Waddesdon is a Rothschild house and gardens
managed by the Rothschild Foundation.
Baron Ferdinand started building the manor
in 1874 to display his outstanding collection of
art treasures and entertain fashionable society.
His choice of a French-style château surprises
many visitors. The highest quality 18th-century
French decorative arts are displayed alongside
magnificent English portraits and Dutch
Old Master paintings in 40 elegant interiors.
Outside is one of the finest Victorian gardens
in Britain, famous for its parterre and ornate
working aviary, and enhanced with classical
and contemporary sculpture. Today, the manor
continues its tradition of entertainment and
hospitality, with events celebrating food and
wine. Visitors can explore Waddesdon's history,
collections and gardens through changing
exhibitions, talks and tours.

Note: house admission by timed ticket
(including members), available by telephone
(booking fee) or at waddesdon.org.uk.
Advance booking strongly advised
(weekends/holidays/Christmas essential).
Booking fee (including members). Summer
festival weekend and timed tickets for
Christmas-decorated interiors event charge,
applies (including members).

Eat, shop, stay: two licensed restaurants for
breakfasts, lunches and afternoon teas. Snacks
and drinks at The Treaterie, Summer House and
Coffee Bar. Gift and wine shop; wine tastings
and cellar tours. Five Arrows hotel, restaurant
and bar in the village. None National Trust.

Waddesdon in Buckinghamshire: the Victorian Parterre, above, and elaborate château-style house, below

Things to see and do: **Indoors** Furnished interiors displaying the collections and new Rothschild Treasury – timed ticket entry March to October (advance booking advised for weekends and holidays). Exhibitions. Wine cellars. Expert talks and tours about the house, collection, archive and exhibitions. November to December – festive decorations, east wing only (advance booking essential). **Outdoors** March to October – daily free guided garden walks and tours of the aviary and cellars. Dog walks and online trails. Winter garden colour, snowdrops and bulbs, walking maps. Woodland playground and den-building. Weekend and holiday family events. Open-air cinema and theatre. Food and wine festivals, Winter Light and Christmas fair. **Dogs**: welcome outdoors on short leads (except parterre, aviary and woodland playground).

Access: [icons]
House [icons] Coach House Gallery [icon]
Grounds [icons]

Find out more: 01296 820414 or waddesdon@nationaltrust.org.uk

The ornate Grey Drawing Room at Waddesdon

Waddesdon		M	T	W	T	F	S	S
Gardens, aviary, playground, wine cellars, shops, restaurant								
1 Jan–5 Jan	11–6			W	T	F	S	S
1 Feb–16 Feb	10–4			W	T	F	S	S
17 Feb–23 Feb	10–4	M	T	W	T	F	S	S
26 Feb–22 Mar	10–4			W	T	F	S	S
25 Mar–1 Nov	10–5			W	T	F	S	S
14 Nov–20 Dec	11–6			W	T	F	S	S
21 Dec–31 Dec	11–6	M	T	W	T			S
House*								
25 Mar–30 Oct	12–4			W	T	F		
28 Mar–1 Nov	11–4						S	S
25 May–29 May	12–4	M	T	W	T	F		
31 Aug–4 Sep	12–4	M	T	W	T	F		
26 Oct–30 Oct	12–4	M	T	W	T	F		
Christmas house (partial opening)*								
1 Jan–5 Jan	11:30–6			W	T	F	S	S
14 Nov–20 Dec	11:30–6			W	T	F	S	S
21 Dec–31 Dec	11:30–6	M	T	W	T			S

Open Bank Holiday Mondays (plus 14 April, 26 May, 26 and 27 October) – grounds 10 to 5, house 12 to 4.
*House: recommended entry before 2:30; last entry 3:10; special ticketed events 4 and 5 July, and Christmas in the house. Everything closed 24, 25 and 26 December.

West Wycombe Park

West Wycombe, Buckinghamshire HP14 3AJ

🏛 ✝ 🏚 📷 1943

Parking: 250 yards.

Alongside this historic village lies an exquisite Palladian villa. This lavish home and serene landscape garden reflect the wealth and personality of its creator, the infamous Sir Francis Dashwood, founder of the Hellfire Club. Still home to the Dashwood family and their fine collection, it remains a busy, private estate. **Note**: opened in partnership with the Dashwood family. The Hellfire Caves and café are privately owned – National Trust members receive a discount on the admission charge.

Eat, shop, stay: refreshments at Hellfire Caves and café (not National Trust) – discount for members. Variety of shops and pubs in the National Trust village, offering refreshments and local produce (none National Trust).

Things to see and do: **Indoors** Guided tours, Monday to Thursday (freeflow access Sundays). **Outdoors** Centuries-old historic village. West Wycombe Hill, iconic Dashwood Mausoleum, church and Golden Ball. **Dogs**: welcome on West Wycombe Hill. Assistance dogs only in park.

West Wycombe Park, Buckinghamshire, above and below

Access: 🅿 🅿 ♿ 📶 ∴ ♿ ♿ ♿

Find out more: 01494 755571 (Infoline). 01494 513569 or westwycombe@nationaltrust.org.uk

West Wycombe Park	M	T	W	T	F	S	S
Grounds							
1 Apr–31 Aug	2–6	M	T	W	T	.	.	S
House*							
1 Jun–31 Aug	2–6	M	T	W	T	.	.	S

*House: entry Monday to Thursday by guided tour (timed tickets). Freeflow on Sundays and Bank Holidays. Last admission 45 minutes before closing.

West Wycombe Village and Hill

West Wycombe, Buckinghamshire HP14 3AJ

✚ 🚰 ♿ 1934

West Wycombe Village and Hill in Buckinghamshire

Parking: roadside parking in village and on West Wycombe Hill.

This historic village, with its many buildings of architectural interest, was an important coaching stop between London and Oxford. West Wycombe Hill offers commanding views over West Wycombe Park and the surrounding countryside. On top of the hill is St Lawrence Church with its famous golden ball. **Note**: church and mausoleum not National Trust.

Eat, shop, stay: refreshments available at the Hellfire Caves and café (not National Trust). Variety of shops and pubs in the National Trust village, offering refreshments and local produce (none National Trust).

Things to see and do: centuries-old historic cottages and coaching inns. West Wycombe Hill, iconic Dashwood Mausoleum and church with golden ball. **Dogs**: welcome on West Wycombe Hill and in village.

Find out more: 01494 755571 (Infoline). 01494 513569 or westwycombe@nationaltrust.org.uk

Westbury Court Garden

Westbury-on-Severn, Gloucestershire GL14 1PD

✤ 1967

Parking: car park 300 yards from main road.

Originally laid out between 1696 and 1705, this is the only restored Dutch water garden in the country. There are canals, clipped hedges, working 17th-century vegetable plots and many old varieties of fruit trees. **Note**: credit cards not accepted.

Eat, shop, stay: hot drinks machine on site. Bottled water and juice for sale. Light refreshments available in the local church (not National Trust) on some Sunday afternoons.

Things to see and do: evening garden tours, Easter egg trails and Apple Day. **Dogs**: welcome on short leads at all times.

Access: 🅿️♿🏠🎵👓 **Garden** ♿♿♿
Pavilion and summerhouse ♿

Find out more: 01452 760461 or westburycourt@nationaltrust.org.uk

Westbury Court Garden		M	T	W	T	F	S	S
4 Mar–31 May	10–5	·	·	W	T	F	S	S
1 Jun–30 Sep	10–5	M	T	W	T	F	S	S
1 Oct–25 Oct	10–5	·	·	W	T	F	S	S

Open Bank Holiday Mondays, and other times by appointment.

Unique Westbury Court Garden in Gloucestershire

White Horse Hill

Uffington, Oxfordshire

🏛️ 👫 🐕 1979

Satnav: use SN7 7QJ. **Parking**: on site.

The White Horse at Uffington is part of an ancient landscape, steeped in history and mythology. It's the oldest chalk figure in the country, dated to the late Bronze Age about 3,000 years ago. Its linear form dominates the landscape, yet no one knows how it was made. The walls of an Iron Age hill fort are visible on the hilltop, the highest point in Oxfordshire. You can also look down on a valley known as The Manger and a natural outcrop known as Dragon Hill, where St George was said to have fought and slain the dragon. **Note**: archaeological monuments under English Heritage guardianship. Sorry no toilet.

Things to see and do: guided walks and events to rechalk the White Horse. Stunning views can be enjoyed from the top of the hill. Ashdown House woodland walks nearby. **Dogs**: welcome on leads at all times (stock grazing and nesting birds).

Access: 🅿️♿

Find out more: 01793 762209 or whitehorsehill@nationaltrust.org.uk

White Horse Hill, Oxfordshire: the White Horse at Uffington, above, and examining a distance marker point, below

An inviting path through picturesque woodland at Woodchester Park, Gloucestershire

Woodchester Park

Nympsfield, near Stroud, Gloucestershire

1994

Satnav: nearest GL10 3TS, then follow signs.
Parking: accessible from Nympsfield road, 300 yards from junction with B4066.

This tranquil wooded valley contains a 'lost landscape': remains of an 18th- and 19th-century landscape park with a chain of five lakes. The restoration of this landscape is an ongoing project. Waymarked trails (steep in places) lead through picturesque scenery, passing an unfinished Victorian mansion. **Note**: toilet not always available. Mansion managed by Woodchester Mansion Trust (not National Trust). Admission to mansion: charges apply (including members).

Eat, shop, stay: seasonal café, shop and toilets at Woodchester Mansion (not National Trust).

Things to see and do: waymarked trails through valley and popular woodland play trail for children built along shortest route, including rope swings, see-saw and balance beams. Events all year. **Dogs**: welcome under close control, on leads where requested.

Find out more: 01452 814213 or woodchesterpark@nationaltrust.org.uk

Additional countryside car parks in The Cotswolds, Buckinghamshire and Oxfordshire

Buckinghamshire

Ivinghoe Beacon	HP4 1NF
Pulpit Wood, Whiteleaf Fields	HP27 0NB

Gloucestershire

Mayhill	GL18 1JS
Dover's Hill	GL55 6PN

Oxfordshire

Buscott village	SN7 8DA

Berkshire, Hampshire and the Isle of Wight

Searching for seaside treasures at
St Helens Duver, Isle of Wight

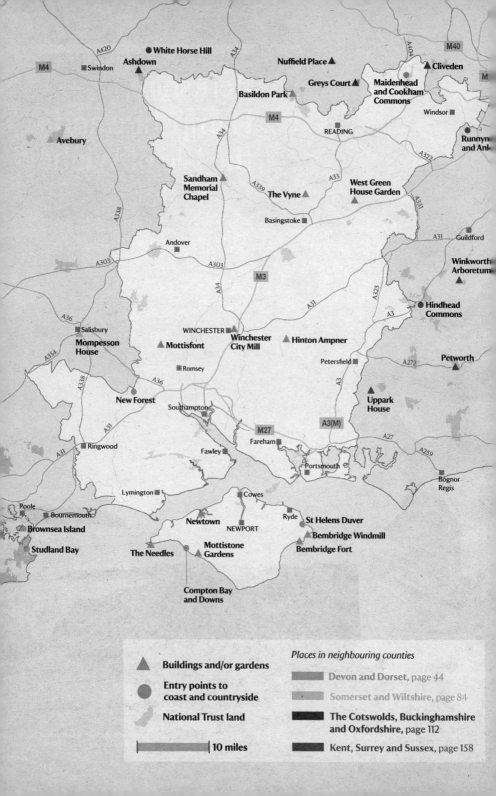

White Horse Hill
Ashdown
Swindon
A420
M4
A34
Nuffield Place ▲
Greys Court ▲
Basildon Park ▲
M4
Maidenhead and Cookham Commons ▲
Cliveden ▲
M40
M
Windsor
READING
A322
Runnym and Anl

Avebury
A34
Sandham Memorial Chapel ▲
A339
The Vyne ▲
A33
West Green House Garden ▲
A33
A331
A31
Guildford
Basingstoke
Andover
A303
A303
M3
A34
A31
Winkworth Arboretum ▲
A325
A3
Hindhead Commons ●
A36
Salisbury
Mompesson House
A354
A338
WINCHESTER
Mottisfont ▲
Winchester City Mill
Hinton Ampner ▲
Petersfield
A3
A272
Petworth ▲
Romsey
A36
New Forest ●
Southampton
A3
Uppark House ▲
A31
Ringwood
Fawley
M27
Fareham
A3(M)
A27
A27
A259
Portsmouth
Bognor Regis
Lymington
Cowes
Ryde
St Helens Duver
Poole
Bournemouth
Newtown
NEWPORT
Bembridge Windmill
Brownsea Island
The Needles
Mottistone Gardens
Bembridge Fort
Studland Bay
Compton Bay and Downs

▲ Buildings and/or gardens

● Entry points to coast and countryside

National Trust land

|——————————————| 10 miles

Places in neighbouring counties

Devon and Dorset, page 44

Somerset and Wiltshire, page 84

The Cotswolds, Buckinghamshire and Oxfordshire, page 112

Kent, Surrey and Sussex, page 158

Saved from destruction in the 1950s, Basildon Park in Berkshire has been restored to its former glory

Basildon Park

near Reading, Berkshire

🏠🔆🎈 1978

Satnav: not reliable, please follow brown signs.
Parking: 400 yards.

Sitting elegantly in 162 hectares (400 acres) of historic parkland and gardens, this 18th-century mansion was saved from destruction by Lord and Lady Iliffe in the 1950s, when it was derequisitioned after the Second World War. In a true labour of love, the Iliffes spent nearly 50 years renovating and returning the house to its former glory, acquiring a collection of fine furnishings and carefully selected Old Masters. The wooded parkland showcases glorious seasonal colour all year round, while the landscape has been restored to offer wonderful views, peaceful trails and picnic places. **Note**: entrance to main show rooms of mansion on first floor – 21 steps from ground level.

Eat, shop, stay: mansion tea-room serving coffee, lunch, afternoon tea and snacks. Shop selling books, plants, local food, ice cream and much more.

Things to see and do: **Indoors** Exhibition space in the South Pavilion.

Outdoors Woodland and parkland walks. Wild Play and family activities. **Dogs**: welcome on leads in grounds. Assistance dogs only in house.

Access: 🅿️♿🧺🚻🔆🎁🏛️🚼 :·🅿️
Mansion 🔆♿ **Grounds** ➡️♿

Find out more: 01491 672382 or basildonpark@nationaltrust.org.uk
Lower Basildon, near Reading, Berkshire RG8 9NR

Basildon Park	
Open every day all year	10–5*

*House: freeflow from 11. 1 January to 1 March and 2 November to 31 December: closes at 4. Closed 24 and 25 December.

Bembridge Fort

Bembridge Down, near Bembridge, Isle of Wight PO36 8QY 1967

In a commanding position on top of Bembridge Down, this unrestored Victorian fort is open for volunteer-run guided tours. **Note**: sorry no toilets. Not suitable for children under 10. Open Tuesdays, 7 April to 27 October, 2 to 3:45 (access by guided tour only, booking essential).

Find out more: 01983 741020 or bembridgefort@nationaltrust.org.uk
c/o Longstone Farmhouse, Strawberry Lane, Mottistone, Isle of Wight PO30 4EA

Bembridge Windmill

Bembridge, Isle of Wight

Satnav: do not use, follow brown signs.
Parking: free (not National Trust),
100 yards in lay-by.

The Isle of Wight's only surviving windmill
(above), and one of the island's most iconic
buildings, built more than 300 years ago. The
sails last turned in 1913, but inside most of its
original machinery is still intact. Climb to the
top and follow the milling process down four
floors. **Note**: steep steps inside the windmill.

Eat, shop, stay: hot and cold drinks, ice cream,
postcards, gifts and flour available. Picnic
tables in grounds. Holiday cottages nearby –
Chert, Little Chert, Wydcombe and Knowles
Farm cottages, and a Shepherd's Hut.

Things to see and do: **Indoors** Hunt for the
hidden millers. **Outdoors** Walks, including
the start of Culver Trail. Nature ID trails
and children's activities (school holidays).
Bembridge Fort nearby. **Dogs**: welcome in
grounds on leads. Assistance dogs only
in windmill.

Access: 🅿️ 🏞️ 🏢 ♿ 🔎 Building 🔆 🏛️ ♿

Find out more: 01983 873945 or
bembridgemill@nationaltrust.org.uk
High Street/Mill Road, Bembridge,
Isle of Wight PO35 5SQ

Bembridge Windmill		M	T	W	T	F	S	S
7 Mar–1 Nov	10:30–5	M	T	W	T	F	S	S

Closes dusk if earlier. Conducted school groups and special
visits March to end October (telephone or email to book).

Compton Bay and Downs

Compton, Isle of Wight

Satnav: use PO30 4HB. **Parking**: on site.

With sandy beaches and colourful cliffs,
Compton Bay is considered one of the best
beaches on the island. It's also a prime site for
fossil-hunting – look out for dinosaur foot
casts. The clifftops and downs are rich in
wildlife and easy-to-access walks, with
views as far as Dorset. **Note**: steep steps
down to the beach.

The sandy beach at Compton Bay and Downs, Isle of Wight

Eat, shop, stay: licensed van selling hot and
cold snacks, drinks and ice cream. Two holiday
cottages, Compton Farm Cottages, within
walking distance – both ideally placed for
exploring the coast and downs.

Things to see and do: excellent spot for
swimming, surfing and fossil-hunting.
Scenic views from three walking trails
available to download from the website.
Dogs: welcome on beach between
Hanover Point and Brook Chine all year.

Find out more: 01983 741020 or
comptonbay@nationaltrust.org.uk

Hinton Ampner

near Alresford, Hampshire

🏠✝🌸♿🍴 1986

Satnav: use SO24 0NH – takes you to Hinton Arms pub, 21 yards west of main entrance.
Parking: on site.

Hinton Ampner is the fulfilment of one man's vision. After a catastrophic fire in 1960, Ralph Dutton rebuilt his home in the light and airy Georgian style he loved. A passionate collector, he filled the sunny rooms with ceramics and art. Outside, Dutton designed a series of tranquil garden rooms, each with their own distinctive planting still apparent today. Geometric topiary, exotic-coloured dahlias and borders of repeat-flowering roses lead onto terraces with panoramic views across the South Downs. Extensive lawns, a park with ancient oaks and beech woodland provide plenty of space to stroll, play, relax and picnic.

Eat, shop, stay: large café (licensed) offering a self-service cake counter, barista coffee and hot food. Indoor and outdoor seating. Picnics welcome.

Hinton Ampner, Hampshire: the elegant library, below, and the view across the Pool Garden, above

Things to see and do: **Indoors** Significant hard stones collection. **Outdoors** Estate walking trails and free seasonal garden walks. Events, including open-air theatre and music in the summer. Children's trails. **Dogs**: welcome on short leads in the grounds. Assistance dogs only in the walled garden.

Access: 🅿♿♿♿♿♿🖼🎵♿
Building 🏠♿ Grounds ♿➡♿

Find out more: 01962 771305 or hintonampner@nationaltrust.org.uk
Near Alresford, Hampshire SO24 0LA

Hinton Ampner		M	T	W	T	F	S	S
House								
Open all year*	11–3:30	M	T	W	T	F	S	S
Estate, garden, shop and tea-room								
Open all year**	10–5	M	T	W	T	F	S	S

*1 to 10 January: entrance hall only open, 11 to 2;
11 January to 23 February: ground floor only.
**1 January to 2 February and 2 November to 31 December, open 10 to 4. Everything closed 24 and 25 December.

Maidenhead and Cookham Commons

near Maidenhead, Berkshire

🏛 ♿ 1934

Maidenhead and Cookham Commons, Berkshire

Satnav: use SL6 9SB for Cookham Moor car park. **Parking**: eight car parks (height restrictions at Henley Road and Pinkneys Drive car parks).

This chain of ancient commons offers footpaths through broadleaf woodlands, chalk downland, marshes dotted with orchids and hay meadows buzzing with insects in summer. These rich habitats are great for spotting wildlife throughout the year – you might see emperor dragonflies, marbled white butterflies, redwings, skylarks and fieldfares.

Eat, shop, stay: numerous shops, restaurants, pubs and cafés in nearby Cookham, Cookham Dean, Pinkneys Green and Maidenhead (none National Trust). Picnic on wildflower meadows.

Things to see and do: enjoy walking and horse-riding along bridleways and tree-lined avenues. Let your imagination run wild on family-friendly routes, with great places to try den-building and bug-hunting. **Dogs**: welcome under close control (grazing livestock and ground-nesting birds).

Find out more: 01628 605069 or maidenheadandcookham@nationaltrust.org.uk

Mottisfont

near Romsey, Hampshire

🏛 ✿ ♿ 1957

Satnav: use SO51 0LN. **Parking**: on site.

Ancient trees, babbling brooks and rolling lawns frame this 18th-century house with a medieval priory at its heart. Maud Russell made Mottisfont her home in the 1930s, bringing artists here to relax and create works inspired by Mottisfont's past, including an extraordinary drawing room painted by Rex Whistler. We continue those artistic traditions today, with a permanent 20th-century art collection and major exhibitions in our top-floor gallery. Outside, carpets of spring bulbs, walled gardens, rich autumn leaves and a colourful winter garden create a feast for the senses all year. Our world-famous collection of old-fashioned roses flowers once a year in June. There are spaces to run, jump and play, and always something for families to do.

Mottisfont in Hampshire: the rose garden in June, opposite, and exploring the grounds, below

Mottisfont's garden and grounds in winter, above, and summer, right: each season offers its own delights

Eat, shop, stay: Old Kitchen in house serving hot meals on china. Coach House Café in Stables offering lighter lunches on eco-friendly disposable tableware. Seasonal coffee shop, ice-cream horsebox and kiosk. Shop and plant centre at Welcome Centre, second-hand bookshop in Stables.

Things to see and do: **Indoors** Four major exhibitions in the art gallery every year, including family-focused show in summer holidays. Rex Whistler murals and permanent 20th-century art collection. Interpretation around the house telling stories of the building and its inhabitants, as they have changed through time. **Outdoors** Seasonal planting in the garden. Free daily guided walks and talks. Family activities, including activity trails in school holidays and wild play areas. Open-air theatre events in summer. Other seasonal events throughout the year. Wider woodland estate to explore on foot or by bike.
Dogs: welcome on short leads outside, excluding rose gardens, formal lawns and play areas.

Access: 🅿🚻♿🏠🚐♿📷🎵
House ♿🏠🚹 Gallery ♿ Grounds 🏠➡♿

Find out more: 01794 340757 or mottisfont@nationaltrust.org.uk
near Romsey, Hampshire SO51 0LP

Mottisfont	
Open every day all year	10–5*

*1 January to 2 February and 2 November to 31 December: closes 4. House and gallery: open at 11. House: closed 6 to 10 January and 9 to 20 November. Gallery: closed between exhibitions. Gardens: 4 to 20 June, open to 8, Thursday to Saturday. Everything closed 24 and 25 December.

Mottistone Gardens and Estate

Mottistone, near Brighstone,
Isle of Wight PO30 4ED

⊞ ⊕ ⛫ ⊞ 1965

Parking: 50 yards.

Set in a sheltered valley, these 20th-century gardens are filled with shrub-lined banks, hidden pathways and colourful borders. They surround an ancient manor house (not open) and have a Mediterranean-style planting scheme, taking advantage of the southerly location, including drought-tolerant plants and an olive grove. Other features include a monocot border, an organic kitchen garden and a tea garden alongside The Shack, a cabin retreat designed as their summer drawing office by architects John Seely (2nd Lord Mottistone) and Paul Paget. A network of footpaths crosses the adjoining Mottistone Estate, taking walkers high onto the downs via the historic Longstone.

Eat, shop, stay: shop selling gifts, books, cards, local products and ice cream. Plant sales. Second-hand books. Tea garden serving drinks, seasonal soups, sandwiches, cake, cream teas and light refreshments. Three holiday cottages nearby – Mottistone Manor Farmhouse, Longstone Cottage and Rose Cottage.

Things to see and do: family events and garden tours. Flowerpot trail and estate walks. '50 things to do before you're 11¾' activities around the garden and a 'Wild Area' for adventurous children. **Dogs**: welcome on leads in the gardens, under close control around livestock on the estate.

Access: ⓟ🅳♿🆆🅻🅿🎫🖼🚪🅰
The Shack 🅻🅷 Garden 🅻🅹➡

Find out more: 01983 741302 or mottistonegardens@nationaltrust.org.uk

Mottistone Gardens		M	T	W	T	F	S	S
Gardens								
7 Mar–1 Nov	10:30–5	M	T	W	T	F	S	S
Shop								
6 Nov–20 Dec	11–3	·	·	·	·	F	S	S

Estate: open every day all year.

Mediterranean-style planting at Mottistone Gardens and Estate, Isle of Wight, is ideal for the sheltered site

The Needles Batteries and Headland

West High Down, Alum Bay,
Isle of Wight PO39 0JH

🏠🦽🗺️🚻 1975

Parking: no parking on site (limited disabled parking by arrangement). Nearest at Alum Bay, ¾ mile, not National Trust (minimum charge £5, with 20% reduction for National Trust members). Freshwater Bay, 3½ miles (not National Trust), or Highdown (196:SZ325856), 2 miles.

Walking from Freshwater Bay to The Needles Headland along Tennyson Down, there are views as far as Dorset. At the end, high above The Needles, amid acres of countryside, is the Needles Old Battery. This Victorian fortification built in 1862 was used throughout both world wars. The Parade Ground has two original guns, and the military history is brought to life with displays, models and a series of vivid cartoons. An underground tunnel leads to a searchlight emplacement with dramatic views over The Needles rocks at the tip of the island.

The New Battery, further up the headland, was once a secret rocket-testing site and has an exhibition on the rocket tests carried out there during the Cold War. **Note**: steep paths and uneven surfaces. Spiral staircase to tunnel. Toilet at Old Battery only.

Eat, shop, stay: clifftop 1940s-style tea-room with stunning views serving soup, sandwiches, cakes, cream teas and light lunches. Picnic tables. Shop selling ice cream, confectionery and gifts. Drinks, snacks and ice cream available at New Battery. Stay on at Coastguard clifftop holiday cottages.

The Needles Batteries and Headland, Isle of Wight:
New Battery, above; fascinating rocks and history, left

Things to see and do: Indoors Exhibition
rooms detailing the Victorian Fort's hidden past
at the Old Battery and the 'Secret Rocket
Testing' at the New Battery. Soldier and photo
trails. Children's games on the Victorian Parade
Ground. **Outdoors** The closest view from land
of the Needles Lighthouse. Clifftop walks to
Tennyson Monument and beyond. Watch the
seabirds glide on the wind. **Dogs**: welcome
on leads. Assistance dogs only in upstairs
tea-room; all dogs welcome downstairs.

Access: 🅿️🖼️🛈🍴🎁📷🚻♿
Old Battery ♿🚶🍴♿ New Battery ♿

Find out more: 01983 754772 or
needles@nationaltrust.org.uk

The Needles		M	T	W	T	F	S	S
Old Battery and tea-room								
7 Mar–1 Nov	10:30–5	M	T	W	T	F	S	S
Old Battery tea-room								
1 Jan–5 Jan	11–3	·	·	W	T	F	S	S
9 Jan–16 Feb	11–3	·	·	·	T	F	S	S
17 Feb–1 Mar	11–3	M	T	W	T	F	S	S
5 Nov–20 Dec	11–3	·	·	·	T	F	S	S
26 Dec–31 Dec	11–3	M	T	W	T	·	S	S
New Battery								
4 Apr–27 Sep	11–4	M	T	W	T	F	S	S

Needles Batteries close in high winds. 10 May: no disabled
vehicular access due to Walk the Wight. 30 May: Old Battery
early opening for Round the Island yacht race.

New Forest Commons and Foxbury

near East Wellow, Hampshire

🏊 1928

Satnav: follow the Omega signs; for Foxbury use SO51 6AQ, Bramshaw Commons SO51 6AQ; Hale Purlieu SP6 2QZ; Hightown Common BH24 3HH; Rockford and Ibsley Commons BH24 3NA. **Parking**: for Foxbury at Half Moon car park on Blackhill Road.

Woodland, grassland, heathland, bogs and mires make up the unique landscape of the New Forest Commons, a wilderness that's teeming with wildlife. The National Trust looks after commons at the following places: Bramshaw, Foxbury, Hale Purlieu, Hightown, as well as Rockford and Ibsley. Foxbury, a gateway to the New Forest, is a 150-hectare (370-acre) area of heathland restoration. Wide open spaces, gentle hillsides and hidden ponds are there to be discovered in this recovering landscape. This is a fragile conservation site for wildlife and we only allow access for special seasonal events. **Note**: all chargeable entrance and event fees in Foxbury apply to members.

Things to see and do: programme of events throughout the year at Foxbury focusing on the site's rich wildlife, including seasonal bird walks, volunteer tree-planting and Forest School for young children. **Dogs**: welcome on leads or under close control March to July (due to nesting birds).

Find out more: 01425 650035 or newforest@nationaltrust.org.uk

New Forest

For your safety we would not advise access to the New Forest between dusk and dawn. Foxbury is accessible for special seasonal events only.

Den-building at New Forest Commons and Foxbury in Hampshire, above, and meeting the locals, below

For other ways to get involved go to nationaltrust.org.uk/volunteer

Newtown National Nature Reserve and Old Town Hall

Newtown, near Shalfleet,
Isle of Wight PO30 4PA

🏚️🧺♿🚻🐾 1933

Parking: 15 yards.

On the water's edge, Newtown is home to a tranquil harbour, wildflower meadows and ancient woodland with rare butterflies and red squirrels. The only National Nature Reserve on the island, Newtown has been cared for by the National Trust since 1963. Tucked away in a tiny hamlet adjoining the National Nature Reserve is the small and quirky 17th-century Old Town Hall, the only remaining evidence of Newtown's former importance. This historic building was the second to be bought and donated to the National Trust by Ferguson's Gang who were battling against the sprawling development of England in the 1930s. **Note**: nearest toilet in the car park by the visitor point.

Eat, shop, stay: information, postcards, guidebooks, maps, gifts and cold drinks available at the Old Town Hall. Information and walks leaflets available at the visitor point.

Things to see and do: **Indoors** Children's quiz sheet. **Outdoors** National Nature Reserve walks. Bird hides. Family activities. Seasonal events. Butterfly Trail. '50 things to do before you're 11¾' activities. **Dogs**: welcome on leads on National Nature Reserve. Assistance dogs only in Old Town Hall.

Access: 🅿️🚫♿🚻📷🔊🔍 **Building** ♿🔍

Find out more: 01983 531785 (Old Town Hall). 01983 531622 (visitor point) or newtown@nationaltrust.org.uk

Newtown		M	T	W	T	F	S	S
Old Town Hall								
7 Mar–24 Oct	10:30–5*	·	T	W	T	·	S	S
Nature Reserve								
Open all year		M	T	W	T	F	S	S
Bird hide								
7 Mar–24 Oct	10–4	M	T	W	T	F	S	S

*Old Town Hall, last admission 15 minutes before closing. Closes dusk if earlier.

Newtown National Nature Reserve and Old Town Hall, Isle of Wight: the reserve is a vital haven for wildlife

St Helens Duver

near St Helens, Isle of Wight

🏛️ ♿ 1928

Satnav: use PO33 1XY. **Parking**: on site.

Once a Victorian golf course with royal patronage, St Helens Duver has sandy beaches, hidden rock pools, undulating sand dunes and coastal woods to explore. It's also a fascinating place to look for wildlife, from burrowing digger wasps to wasp spiders and waterbirds over the harbour. **Note**: sorry no toilets.

Eat, shop, stay: two charming holiday cottages close to the Duver – Old Church Lodge, a Victorian stone cottage, sleeps four; the Old Club House, an attractive wooden chalet overlooking the Duver, sleeps five.

Things to see and do: great spot for relaxing on the beach, exploring rock pools, admiring spring flowers or birdwatching. Coastal walks and walk to Bembridge Windmill.
Dogs: welcome under close control.

Find out more: 01983 741020 or sthelensduver@nationaltrust.org.uk

St Helens Duver, Isle of Wight: once a Victorian golf course, the beaches and woods are now open to be explored

Sandham Memorial Chapel

Harts Lane, Burghclere, near Newbury, Hampshire RG20 9JT

✝️ ❖ 1947

Parking: opposite Chapel entrance (accessible parking at rear).

Nestled in a quiet village, the Chapel (above) hides an unexpected treasure – an epic series of paintings by the acclaimed artist Stanley Spencer, depicting scenes inspired by his experiences in the First World War. The orchard is perfect for picnics and the garden of reflection provides a peaceful space for contemplation. **Note**: conservation work planned for this summer (call for details).

Eat, shop, stay: small shop selling books, postcards, plants, gifts and local artists' work. Picnics welcome in the gardens and orchard.

Things to see and do: **Indoors** Exhibition about the Chapel, paintings and the people instrumental in its creation. **Outdoors** Orchard, wildflower meadow and garden of reflection. Events all year. **Dogs**: welcome on leads in grounds only.

Access: 🅿️♿🔍🎨📷🚻♿👁️♿
Chapel 🔍♿♿ Visitor reception/exhibition 🔍♿♿
Grounds 🔍➡️♿

Find out more: 01635 278394 or sandham@nationaltrust.org.uk

Sandham Memorial Chapel		M	T	W	T	F	S	S
26 Feb–1 Nov*	11–4	·	·	**W**	**T**	**F**	**S**	**S**
6 Nov–20 Dec	11–3	·	·	·	·	**F**	**S**	**S**

*1 June to 30 August: open to 5, weekends only. Open Bank Holiday Mondays, 11 to 4. Car park opposite Chapel available during normal opening hours, locked 15 minutes after closing. Chapel may be closed on certain days due to rehearsals for special events (please check before visiting).

Why not share your pictures with us? #nationaltrust

The Vyne

Sherborne St John, near Basingstoke, Hampshire

🏠 ✝ 🏦 ⚅ 🐾 ♿ ⟨T⟩ 1956

Satnav: not reliable, follow brown signs.
Parking: on site, limited in winter (October to April) due to ground conditions.

The Vyne has opened more rooms than ever before, including an exhibition space revealing stories covering 500 years of history. Visitors can discover the story of a brother and sister who became intertwined with The Vyne's survival; one the unexpected heir to the grand Tudor mansion, the other adopted as a companion. Outside, acres of wildlife-rich gardens and woods create a wonderful space for relaxation and exploration, while the play space gives children freedom to let their imagination take them on an adventure.

Sweeping lawns offer lakeside picnicking, and a short stroll reveals a bird hide overlooking water meadows.

Eat, shop, stay: tea-room serving light lunches, soup, sandwiches, cakes and scones. Gift shop and plant sales. Second-hand bookshops in house and garden. Picnics welcome.

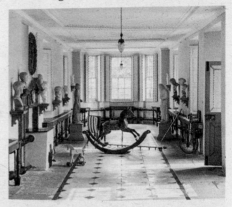

The Vyne, Hampshire: the Stone Gallery, above, and glorious colour in the garden, below

Things to see and do: **Indoors** Events and activities all year. Free guided tours. **Outdoors** Open-air theatre. Garden tours, trails and woodland walks. **Dogs**: welcome on short leads in woodland and gardens.

Access: 🅿️ 🚻 ♿ 🎧 🔄 📷 🖥️ ♿ 📶 📷
House ♿ 🚻 ♿ Grounds ♿ ♿ ♿ ➡️ ♿

Find out more: 01256 883858 or thevyne@nationaltrust.org.uk
Vyne Road, Sherborne St John, near Basingstoke, Hampshire RG24 9HL

The Vyne	
Open every day all year	10–5*

*1 January to 7 February and 2 November to 31 December: closes 4. House: opens 11 for visit by tour or timed ticket (telephone for details). Shop: opens 11. Last entry one hour before closing. Closed 24 and 25 December.

The Vyne: the grand Tudor mansion seen from across its lake, above, and spotting birds from a hide, below

West Green House Garden

West Green, Hartley Wintney,
Hampshire RG27 8JB 1957

Four seasons of beauty, contrast and
inspiration. Created by acclaimed garden
designer and writer Marylyn Abbott.
Note: maintained on behalf of the National
Trust by Marylyn Abbott. Facilities not National
Trust. Open Wednesday to Sunday, 11 March
to 31 October, 11 to 4:30, and 11 November to
23 December, 11 to 4. 8 to 23 December, open
to 7. Also open Bank Holiday Mondays.

Find out more: 01252 844611 or
westgreenhouse@nationaltrust.org.uk

Winchester City Mill

Bridge Street, Winchester, Hampshire

1929

Satnav: do not use.
Parking: at Chesil car park or park
and ride, neither National Trust
(charge including members).

This restored working watermill has stood
at the heart of the city of Winchester for a
millennium and is probably the oldest working
watermill in the UK. As the official Gateway
to the South Downs National Park, City Mill
provides information for visitors wishing
to explore local walks and attractions.
Note: nearest toilet 220 yards
(not National Trust).

Eat, shop, stay: shop selling local produce,
gifts and books, as well as our freshly milled
wholemeal flour.

Things to see and do: school holiday quizzes
and trails and seasonal family events, including
Easter egg hunts. Flour-milling demonstrations
every weekend and regular baking
demonstrations. **Dogs**: assistance dogs only.

Access: ⬚⬚⬚⬚⬚⬚⬚ Building 🏚

Find out more: 01962 870057 or
winchestercitymill@nationaltrust.org.uk
Bridge Street, Winchester,
Hampshire SO23 9BH

Winchester City Mill		M	T	W	T	F	S	S
1 Jan–24 Dec	10–5*	**M**	**T**	**W**	**T**	**F**	**S**	**S**

*1 January to 1 March and 2 November to 24 December: closes
4. Closed 25 to 31 December.

Winchester City Mill, Hampshire, on the River Itchen

Additional coastal and countryside car parks in Berkshire, Hampshire and the Isle of Wight

Berkshire

Cookham Common	SL6 9SB
Simon's Wood	RG45 6AE

Isle of Wight

Bembridge and Culver Downs	PO36 8QY
Borthwood Copse	PO36 0LD
Knowles Farm	PO38 2NP
St Catherine's Hill and Down	PO38 2JB
Tennyson Down	PO39 0HY
Ventnor Downs	PO38 1AH

Family time at Birling Gap, East Sussex.
Photo by Hannah Slater, competition runner up

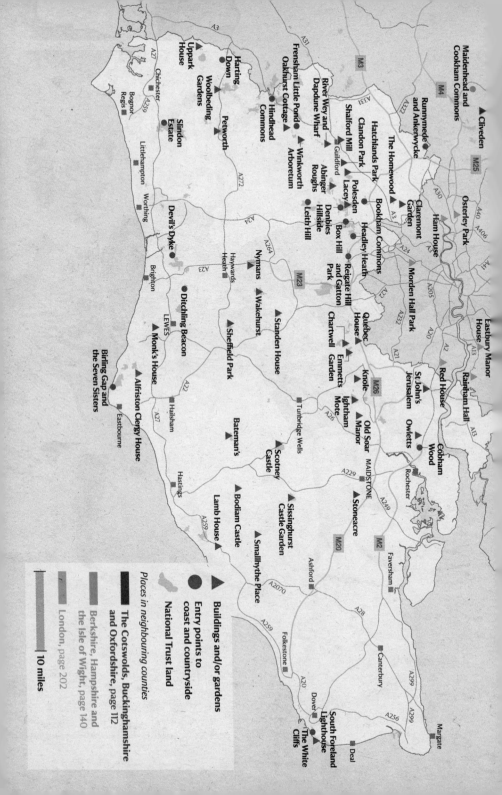

Places in neighbouring counties

The Cotswolds, Buckinghamshire
and Oxfordshire, page 112

Berkshire, Hampshire and
the Isle of Wight, page 140

London, page 202

Buildings and/or gardens

Entry points to
coast and countryside

National Trust land

10 miles

Maidenhead and
Cookham Commons

Cliveden

Runnymede
and Ankerwycke

Osterley Park

Ham House

Claremont
Garden

The Homewood

Frensham Little Pond
Oakhurst Cottage

Harting
Down

Uppark
House

Woolbeding
Gardens

Petworth

Slindon
Estate

Hindhead
Commons

River Wey and
Dapdune Wharf

Shalford Mill

Clandon Park

Hatchlands Park

Winkworth
Arboretum

Polesden
Lacey

Abinger
Roughs

Denbies
Hillside

Leith Hill

Box Hill

Headley Heath

Bookham Commons

Reigate Hill
and Gatton
Park

Morden Hall Park

Eastbury Manor
House

Rainham Hall

Red House

Owletts

Cobham
Wood

St John's
Jerusalem

Quebec
House

Chartwell

Emmetts
Garden

Knole

Ightham
Mote

Old Soar
Manor

Stoneacre

Sissinghurst
Castle Garden

Standen House

Sheffield Park

Wakehurst

Nymans

Bateman's

Scotney
Castle

Bodiam Castle

Lamb House

Smallhythe
Place

Ditchling Beacon

Monk's House

Devil's Dyke

Alfriston Clergy House

Birling Gap and
the Seven Sisters

South Foreland
Lighthouse

The White
Cliffs

Chichester

Bognor
Regis

Littlehampton

Worthing

Brighton

LEWES

Haywards
Heath

Eastbourne

Hailsham

Hastings

Tunbridge Wells

MAIDSTONE

Rochester

Ashford

Faversham

Canterbury

Dover

Deal

Margate

Folkestone

A3

A31

A331

A272

A24

A264

A23

A22

A21

A26

A229

A249

A20

A28

A2070

A259

A2

A13

A41

A20

A205

A232

A30

A40

A106

A3

M3

M4

M25

M23

M26

M20

M2

A27

A259

A259

Abinger Roughs and Netley Park

White Downs Lane, Abinger Hammer, Surrey RH5 6QS 1940

Hidden woods, flower-filled grasslands, natural play and picnic benches make this the perfect spot for young nature explorers and families. **Note**: sorry no toilets.

Find out more: 01306 887485 (rangers) or abingerroughs@nationaltrust.org.uk

Alfriston Clergy House

The Tye, Alfriston, Polegate, East Sussex BN26 5TL

1896

Tranquil Alfriston Clergy House in East Sussex, was the first building the National Trust saved for the nation

Parking: 500 yards in village car parks (not National Trust).

This rare 14th-century Wealden 'hall-house' was the first building to be acquired by the National Trust, in 1896. The thatched, timber-framed house is in an idyllic setting, with views across the River Cuckmere, and is surrounded by a tranquil cottage garden full of wildlife. **Note**: nearest toilet in village car park.

Eat, shop, stay: shop selling souvenirs, plants and gifts.

Things to see and do: **Indoors** Children's quizzes and trails. Varied events all year. **Outdoors** Short circular walks and longer hikes over the South Downs. **Dogs**: assistance dogs only.

Access:
Building **Grounds**

Find out more: 01323 871961 or alfriston@nationaltrust.org.uk

Alfriston Clergy House		M	T	W	T	F	S	S
2 Mar–28 Jun*	10:30–5	M	T	W	·	·	S	S
29 Jun–30 Aug	10:30–5	M	T	W	T	F	S	S
31 Aug–1 Nov	10:30–5	M	T	W	·	·	S	S
7 Nov–20 Dec	11–4	·	·	·	·	·	S	S

*Open Good Friday and May Bank Holiday.

Bateman's

Bateman's Lane, Burwash,
East Sussex TN19 7DS

🏛️🖼️❀🍴☂️ 1940

Parking: 30 yards.

Bateman's remains today as Kipling described
it in 1902: 'A grey stone lichened house –
AD 1634 over the door – beamed, panelled,
with oak staircase all untouched and unfaked…
It is a good and peaceable place, standing in
terraced lawns nigh to a walled garden of old
red brick and two fat-headed old oast houses
with red brick stomachs and an aged silver-grey
dovecot [*sic*] on top.' Much of Kipling's
belongings remain as he left them. Paths wind
past Kipling's 1928 Rolls-Royce, through
manicured lawns and a wildflower meadow.
A 17th-century working watermill stands
beside the River Dudwell.

Eat, shop, stay: shop selling a range of gifts,
Kipling books and plants from the garden.
Scullery bookshop specialising in pre-loved
classics. Tea-room offering seasonal lunches,
using fresh produce from our kitchen garden,
homemade cakes and light bites. Seasonable
'grab and go' facility.

Looking across the lily pond towards Bateman's,
East Sussex, above, and Rudyard Kipling's study, left

Things to see and do: Indoors Kipling's family
home in the beautiful Sussex Weald setting
which inspired many of his best-known
works. Working 17th-century watermill.
Outdoors Walks, trails, storytelling and
children's play area. **Dogs**: welcome on
short leads in the garden and on the estate
(seasonal cattle grazing).

Access: 🅿️♿🚽👶🔦📷🎧🚶‍♂️💺♿
Building 🔆♿♿ Grounds 🔆➡️♿

Find out more: 01435 882302 or
batemans@nationaltrust.org.uk

Bateman's		M	T	W	T	F	S	S
House								
1 Jan–14 Feb*	11–3:30	M	T	W	T	F	S	S
15 Feb–1 Nov	11–5	M	T	W	T	F	S	S
2 Nov–31 Dec	11–3:30	M	T	W	T	F	S	S
Garden, shop and tea-room								
Open all year	10–5**	M	T	W	T	F	S	S

*House: 6 January to 14 February, weekday entry by guided
tour only. **1 January to 14 February and 2 November to
31 December: close 4. Closed 24 and 25 December.

Birling Gap and the Seven Sisters

near Eastbourne, East Sussex

[icons] 1931

Satnav: use BN20 0AB.
Parking: at Birling Gap.

For drama, nothing beats the point where the sheer chalk cliffs of the South Downs meet the sea. One of the south coast's longest undeveloped stretches, the Seven Sisters are truly iconic. If you venture down the steps onto the beach, you can discover fascinating rock pools and the intricate wave-cut platform. The café and shop are a delightful place to start or end your peaceful downland walk. Before you explore the rare chalk heath and grassland, why not get some friendly advice from the visitor welcome team? **Note:** unstable cliff edge, stay away from edge and from cliff base.

Eat, shop, stay: licensed clifftop café serving hot and cold drinks, bottled beer and wine, light lunches, cream teas and cakes. Drinks and sandwiches available to take away. Seaside shop selling gifts and seasonal items. Picnic area outside shop.

Things to see and do: rock-pooling, countryside walks and stargazing. Crowlink downland, on top of the Seven Sisters, Alfriston Clergy House and Monk's House nearby. Events and activities for all ages.
Dogs: welcome in café, shop and on beach. Always on leads near livestock.

Access: [icons] Café [icon] Shop [icon]

Find out more: 01323 423197 or birlinggap@nationaltrust.org.uk

Birling Gap and the Seven Sisters								
Café and shop								
1 Jan–14 Feb	10–4	M	T	W	T	F	S	S
15 Feb–1 Nov	10–5*	M	T	W	T	F	S	S
2 Nov–31 Dec†	10–4**	M	T	W	T	F	S	S

*4 April to 29 September: close 5:30 at weekends and Bank Holiday Mondays; 20 July to 1 September: open daily, 9:30 to 5:30. †Closed 24 and 25 December.
**26 December: open 10:30 to 3:30.

Birling Gap and the Seven Sisters, East Sussex: the world-famous cliffs, below, and a marine treasure, above

Bodiam Castle

Bodiam, near Robertsbridge,
East Sussex TN32 5UA

[symbols] 1926

Parking: 400 yards.

A brooding symbol of power for more than
700 years, the strong stone walls of Bodiam
Castle rise up proudly from the peaceful
river valley setting. A wide moat encircles
the seemingly untouched medieval exterior.
Once inside, spiral stairways, tower rooms
and battlements are ripe for exploration.
Panoramic views across the Sussex countryside
can be enjoyed from the top of the towers.
Visitors of all ages are captivated by this
evocative medieval ruin, a place where you
can let your imagination run free. In spring
and early summer Bodiam is home to a
nationally significant bat maternity roost.
Note: popular with schools. Main toilets in
car park. Portaloos at top of site (main season).

Eat, shop, stay: shop selling castle-inspired
gifts, food, homewares, garden décor and
plants. Wharf tea-room serving main meals,
afternoon teas and a selection of drinks.
Dog-friendly Castle View Café opposite
castle entrance serving takeaway hot drinks,
snacks and ice cream.

Things to see and do: Indoors Story of
Bodiam display and film. Seasonal fun-packed
family events programme throughout the year,
including storytelling and crafts. **Outdoors**
'50 things' activities, trails and guided walks.
Dogs: welcome on leads in grounds only.

Access: [symbols]
Castle [symbols] Grounds [symbols]

Find out more: 01580 830196 or
bodiamcastle@nationaltrust.org.uk

Bodiam Castle		M	T	W	T	F	S	S
Castle								
1 Jan–14 Feb*	10:30–3:30	M	T	W	T	F	S	S
15 Feb–1 Nov	10:30–5	M	T	W	T	F	S	S
2 Nov–31 Dec**	10:30–3:30	M	T	W	T	F	S	S
Shop, tea-room and grounds								
Open all year**	10–5†	M	T	W	T	F	S	S

*6 January to 14 February: weekday entry by guided tour only,
half past each hour (booking not necessary).**Closed 24 and
25 December. †1 January to 14 February and 2 November to
31 December: close 4. Castle View Café: open daily, 11 to 30
minutes before castle closes.

With its wide moat and castellations, medieval Bodiam Castle in East Sussex is the perfect fairy-tale castle

Bookham Commons

near Great Bookham, Surrey

 1923

Satnav: use KT23 3LT.
Parking: at Tunnel, Mark Oak Gate and Hundred Pound Bridge car parks.

Enchanting ancient oak woodland, grassland plains and tranquil ponds. Listen out for tuneful nightingales and warblers in the spring and in summer look for insects hovering over the ponds. If you're lucky, you may also spot the beautiful, but elusive, purple emperor butterfly. **Note**: sorry no toilets.

Eat, shop, stay: refreshments available at Ye Olde Windsor Castle, Little Bookham and in Great Bookham village (none National Trust).

Things to see and do: bird hide and natural play area. Seasonal guided walks.
Dogs: welcome (on leads near livestock).

Access:

Find out more: 01306 887485 or bookhamcommons@nationaltrust.org.uk

Holly Blue butterfly at Bookham Commons in Surrey: an enchanting haven for so much flora and fauna

Box Hill

Tadworth, Surrey

 1914

Box Hill, Surrey: braving the steep bends of Zig Zag Road

Satnav: use KT20 7LB (doesn't work for all satnavs). **Parking**: off the Box Hill Zig Zag Road (short walk to café and viewpoint).

A great place for family adventures: delving into the ancient woodland, exploring the natural play trail, finding the tower or discovering the River Mole at the Stepping Stones. On a clear day you can see for miles from the top of Box Hill, so if you're hiking up, the stunning views are well worth it. You can pick up free trail leaflets from the shepherd's hut and outside the café, or find your own way along the many footpaths. Box Hill and Westhumble and Dorking railway stations are within easy reach.

Eat, shop, stay: the Box Hill café has indoor and outdoor seating and serves light lunches, snacks, sandwiches and cakes. The servery offers takeaway hot drinks, sandwiches and cakes as well as the famous 'revival' flapjack! Plenty of picturesque picnic spots.

Things to see and do: home to the popular Box Hill Bugs (booking essential), borrow a children's Tracker Pack from the shepherd's hut. Guided walks and a variety of self-led trails available. **Dogs**: welcome under close control where livestock are grazing. Assistance dogs only in café.

Access: 🅿️♿🚻👶🚏 Café ♿ Grounds ➡️

Find out more: 01306 888793. 01306 878554 (learning and events) or boxhill@nationaltrust.org.uk

Box Hill	
Café	
Open every day all year	10–5*

*1 January to 29 March and 25 October to 31 December: closes 4. Closed 25 December. Extended summer opening hours – see website for details.

Glorious golden autumn hues at Box Hill, above, and fresh green summer foliage, below

Chartwell

Mapleton Road, Westerham, Kent TN16 1PS

🏠♣️🐾🔔🍽️ 1946

Churchill's Chartwell, Kent: the drawing room and garden

Parking: on site.

Chartwell was the family home of Sir Winston Churchill, the place that brought him comfort and inspiration. Filled with treasures and personal belongings from every aspect of his life, this intimate house invites you into the private world of one of Britain's greatest leaders. Follow in the footsteps of one of the many frequent guests who are recorded in the visitor book. His studio contains the largest collection of Churchill's paintings and offers an insight into Churchill the painter. The garden reflects Churchill's love of landscape and nature, including the lakes he created. There are lots of fun things to do in our woodland area: a tree house, Donkey Jack's caravan, swings, a bomb crater and much more to explore. **Note**: house entry by timed ticket (available on website). Steep slopes; challenging for less able.

Kent, Surrey and Sussex

Eat, shop, stay: café serving food inspired by Churchill's family cook – hot dishes, salads, light bites, cream teas, cakes and delicious desserts. Shop stocking Churchill memorabilia, books, garden ornaments, plants, local produce and a special range of Chartwell-inspired items.

Things to see and do: Indoors Free family house guide. Daily talks in the studio about Sir Winston's love of painting. New public access to Secretaries' Office (weekdays during school term; from April). **Outdoors** New, free audio guide. Tree house in the woods, inspired by one Churchill built for his children. Guided tours of Churchill's family garden on selected days (March to October). Themed family trails during school holidays. The woodland trail offers distant views of the house and connects with the hilly 5-mile circular Weardale Walk to Emmetts Garden. **Dogs**: welcome on short leads in the garden and off lead in the wider estate.

Access: [icons] House [icons] Studio [icon] Grounds [icons]

Find out more: 01732 868381 or chartwell@nationaltrust.org.uk

Chartwell		M	T	W	T	F	S	S
House*								
29 Feb–1 Nov	11:30–5**	M	T	W	T	F	S	S
5 Dec–20 Dec	11–3	.	.	.	.	.	S	S
Secretaries' Office and Family Room								
2 Mar–30 Oct	11:30–5	M	T	W	T	F	.	.
Garden, exhibition, studio, shop and café								
Open all year	10–5†	M	T	W	T	F	S	S

*House: entry by timed ticket (available on day from visitor welcome centre); also available at least 24 hours in advance via website or call 0344 249 1895. **Last entry 3:50.
†1 January to 3 February and 28 October to 31 December close 4. Studio opening times vary. Closed 24 and 25 December.

Chartwell: statue of Clementine and Sir Winston Churchill

Clandon Park

near Guildford, Surrey

[icons] 1956

Clandon Park in Surrey: aftermath of the 2015 fire

Satnav: follow brown signs to the entrance on the A247. **Parking**: 250 yards.

A major restoration project is under way at Clandon Park, to remake this Palladian marvel following the fire in 2015. The house and garden will offer different types of access throughout the year, providing a unique opportunity to follow the Trust's progress as Clandon is rebuilt. **Note**: please check the website for the latest information.

Access: [icons] Building [icon]

Find out more: 01483 222482 or clandonpark@nationaltrust.org.uk
West Clandon, near Guildford, Surrey GU4 7RQ

Clandon Park		M	T	W	T	F	S	S
18 Mar–1 Nov*	10–5	.	.	.	W	T	F	S	S

*Different parts of the house and wider site may open at different times as the project progresses. Also open Bank Holiday Mondays.

Parking is free for members, but don't forget to scan your card in the car park when you visit

Claremont Landscape Garden

near Esher, Surrey

✤ 1949

Satnav: unreliable; instead follow brown signs from Cobham and Esher.
Parking: main car park at entrance. Space limited at busy times – please use car park in West End Lane opposite.

One of the earliest 18th-century landscape gardens, Claremont was once described as 'the noblest of any in Europe', combining the innovative work of designers Vanbrugh, Bridgeman, Kent and 'Capability' Brown. Once a playground for the wealthy and influential, and a sanctuary for British, French and Belgium royalty, retrace the steps of Queen Victoria, Princess Charlotte and Prince Leopold. The impressive turf amphitheatre offers wonderful views over the lake and walks take in features such as the grotto and camellia terrace. There are play areas for climbing, Badger's Basecamp for den-building and the Thatched Cottage for dressing-up and games.

Eat, shop, stay: café located outside pay barrier serving seasonal hot lunches, along with freshly made sandwiches and bakes. We have free Wi-Fi and a shop area. The Cube kiosk by the play area also offers hot and cold drinks and snacks.

Claremont Landscape Garden, Surrey, above and below

Things to see and do: events throughout the year, including children's trails and crafts during school holidays. Guided walks. Belvedere Tower open on selected dates (April to October). Boat hire, subject to availability. **Dogs**: welcome on short leads between 1 October and 30 April only.

Access: 🅿♿🚽👶♿📷👓🅿 Grounds 🖼➡♿

Find out more: 01372 467806 or claremont@nationaltrust.org.uk
Portsmouth Road, near Esher, Surrey KT10 9JG

Claremont Garden		M	T	W	T	F	S	S
1 Jan–31 Jan	10–4	M	T	W	T	F	S	S
1 Feb–31 Mar	10–5	M	T	W	T	F	S	S
1 Apr–31 Oct	10–6	M	T	W	T	F	S	S
1 Nov–31 Dec*	10–4	M	T	W	T	F	S	S

Café and shop close 30 minutes earlier than garden.
*Closed 24 and 25 December.

Cobham Wood and Mausoleum

near Cobham, Kent 2014

Sitting proud in historic woodland pasture, the 18th-century Darnley Mausoleum commands stunning views across the North Kent downs. **Note**: for satnav use DA12 3BS. Access to mausoleum on foot only, about 1 mile from South Lodge Barn. Mausoleum and South Lodge Barn normally open first Sunday of month, April to September, and selected other dates (please see website for additional dates). Mausoleum open 12:30 to 4:30; South Lodge Barn 12 to 5.

Find out more: 01732 810378 or cobham@nationaltrust.org.uk

Denbies Hillside

near Dorking, Surrey

1963

Belted Galloway cattle graze on Denbies Hillside, Surrey

Satnav: use RH5 6SR.
Parking: at Denbies Hillside.

Denbies Hillside is a dramatic chalk escarpment with panoramic views of the Surrey countryside. It's a great place to walk, picnic and watch wildlife – you may even spot chalk downland species such as the Adonis blue and chalkhill blue butterflies.

Eat, shop, stay: picnic area with benches in Steers Field.

Things to see and do: self-guided trail and spectacular views. Walk west along the North Downs Way to discover several Second World War pillboxes. Spot red kites, kestrels and buzzards.
Dogs: welcome (on leads near livestock).

Access:

Find out more: 01306 887485 or denbieshillside@nationaltrust.org.uk

Devil's Dyke

near Brighton, West Sussex

1995

Satnav: use BN1 8YJ. **Parking**: on site.

At nearly a mile long, the Dyke Valley is the longest, deepest and widest 'dry valley' in the UK. Legend has it that the Devil dug this chasm to drown the parishioners of the Weald. On the other hand, scientists believe it was formed naturally just over 10,000 years ago in the last ice age. The walls of the Iron Age hill fort can be seen when you walk around the hill, and there is a carpet of flowers and a myriad of colourful insects to discover in the valley.

Eat, shop, stay: Devil's Dyke pub (not National Trust) beside car park.

Devil's Dyke, West Sussex, was formed in the last ice age

Ditchling Beacon

near Ditchling, East Sussex

1953

Satnav: use BN6 8XG. **Parking**: small car park off Ditchling Road – very busy at weekends.

Just 7 miles north of Brighton, at 248 metres above sea level, Ditchling Beacon is the highest point in East Sussex and offers panoramic views all around the summit. To the south visitors can see the sea, while to the north you look across the Weald or east–west across the Downs. The site also has the remains of an Iron Age hill fort. Situated on the South Downs Way, it makes an excellent place to start a walk heading west towards Devil's Dyke or east towards Black Cap and Lewes.

Things to see and do: self-guided walks leaflet, orienteering course map and family Discovery Packs available from information trailer (open April to September, weekends and some weekdays). Numerous bridleways are great for cycling. **Dogs**: welcome (on leads near livestock).

Access: P♿ D♿ ♿ ♫ ➡

Find out more: 01273 857712 or devilsdyke@nationaltrust.org.uk

Ditchling Beacon, East Sussex, offers far-reaching panoramic views in all directions

Set on the South Downs Way, Ditchling Beacon, above and below, is the perfect starting point for bracing walks

Eat, shop, stay: refreshments available from ice-cream van. Picnics welcome.

Things to see and do: great for bracing walks with amazing views on the South Downs. Traces of the rampart and ditch of the hill fort to discover. Why not visit nearby Ditchling Down? **Dogs**: welcome on leads at all times.

Access: [P♿]

Find out more: 01323 423197 or ditchlingbeacon@nationaltrust.org.uk

Emmetts Garden

Ide Hill, Sevenoaks, Kent TN14 6BA

[❀] [⚲] [1965]

Parking: 100 yards.

Emmetts is a rare, stunning Edwardian garden known for its beautiful bluebells and spring colour. Summer brings the romantic rose garden, followed by vibrant autumn foliage, and more than 1,000 winter bulbs newly planted – there is something to see all year, as well as wonderful views across the Weald of Kent that can be enjoyed from the garden and on our countryside walks. Emmetts is a garden to enjoy with friends and family, a place where you can let off steam, play games, picnic in our meadow or simply sit back and relax. **Note**: a five-year restoration scheme is under way in some areas of the garden.

Eat, shop, stay: the Old Stables serving cakes, bakes and light refreshments. Shop selling a variety of products for the home, garden and outdoors, books, souvenirs and children's toys. Venture outside to the plant area for an array of plants and garden products.

Things to see and do: Indoors New interpretation in Discovery Cabin. **Outdoors** Children's trails in the school holidays, wild play area, swings, a tepee, and games to borrow. Garden tours (selected days). Downloadable walks available. **Dogs:** welcome on short leads in gardens and off lead in the wider countryside.

Access: 🅿️♿🚼🦽🅾️♨️🚫 **Grounds** 🏛️➡️♿

Find out more: 01732 751507 or emmetts@nationaltrust.org.uk

Emmetts Garden	
Open every day all year	10–5*

*1 January to 3 February and 2 November to 31 December: closes 4. Closed 24 and 25 December.

Emmetts Garden in Kent: new treasures every season

Frensham Little Pond

Priory Lane, Frensham, Surrey GU10 3BT

♿ 1974

Great crested grebes at Frensham Little Pond in Surrey

Parking: at Priory Lane corner and main car park.

Originally created in the 11th century to supply the Bishop of Winchester with fish, the pond and surrounding area is now a sanctuary for wildlife. The heathland is a colourful mosaic of purple heathers, fragrant bright-yellow gorse and rich green bracken with many footpaths to explore. **Note:** to protect the wildlife habitats, swimming and inflatables are not allowed.

Eat, shop, stay: Tern Café (outside seating only) serving snacks, homemade sandwiches and cakes. Picnics welcome (no barbecues please). Toilet available only when café open.

Things to see and do: bird hide and telescope next to café. Swimming and large beach available at nearby Frensham Great Pond (Bacon Lane, Churt, Surrey GU10 2QB). **Dogs:** welcome on leads from March to September and around café at all times.

Access: ♨️

Find out more: 01428 681050 (rangers) or frenshamlittlepond@nationaltrust.org.uk

Frensham Little Pond		M	T	W	T	F	S	S
Café								
1 Jan–29 Mar*	10–3	·	·	W	T	F	S	S
30 Mar–1 Nov	10–5	M	T	W	T	F	S	S
4 Nov–27 Dec**	10–3	·	·	W	T	F	S	S

*17 to 23 February: open daily, 10 to 3.
**Closed 24 and 25 December.

Harting Down

near South Harting, West Sussex 1994

A tapestry of downland with scattered scrub and woodland, rich in wildlife and steeped in history. **Note**: nearest toilets at South Harting or Uppark. Satnav unreliable.

Find out more: 01730 816638 or hartingdown@nationaltrust.org.uk

Hatchlands Park

East Clandon, Guildford, Surrey GU4 7RT

🏛️✣🐾 1945

Satnav: when nearby, follow brown signs to main car park entrance on A246.
Parking: 300 yards.

With open fields grazed by sheep and cattle, ancient woodland and wildflower meadows, the parkland is perfect for relaxation and exploration. The natural adventure area, with its tree house and bug burrow, is perfect for families to get even closer to nature. Nestled in the parkland is a Georgian country house, built for naval hero Admiral Boscawen and his bluestocking wife, Fanny. Now home to tenant Alec Cobbe, it contains his collection of Old Master paintings and the Cobbe Collection – Europe's largest array of keyboard instruments, including some which inspired world-famous composers such as J S Bach and Elgar. **Note**: only six ground-floor rooms open.

The grounds of Hatchlands Park in Surrey, left, and searching for a bargain in the plant sale, above

Eat, shop, stay: café in the original kitchen. Dog-friendly Coach House Café. Gift shop. Pre-loved bookshop in the Old Stable. Picnic areas.

Things to see and do: Indoors Introductory talks, guided house tours and cellar tours (all on selected days). **Outdoors** Children's adventure area, courtyard garden and open-air theatre. **Dogs**: welcome under close control in the parkland and designated areas. Dog-friendly Coach House Café.

Access: 🅿️🏛️🎦🔊🎧🖼️🚹 ∴ 🎡
Building 🦽♿🪑 Grounds ➡️♿

Find out more: 01483 222482 or hatchlands@nationaltrust.org.uk

Hatchlands Park		M	T	W	T	F	S	S
House and garden								
1 Apr–29 Oct*	2–5**		·	T	W	T	·	S
Park walks, shop and café								
Open all year	10–5†	M	T	W	T	F	S	S

*Also open Bank Holiday Mondays and Fridays in August. Possible additional dates (check before visiting).
**Garden: open 10 to 5 on house open days.
†1 January to 3 February and 2 November to 31 December: close 4. Closed 24 and 25 December.

Headley Heath

Headley Common Road, Headley Heath, Surrey KT18 6NN [1946]

A wide network of tracks to explore, featuring a wonderful mosaic of heath, chalk downland and mixed woodland. **Note**: cattle grazing (dogs welcome on leads, please look out for notices). Car parks at Headley Heath and Brimmer.

Find out more: 01306 885502 or headleyheath@nationaltrust.org.uk

Hindhead Commons and the Devil's Punch Bowl

near Hindhead, Surrey

[1906]

Hindhead Commons and the Devil's Punch Bowl, Surrey

Satnav: use GU26 6AB.
Parking: off the London Road.

Spectacular views from Hindhead Commons and uninterrupted walks to the Devil's Punch Bowl make this an unforgettable place to relax and take in some of the best countryside in the South East. Since the opening of the A3 tunnel, paths and bridleways have been reconnected and natural contours restored. Peace and calm now reign and the glorious landscape, with its carpets of purple heather in the summer and grazing Highland cattle, is there to enjoy.

Eat, shop, stay: café serving drinks, hot food, sandwiches and cakes (indoor and outdoor seating). 'Grab and go' kiosk offering takeaway options.

Things to see and do: walks leaflets available from the café and visitor den. Borrow a children's Tracker Pack to explore the wild and make the most of your visit.
Dogs: welcome under close control during bird-nesting season (March to October); café – assistance dogs only.

Access: 🅿️♿🚻♿🍴
Café and shop ♿ Grounds ➡️

Find out more: 01428 681050 (rangers). 01428 608771 (café) or hindhead@nationaltrust.org.uk

Hindhead Commons	
Café	
Open every day all year*	9–5**

*Closed 25 December. **1 January to 14 February and 2 November to 31 December: closes 4.

The Homewood

Portsmouth Road, Esher, Surrey KT10 9JL [1999]

Patrick Gwynne's extraordinary early 20th-century family home is a masterpiece of Modernist design in the midst of a picturesque garden. **Note**: administered on behalf of the National Trust by tenant. Toilets and café at Claremont. **Access by booked tour only, via minibus from Claremont Landscape Garden**. Additional charge for tours (including members). Usually open once a week on either Friday or Saturday, 1 April to 31 October. Guided tours at 10:30, 11:30, 12:30, 2 and 3 (45 minutes).

Find out more:
01372 467806 (Claremont Landscape Garden) or thehomewood@nationaltrust.org.uk
c/o Claremont Landscape Garden, Portsmouth Road, Esher, Surrey KT10 9JG

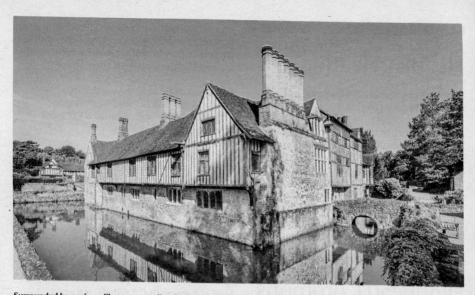

Surrounded by a mirror-like moat, medieval Ightham Mote is hidden away within a secluded Kent valley

Ightham Mote

Mote Road, Ivy Hatch, near Sevenoaks, Kent TN15 0NU

🏠 ✤ ♿ 🍴 | 1985 |

Satnav: use TN15 0NU. **Parking**: 100 yards.

Hidden away in a secluded Kent valley – a location it owes to the wealth of natural resources and proximity to water – this perfectly preserved medieval moated manor house celebrates 700 years of history this year. Ightham Mote's architecture and decoration reflect the development of the English country house, while its past owners provide the many stories about this once-cherished family home, evoking a deep sense of history. In the tranquil gardens there are streams and lakes fed by natural springs, an orchard, flower borders and a cutting garden. The wider estate offers walks with secret glades and countryside views. **Note**: very steep slope from visitor reception – passenger buggy or lower drop-off available.

Eat, shop, stay: licensed café serving freshly baked produce, barista-style coffee, sandwiches, light lunches, cream teas and cakes. Free Wi-Fi. Seating indoors and outside.

Takeaway kiosk open during busy periods. Picnic facilities available. Shop selling souvenirs, gifts, local products and plants.

Things to see and do: Indoors Introductory talks daily. Conservation exhibition and tower/hidden house/attic tours. Quizzes. **Outdoors** Tours and walks. Events, including music. Natural play area, garden trails and school holiday events for families. **Dogs**: welcome on wider estate and café patio. On leads in garden (November to February).

Access: 🅿️♿🚻🔛🔊🔈🎧📷💺♿ ⟶ 📷 Building 🔛♿♿🚶♿ Grounds ♿➡️

Find out more: 01732 810378 or ighthammote@nationaltrust.org.uk Mote Road, Ivy Hatch, near Sevenoaks, Kent TN15 0NT

Ightham Mote		M	T	W	T	F	S	S
House								
1 Jan–5 Jan	11–3*			W	T	F	S	S
29 Feb–1 Nov	11–5	M	T	W	T	F	S	S
28 Nov–31 Dec	11–4*	M	T	W	T	F	S	S
Garden, café, exhibition and shop								
Open all year	10–5**	M	T	W	T	F	S	S

Estate open all year. *House and grounds: partial access in winter, with selected rooms decorated for Christmas. **Garden, café, exhibition and shop: 1 January to 28 February and 2 November to 31 December, close 4. Closed 24 and 25 December.

Knole

Sevenoaks, Kent

🏛️ 👨‍👩‍👧 1946

Satnav: use TN13 1HX and follow brown signs to Sevenoaks High Street (entrance opposite St Nicholas Church). **Parking**: 60 yards. Additional parking in town centre.

Sitting proudly within Kent's last medieval deer park, Knole offers a vast estate where you can follow in the footsteps of tourists who have visited Knole's show rooms for 400 years. The recently conserved rooms showcase one of the finest collections of Royal Stuart furniture and textiles, and feature paintings by renowned artists. Spend the day and take in panoramic views from the top of the Gatehouse Tower, where you can also discover the life and loves of a former resident. See the scale and magnificence of this 600-year-old estate by exploring the grand courtyards or wandering through the parkland.

Eat, shop, stay: Brewhouse Café serving delicious hot and cold food, with outdoor seating available on the roof terrace. Enclosed picnic area in the park. Gift shop and bookshop with children's area (right).

Things to see and do: **Indoors** Explore the courtyards, Orangery, historic show rooms and tower, book on a tour of the attics.

Outdoors Join a guided walk or follow waymarked trails to explore the ancient parkland. **Dogs**: welcome in parkland and courtyards on leads. Café, shop, tower, show rooms – assistance dogs only.

Access: 🅿️♿🚽♿♿🚶🏠 **Show rooms** ♿👫
Gatehouse Tower ♿👫 **Park** ♿♿➡️♿♿

Find out more: 01732 462100 or knole@nationaltrust.org.uk
Sevenoaks, Kent TN15 0RP

Knole		M	T	W	T	F	S	S
Show rooms								
7 Mar–1 Nov*	11–5	·	T	W	T	F	S	S
Gatehouse Tower								
Open all year	11–5**	M	T	W	T	F	S	S
Café, courtyards and shop								
Open all year	10–5**	M	T	W	T	F	S	S
Conservation Studio								
Open all year	11–5**	·	·	W	T	F	S	·

*Open Bank Holiday Mondays, April to August. **November to January (inclusive): close 4. Closed 24 and 25 December.

Immense, imposing and fascinating Knole in Kent

Lamb House

West Street, Rye, East Sussex TN31 7ES

[icons] 1950

Parking: no on-site parking.
Nearest car parks in Rye, not National Trust
(charge including members).

Georgian home of writers Henry James and
E. F. Benson, who depicted the property in the
Mapp and Lucia stories. There is a peaceful
walled garden, full of colour, designed by
Alfred Parsons, as well as a vegetable patch –
unusual in the heart of Rye. **Note**: restricted
access for buggies and wheelchairs.

Eat, shop, stay: small tea-room offering hot
and cold drinks, cakes and cream teas and
savoury platters. Outside seating available
in the courtyard. Selection of James and
Benson books for sale.

Things to see and do: **Indoors** Events all year,
including themed Christmas opening. More
rooms open to explore – changing displays tell
the history of the house. **Outdoors** Inspiring,
relaxing garden. **Dogs**: assistance dogs only.

Access: [icon] Building [icon] Grounds [icon]

Find out more: 01797 222909 or
lambhouse@nationaltrust.org.uk

Lamb House		M	T	W	T	F	S	S
House and tea-room*								
1 Mar–1 Nov	11–5	M	T	·	·	F	S	S
27 Nov–15 Dec	11–4	M	T	·	·	F	S	S

*Tea-room: closes 30 minutes before house.

Lamb House, East Sussex: Rye's Georgian gem

Leith Hill

near Coldharbour, Dorking, Surrey

[icons] 1923

The striking tower at Leith Hill, Surrey: unbeatable views

Satnav: for Rhododendron Wood and Starveall
Corner use RH5 6LU (height restriction
barrier); for Windy Gap RH5 6LX; for Landslip
RH5 6HG. **Parking**: at Rhododendron Wood
for Leith Hill Place. For tower, park at Starveall
Corner (not National Trust), ¾ mile (level);
Windy Gap car park, ¼ mile (steep steps);
Landslip car park, ¾ mile (steep gradient).

Leith Hill Tower is the highest point in
south-east England offering unbeatable views
north to London, and south to see the sea
sparkling through Shoreham Gap. The house
was gifted by composer Ralph Vaughan
Williams, and used for a time as a school
boarding house. Now it is a venue for
exhibitions and workshops. You can enjoy
walks on the hill, where every season is a riot
of colour – starting with the spring bluebells
at Frank's Wood, followed by the early summer
colour at the Rhododendron Wood and then
the stunning autumnal displays of golds and
reds. **Note**: sorry no toilet or parking at tower;
steep spiral stairs to top.

Eat, shop, stay: hot and cold food and drinks available at Leith Hill Tower (not National Trust), tea and cake available at Leith Hill Place, when open. Picnics welcome, but no barbecues please. Self-catering accommodation at Henman Bunkhouse for up to 16 people.

Things to see and do: **Indoors** 'House of Science' exhibition at Leith Hill Place. Concerts and talks. Small history exhibition at tower. **Outdoors** Trail leaflets and seasonal guided walks. **Dogs**: welcome in Leith Hill Place; on leads on heathland (April to July).

Access: ♿🚻 Leith Hill Place 🏞 Leith Hill Tower 🔖

Find out more: 01306 712711 (Leith Hill Tower). 01306 711685 (Leith Hill Place) or leithhill@nationaltrust.org.uk

Leith Hill		M	T	W	T	F	S	S
Leith Hill Place								
13 Mar–1 Nov	11–5*	·	·	·	·	F	S	S
Tower								
Open all year	10–3**	M	T	W	T	F	S	S

*Leith Hill Place open to 5 on Bank Holidays. Closed on 16 August for Ride London event. **Tower open to 5 at weekends and Bank Holidays (weather permitting). Closed 25 December.

Panoramic view showing Leith Hill Place

Monk's House

near Lewes, East Sussex

🏠 ❋ 1980

Monk's House in East Sussex: Virginia Woolf's retreat

Satnav: do not use – wrongly indicates access across railway crossing. **Parking**: 100 yards (2-metre height restriction barrier).

This small 16th-century weatherboarded cottage in the village of Rodmell was the country retreat of novelist Virginia Woolf and her husband Leonard and a meeting place for the Bloomsbury Group. The garden features the room where she created her best-known works and includes cottage garden borders, orchard, allotments and ponds. **Note**: no access to Rodmell from A26.

Eat, shop, stay: gift shop selling Woolf and Bloomsbury-related products.

Things to see and do: why not try your hand at a game of bowls? One of the favoured pastimes of the Woolfs. **Dogs**: welcome on leads in garden.

Access: 📷♿🚻 Building 🔖👥 Grounds 🔖

Find out more: 01273 474760 or monkshouse@nationaltrust.org.uk Rodmell, near Lewes, East Sussex BN7 3HF

Monk's House		M	T	W	T	F	S	S
1 Apr–31 Oct	1–5	·	·	W	T	F	S	S

Open Bank Holiday Mondays. Garden: open 12:30 to 5.

Nymans

Handcross, near Haywards Heath,
West Sussex RH17 6EB

🏠🌿♿🛏🔔 1954

Parking: on site.

A garden for all seasons, with rare and unusual plant collections, set around a romantic house and partial ruins. The comfortable, yet elegant, house reflects the personalities and stories of the talented Messel family. In spring see blossom, bulbs and a stunning collection of subtly fragranced magnolias. The Rose Garden, inspired by Maud Messel's 1920s design, is scented by hints of old-fashioned roses. Dramatic shows of vibrant native tree colour in autumn precede winter's structural form, with pockets of perfumed daphne throughout the garden. Discover hidden corners through stone archways, walk along tree-lined avenues while surrounded by the lush countryside of the Sussex Weald. The adjoining woodland, with lake and bird hides, has plenty of opportunities to spot wildlife.

Eat, shop, stay: large shop and plant centre selling collection of plants grown at Nymans. Hot meals served from 12 to 2:30. Light refreshments and snacks available in the garden during peak periods. Second-hand bookshop. Holiday cottage.

Things to see and do: **Indoors** Family rooms in the house and small gallery showing changing exhibitions, open all year. Regular guided house tours on weekdays. **Outdoors** Wander through the ever-changing gardens with year-round seasonal interest; there are daily guided garden walks. Ruins regularly open to visitors. Family activities every day, with additional activities during school holidays. Daily mobility buggy tours. Gardening and creative workshops all year. Enjoy the surrounding woodlands, with their waymarked walks, and the landscape with stunning views across the Weald towards the South Downs. **Dogs**: assistance dogs only in house. Dogs welcome in garden at set times during year.

Access: 🅿♿🚻♿♿🅿🖼🚶 **Gallery** ♿
House 🚶♿🚻♿ **Garden** ♿🚶♿➡♿♿

Find out more: 01444 405250 or nymans@nationaltrust.org.uk

Nymans	
Garden, house and gallery*	
Open every day all year	10–5**

*Gallery closed for short periods to change exhibitions. Garden open until 8, Fridays in June, July and August.
**2 November to 1 February: close 4. House: closed 24 and 25 December.

Three views of glorious Nymans, West Sussex, this page and opposite: the exceptional garden, with rare plants and year-round colour, surrounds a romantic house

Oakhurst Cottage

Hambledon, near Godalming,
Surrey GU8 4HF 1952

Timber-framed cottage offering a rare insight
into domestic life in the mid-19th century,
with a traditional garden to explore.
Note: nearest toilets and visitor facilities at
Winkworth Arboretum (4 miles approximately).
Open Wednesday, Thursday and weekends,
1 April to 31 October. Admission by booked
guided tour only at 2, 3 and 4 (last tour
at 3 in October). Telephone to book.
Also open Bank Holiday Mondays.

Find out more: 01483 208936
(Winkworth Arboretum) or
oakhurstcottage@nationaltrust.org.uk

Old Soar Manor

Plaxtol, Borough Green, Kent TN15 0QX 1947

Dating from 1290, the remaining rooms of this
knight's house offer a glimpse back to the time
of Edward I. **Note**: sorry no toilet or tea-room.
Narrow lanes, limited off-road parking.
Open daily, apart from Friday, 1 April to
30 September, 10 to 6.

Find out more: 01732 810378 or
oldsoarmanor@nationaltrust.org.uk

Owletts

The Street, Cobham, Gravesend,
Kent DA12 3AP 1938

An architect's 17th-century family home
with a varied history and architectural features,
set within a relaxing, traditional garden.
Note: parking available. Open Sundays,
5 April to 27 September, 11 to 5.

Find out more: 01732 810378 or
owletts@nationaltrust.org.uk

Petworth

Petworth, West Sussex

1947

Satnav: use GU28 9LR.
Parking: on A283, 700 yards.
Separate car park for Petworth deer park.

Inspired by the Baroque palaces of Europe,
Petworth House is an extraordinary and
surprising ancestral seat created by one family
over 900 years. The 17th-century building you
see today comprises grand state rooms which
form the centrepiece of your visit. Designed
to display the taste, lifestyle and artistic
patronage of generations, the state rooms offer
an infinity of paintings and sculpture, including
major works by Van Dyck, Turner, Reynolds and
Gainsborough. This remarkable collection
reflects a journey of survival and success
through the Tudor Reformation, Gunpowder
Plot and the Napoleonic Wars. **Note**: selected
rooms may be closed over the winter for
conservation. Additional charges may apply for
some events, including winter art exhibition.

Eat, shop, stay: hot and cold lunches,
afternoon teas and homemade cakes available
in the Audit Room. Additional seating and
takeaway refreshments served in the
Servants' Hall Café. Gift shops selling
books, products inspired by the collection
and locally sourced souvenirs.

Palatial Petworth in West Sussex, above and opposite, contains extraordinary collections, grand state rooms and is set within a 'Capability' Brown landscape deer park

Things to see and do: **Indoors** Guided tours of the collection, the family of collectors and servants' working life on weekdays (main season). Private rooms used by the family open on selected days. Exhibitions, family trails, costumed interpretation all year, with a festive display for the Christmas season. **Outdoors** The 283-hectare (700-acre) 'Capability' Brown deer park, a landscape masterpiece, is a space for quiet reflection and offers stunning views of the South Downs National Park. You can wander through the Pleasure Ground, with its historic monuments, and enjoy one of our downloadable walks. **Dogs**: welcome under close control in Petworth Park. Assistance dogs only in Pleasure Ground.

Access: 🅿️🅿️♿♿♿♿🎧📷🎬👓📷
Building ♿♿♿

Find out more: 01798 342207 or petworth@nationaltrust.org.uk
Petworth, West Sussex GU28 0AE

Petworth		M	T	W	T	F	S	S
House								
1 Jan–23 Feb*	11–4	M	T	W	T	F	S	S
24 Feb–31 Dec*	11–5**	M	T	W	T	F	S	S
Pleasure Ground, shop and café								
Open all year	10–5†	M	T	W	T	F	S	S
Deer park								
Open all year	8–8††	M	T	W	T	F	S	S

*Selected rooms only. 11 January to 18 March: winter art exhibition. **2 November to 31 December: house closes at 4. Closed 24 and 25 December. †1 January to 3 February and 4 November to 31 December: close at 4. ††Closes 6 in winter, access via deer-park car park only. Car-park gates lock automatically.

Polesden Lacey

near Dorking, Surrey

Satnav: use KT23 4PZ. **Parking**: 200 yards.

Set within the Surrey Hills Area of Outstanding Natural Beauty, this was the party house of indomitable socialite Margaret Greville. Discover the many stories of Margaret's life, her lavish parties and domestic staff within this 19th-century house. There is also an astonishing collection, including pieces by Fabergé, maiolica and paintings by Dutch Masters. Surrounded by 12 hectares (30 acres) of grounds and a 566-hectare (1,400-acre) estate, there's space to walk and explore.

The gardens offer colour and fragrance all year. Highlights include the walled rose garden in summer and the picturesque Graham Stuart Thomas-designed winter garden. Enjoy a woodland walk on the wider estate, home to wildlife, including rare birds and butterflies. The breathtaking views change with every season. **Note**: additional charges may apply for certain events (including members). We offer a reduced entry price if you arrive during the last hour of house opening.

Eat, shop, stay: café and coffee shop offer seasonal dishes, snacks, cream teas, coffee and ice cream. Pop-up outlets open in warmer weather. Shops selling homeware, gifts, souvenirs, local crafts and plants. Second-hand bookshop in the grounds. Holiday cottage in the gardens.

Polesden Lacey, Surrey, this page and opposite: the lavish Saloon and two views of the garden and grounds

Things to see and do: **Indoors** Morning house tours and daily introductory talks (weekdays). Explore at your own pace on weekday afternoons and weekends. Enjoy seasonal exhibitions and festive displays in December. **Outdoors** Regular garden tours. Grade II*-listed gardens, including formal gardens and pleasure grounds. The estate is part of the Surrey Hills Area of Outstanding Natural Beauty, with four waymarked walks. Families will love the natural play area in the grounds and tree swings. You can also borrow binoculars to search for wildlife, meet chickens, visit the bug hotel and bird hide and then join the fun seasonal trails during the school holidays. **Dogs**: welcome on leads in parts of the gardens and on the wider estate.

Access: 🅿️🐕♿🏠🔆🎧📷🖥🪑
House ♿🔆♿ **Grounds** 🔆♿➡🐾♿

Find out more: 01372 452048 or polesdenlacey@nationaltrust.org.uk
Great Bookham, near Dorking, Surrey RH5 6BD

Polesden Lacey	
Open every day all year	10–5*

*House: opens 11; weekday access 11 to 12:30, by guided tour only; freeflow from 12:30 (admission by timed ticket at certain times). Last entry one hour before closing. 1 January to 2 February and 2 November to 31 December: closes 4. Closed 24 and 25 December. House (or part of house) may close occasionally for programming set up or conservation.

Quebec House

Quebec Square, Westerham, Kent TN16 1TD

🏠 ♣ 1918

Georgian simplicity at Quebec House in Kent

Parking: 80 yards in main town car park on A25 (not National Trust).

The childhood home of General James Wolfe, Quebec House retains much of its original charm and feel. Recreated Georgian schoolroom, hands-on collections and objects belonging to Wolfe are used to learn about Georgian family life. Exhibition in the Coach House explores Wolfe's victory at the Battle of Quebec in 1759.

Eat, shop, stay: second-hand books, souvenirs and Quebec-themed gifts for sale in the Coach House, as well as hot and cold drinks and a selection of cakes.

Things to see and do: guided tours (12 and 12:30). On Sundays, volunteers recreate Mrs Wolfe's recipes. Exhibition about the dramatic Battle of Quebec. Historic Westerham nearby. **Dogs**: welcome on short leads in the garden.

Access: 🅿️👓🦽🖼️📷♫🔆🏛️
Building 🏠🦽 **Grounds** 🅿️🦽

Find out more: 01732 868381 or quebechouse@nationaltrust.org.uk

Quebec House		M	T	W	T	F	S	S
26 Feb–1 Nov*	11–5			W	T	F	S	S
7 Nov–13 Dec	1–4						S	S

*House: open from 1, tours only from 12 and 12:30 (bookable on the day at the Coach House); Open Bank Holiday Mondays.

Reigate Hill and Gatton Park

near Reigate, Surrey

🏠 ♣ 1912

Satnav: use RH2 0HX.
Parking: at Wray Lane or Margery Wood car park when Wray Lane is full (KT20 7EJ).

Reigate Hill commands sweeping views across the Weald to the South Downs. It's a great spot for walking, family picnics, flying a kite and watching wildlife. A short walk away is the 19th-century Reigate Fort. The complex is open every day and the fort buildings open for special events. To the east of Reigate Hill is Surrey Hill's hidden gem, Gatton Park, designed by Lancelot 'Capability' Brown. **Note**: areas of Gatton Park opened monthly by the Gatton Trust.

Eat, shop, stay: picnics welcome. Tea kiosk (not National Trust) at Wray Lane.

Reigate Hill and Gatton Park, Surrey, below and opposite

Things to see and do: walks detailed on noticeboards and downloadable from website. Spot the chalk downland species, such as the Adonis blue butterfly. Visit the B-17 plane crash memorial site, west of Reigate Fort. **Dogs**: welcome under close control at all times.

Access: 🚶🧭

Find out more: 01342 843036 or reigate@nationaltrust.org.uk

Reigate Hill and Gatton Park
Reigate Fort buildings open by special arrangement.

River Wey and Godalming Navigations and Dapdune Wharf

Navigations Office and Dapdune Wharf, Wharf Road, Guildford, Surrey GU1 4RR

🏠♿🚻 **1964**

Parking: at Dapdune Wharf.

A hidden haven where you can relax and unwind on a boat trip, explore a restored barge, or enjoy scenic walks. Dapdune Wharf in Guildford brings to life stories of the historic waterway, along 20 miles of waterside towpath. A great place for children to have fun.

Note: boat trip charges, mooring and fishing fees apply to members.

Eat, shop, stay: small tea-room serving sandwiches, cakes, ice cream and drinks. Second-hand book shed. Small shop with plant sales. Picnic areas at Dapdune Wharf.

Things to see and do: **Indoors** Children's dressing-up clothes. **Outdoors** Year-round events, including activities for children at Dapdune and guided walks along towpath and beyond. September River Festival. Overnight moorings. **Dogs**: on leads at Dapdune Wharf and lock areas; elsewhere under control.

Access: 🅿️♿🚻🔈📷🏠

Find out more: 01483 561389 or riverwey@nationaltrust.org.uk

River Wey and Dapdune Wharf		M	T	W	T	F	S	S
Dapdune Wharf*								
21 Mar–8 Nov	11–5**	**M**			**T**	**F**	**S**	**S**

*Open daily during local school half term and summer holidays. **24 October to 8 November: closes 4. River trips from Dapdune Wharf, 11 to 4 (conditions permitting). Access to towpath during daylight all year.

River Wey and Godalming Navigations and Dapdune Wharf, Surrey: lock-keeper's cottage

Runnymede and Ankerwycke

Egham, near Old Windsor, Surrey

🏠 🚲 ♿ 🐾 1931

Satnav: use TW20 0AE and follow brown 'Runnymede Memorials' signs.
Parking: either side of A308 (seasonal opening).

Seen by many as the birthplace of modern democracy, this picturesque landscape beside the Thames was witness to King John's sealing of the Magna Carta more than 800 years ago. Within easy reach of the M25, there is so much to enjoy here –ancient woodlands, countryside walks and picnics by the river. Along with Lutyens's Fairhaven Lodges, Runnymede is home to memorials for the Magna Carta, John F. Kennedy and Commonwealth Air Forces, making it the perfect place to reflect. This year support Runnymede Explored, our vision to unify Runnymede and Ankerwycke through improved pathways, interpretation and a ferry crossing. **Note**: mooring and fishing (during fishing season) available for additional fee (including members).

Picnicking at Runnymede and Ankerwycke in Surrey, below, and the 'Writ in Water' installation, above

Eat, shop, stay: tea-room serving soup, light lunches, sandwiches and tasty treats, along with hot and cold drinks and ice cream. Free Wi-Fi. Shop in tea-room offering Magna Carta-themed books, souvenirs and toys.

Things to see and do: family events throughout the year. Explore contemporary art installations *Writ in Water* and *The Jurors*. River boat trips available with French Brothers Boat Hire (01753 851900). **Dogs**: welcome on site and in the Magna Carta tea-room. On leads near livestock.

Access: 🅿️♿♿♿♿ Grounds ♿

Find out more: 01784 432891 or runnymede@nationaltrust.org.uk

Runnymede and Ankerwycke	
Tea-room	
Open every day all year	10–5*

*1 to 31 January and 29 October to 31 December: closes 3:30; 1 May to 31 August (weekends and Bank Holidays): closes 6. Car parks: locked outside of hours. Closed 24 and 25 December.

St John's Jerusalem

Sutton-at-Hone, Dartford, Kent
DA4 9HQ 1943

Set within a secluded moated garden, this is a rare example of a 13th-century chapel built by the Knights Hospitaller. **Note**: private residence, maintained and managed by a tenant on behalf of the National Trust. Sorry no tea-room or accessible toilet. Open Wednesdays, 1 April to 30 September, 2 to 6, and 7 to 28 October, 2 to 4.

Find out more: 01732 810378 or stjohnsjerusalem@nationaltrust.org.uk

Scotney Castle

Lamberhurst, Tunbridge Wells, Kent TN3 8JN

🏠🖼️🚽✳️🍽️ 1970

Scotney Castle, Kent, lies in a peaceful wooded valley

Parking: 130 yards (limited), overflow parking 440 yards.

The medieval moated Old Scotney Castle lies in a peaceful wooded valley. In the 19th century its owner, Edward Hussey III, set about building a new house, partially demolishing the Old Castle to create a romantic folly, the centrepiece of his picturesque landscape. From the terraces of the new house, sweeps of rhododendrons and azaleas cascade down the slope in summer, followed by highlights of autumn leaf colour, mirrored in the moat. In the house three generations have made their mark, adding possessions and character to the homely Victorian mansion which enjoys far-reaching views out across the estate.

Eat, shop, stay: the coach-house tea-room offers a selection of hot meals and sandwiches, as well as homemade cakes and scones. Take home your own part of Scotney with local honey, ale made using Scotney Castle hops and plants available in the shop.

Frosty winter's day at 14th-century Scotney Castle

Things to see and do: Indoors Children's house trail. Seasonal changing exhibitions and conservation demonstrations all year. **Outdoors** Regular guided and self-led estate walks. Natural play and children's play areas. **Dogs**: welcome on short leads in the garden and on the estate.

Access: 🅿️🚪🏷️👂📷🎥📹📼
House 🔆🔆🔆 Grounds 🔆➡️🔆

Find out more: 01892 893820 (Infoline). 01892 893868 or scotneycastle@nationaltrust.org.uk

Scotney Castle	
Open every day all year*	10–5

*House: opens 11, closing times vary in January, February, November and December (please check before travelling), entry by timed ticket or guided tour. 1 January to 14 February and 2 November to 31 December: everything closes 4. Closed 24 and 25 December.

Shalford Mill

Shalford, near Guildford, Surrey GU4 8BS 1932

Evocative mill, although the machinery no longer works. Discover the story of the Ferguson's Gang. **Note**: sorry no toilet or refreshments. Visits by guided tour only. Open Wednesday, Sunday and Bank Holiday Mondays, 1 April to 1 November, 11 to 4:30.

Find out more: 01483 561389 or shalfordmill@nationaltrust.org.uk

Sheffield Park and Garden

Sheffield Park, Uckfield, East Sussex TN22 3QX

⊞ ⬙ ▽ 1954

Satnav: look out for brown signs on approach.
Parking: on site (overflow car park 600 yards, in use when dry); very busy during May and October.

Originating in the 18th century and developed by each subsequent owner, this garden of colour, perfume and sound excites your senses as you enjoy winding paths, majestic trees, ponds and dappled glades. Falls, cascades and bridges are integral to the garden design. Planting is reflected in ponds so clear that the eye is tricked into thinking up is down. Bold and grand planting has a sculptural form in winter. Spring and summer bring vibrant blooms, fragrant arbours and splashes of colour. Autumn is a blazing kaleidoscope of greens, flame-reds, burnt oranges and bright yellows, planted for their combined display.

The encircling park and woodland provide opportunities for further adventure where nature thrives in riverside meadows and woods.

Eat, shop, stay: tea-room serving homemade cakes, sandwiches, hot lunches and cream teas. Takeaway refreshments and snacks in the garden (available seasonally). Shops in reception building and Coach House selling gifts, local products, gardening items and plants. Second-hand bookshop beside Coach House.

Things to see and do: events and trails in the school holidays and '50 things' self-led activities for families all year. Natural playtrail in Ringwood Toll – try den-building, balance beams, a log see-saw and much more. More than 120 hectares (300 acres) of parkland, with circular walks (just over 1 mile) by the River Ouse. Cricket matches take place on the historic cricket pitch most summer weekends.

Carpets of bluebells in spring, followed by rhododendrons and azaleas. Waterlilies cover the lakes during summer, and autumn brings an outstanding display of colour. Walk Woods is open seasonally. Pulham Falls waterfall (12 to 1, Tuesday and Friday). **Dogs**: welcome in East Park. In parkland on short leads; in garden after 1:30.

Access: 🅿️🚐♿🚻🖐️🗺️📷📺⛵♨️📷
Reception ♿🚻 **Tea-room** ♿🚻
Garden ♿🚻🅿️➡️♿♿

Find out more: 01825 790231 or
sheffieldpark@nationaltrust.org.uk

Sheffield Park	
Open every day all year	10–5*

*Garden: 1 January to 2 February and 2 November to 31 December, closes at 4. Garden, shop and tea-room: closed 24 and 25 December.

There's so much to explore at Sheffield Park and Garden in East Sussex, this page and opposite

Kent, Surrey and Sussex

Sissinghurst Castle Garden

Biddenden Road, near Cranbrook,
Kent TN17 2AB

🏠🌿♿🍴🛍🍵 1967

Parking: 315 yards.

Sissinghurst Castle Garden sits within the ruin of a great Elizabethan house surrounded by the rich Kentish landscape of woods, streams and farmland. The famous garden, with its fairy-tale tower, is the result of the creativity of the formal design of Harold Nicolson and the lavish planting of Vita Sackville-West. The colour schemes, intimacy of the different garden 'rooms' and rich herbaceous borders are the epitome of an English garden. The wider estate, which includes a vegetable garden, lakes and rich variety of wildlife, is waiting to be explored, while our regular exhibitions tell Sissinghurst's stories and show how history and landscape have combined to shape this special place. See the architectural beauty of the garden in winter at weekends. **Note**: limited access for buggies and wheelchairs.

Eat, shop, stay: Granary restaurant serving lunch and afternoon tea made with produce from our vegetable garden (hot food available until 3). The Old Dairy, offering sandwiches, cakes and drinks. Second-hand bookshop and garden shop selling plants grown in the Sissinghurst nursery.

Things to see and do: Indoors Exhibitions and daily talks. The Library contains the National Trust's most significant collection of 20th-century literature, and visitors can learn how we conserve it. Daily guided tours of the South Cottage from 12 to 4 (limited availability, closed June). **Outdoors** Welcome talks and '50 things to do before you're 11¾' activities. Trails available from visitor reception to help you explore. Acres of ancient woodland and lakes. Panoramic views across the Wealden countryside. Discover Delos, our redesigned Mediterranean garden in the heart of Kent. You can see animals on our working farm. Smallhythe Place, Lamb House and Stoneacre nearby. **Dogs**: welcome on leads on estate. Assistance dogs only in garden and vegetable garden.

Access: 🅿♿🚻🧒👨‍🦽🖼📷♿
Building 🛗♿♿ Grounds 🛗♿➡

Find out more: 01580 710700 or sissinghurst@nationaltrust.org.uk

Sissinghurst Castle Garden		M	T	W	T	F	S	S
Garden								
4 Jan–1 Mar	11–4*	.	.	.	.	.	S	S
7 Mar–1 Nov	11–5:30*	M	T	W	T	F	S	S
7 Nov–27 Dec	11–4*	.	.	.	.	.	S	S
South Cottage†								
1 Jan–31 May	Tour	M	T	W	T	F	S	S
4 Jul–31 Dec	Tour	M	T	W	T	F	S	S
Shop and restaurant								
Open all year	10–5:30**	M	T	W	T	F	S	S
Estate								
Open all year	Dawn–dusk	M	T	W	T	F	S	S

*Garden: last entry 45 minutes before closing; for conservation reasons, no food, drink or buggies in garden (carriers provided). Tower and library open in winter.
**Shop and restaurant: close 4:30, November to February.
†South Cottage: closed June; limited timed tickets.
Closed 24 and 25 December.

Two views of Sissinghurst Castle Garden, Kent, this page, and the tower, seen from the top courtyard, opposite

Kent, Surrey and Sussex

Slindon Estate

near Arundel, West Sussex

🏠 🏛 ♿ 🛏 👪 ⛺ ⛺ 1950

Satnav: use BN18 0QY for Park Lane; BN18 0SP Duke's Road; RH20 1PH Bignor Hill. **Parking**: at Park Lane, Duke's Road and Bignor Hill.

Slindon Estate is a patchwork of woodland, downland, farmland and parkland, with an unspoilt Sussex village at its centre. Historic features cover the landscape, such as Stane Street, the Roman road from Chichester to London. Slindon has a rich and wonderfully varied wildlife with bats, badgers, butterflies and downland flowers. **Note**: sorry no toilets.

Eat, shop, stay: The Forge in Slindon village (tenant-run) stocks everything from locally baked bread, deli items, fruit and vegetables, to sandwiches and cakes. Fresh coffee and tea, beer, light meals also available.

Slindon Estate, West Sussex, above and below: a patchwork of farmland, woods, downs and parkland

Things to see and do: there are more than 25 miles of rights of way to explore on the estate, as well as the village to discover. **Dogs**: welcome under close control.

Access: ➡

Find out more: 01243 814730 or slindonestate@nationaltrust.org.uk

Smallhythe Place

Smallhythe, Tenterden, Kent TN30 7NG

🏠♿🔔🍽 1939

Parking: 50 yards (not National Trust).

Surrounded by the rolling Kent countryside, the corridors of this early 16th-century cottage resonate with the vibrant spirit of its theatrical former owner, Victorian actress Ellen Terry. Bursting with memorabilia from her life-long career on stage, visitors can see unique theatrical artefacts and visit the Barn Theatre.

Eat, shop, stay: charming vintage tea-room attached to the Barn Theatre selling soup, sandwiches, cakes, as well as soft and alcoholic drinks.

Things to see and do: **Indoors** Diverse variety of plays and music performed in the Barn Theatre. **Outdoors** Open-air theatre (summer). Sissinghurst Castle Garden, Lamb House and Stoneacre nearby. **Dogs**: welcome on leads in grounds.

Access: 🚐📷♿😊🅿
Building 🔛🔛 Grounds 🔛➡

Find out more: 01580 762334 or smallhytheplace@nationaltrust.org.uk

Smallhythe Place		M	T	W	T	F	S	S
4 Mar–1 Nov	11–5*			W	T	F	S	S

*Tea-room: closes 4:30. Open Bank Holiday Mondays.

The Barn Theatre at Smallhythe Place in Kent

South Foreland Lighthouse

The Front, St Margaret's Bay, Dover, Kent

🏠♿🚗🍽 1989

Parking: no on-site parking, nearest at White Cliffs (2 miles); St Margaret's car park (1 mile).

This historic landmark (above), dramatically situated on The White Cliffs of Dover, guided ships past the infamous Goodwin Sands and has a fascinating tale to tell. It was the first lighthouse powered by electricity and the site of the first international radio transmission. **Note**: access to lighthouse by road is not permitted. Nearest parking at White Cliffs Visitor Centre.

Eat, shop, stay: loose-leaf tea and homemade cakes in Mrs Knott's tea-room. Shop selling ice cream, sandwiches, cold drinks and gifts.

Things to see and do: **Indoors** Tours run by knowledgeable guides. Interactive and hands-on displays. **Outdoors** Family fun with kite-flying and games. **Dogs**: welcome on leads in grounds. Please be aware of cliff edges.

Access: 🚐🚐♿📺😊🅿
Lighthouse 🔛🚹 Tea-room 🔛🚹 Grounds 🔛

Find out more: 01304 853281 or southforeland@nationaltrust.org.uk
Langdon Cliffs, Dover, Kent CT16 1HJ

South Foreland Lighthouse		M	T	W	T	F	S	S
Lighthouse*								
27 Mar–1 Nov	11–5:30**	M				F	S	S
Tea-room								
1 Feb–22 Mar	11–3						S	S
27 Mar–1 Nov	11–5**	M	T	W	T	F	S	S

*Significant conservation work may affect opening. Open daily during local school holidays. Last tour at 5.
**25 October to 1 November: closes 3.

Standen House and Garden

West Hoathly Road, East Grinstead,
West Sussex RH19 4NE

🏠 ✣ 🚻 🛏 🍴 1973

Parking: 200 yards (steep hill).

Nestled in the Sussex countryside with views across the High Weald, James and Margaret Beale chose an idyllic location to build their rural retreat. Designed by Philip Webb, the house is one of the finest examples of Arts and Crafts workmanship with Morris & Co. interiors and decorative art of the period. The 5-hectare (12-acre) hillside garden established by Mrs Beale is restored to its 1920s glory. Each garden room offers something for every season, from colourful spring bulbs to autumn shades. On the wider estate, footpaths lead into the woodlands and the High Weald Area of Outstanding Natural Beauty.

Eat, shop, stay: Barn Café serving homemade cakes, hot lunches and cream teas (Wi-Fi). Takeaway drinks, sandwiches and ice cream. Arts and Crafts-inspired gifts in shop. Plant centre. Second-hand bookshop. Kitchen garden produce. Picnics welcome. Holiday apartment within house.

Standen House and Garden, West Sussex, above and below

Things to see and do: Indoors Daily talks. Exhibitions exploring the Arts and Crafts movement. Family Christmas. **Outdoors** Restored garden. Spring tulips. Woodland walks. Family trails (school holidays). Natural play area. Seasonal water tower tours. **Dogs**: welcome on short leads in formal garden, woodland estate and Potting Shed.

Access: 🅿️ D♿ 🚪♿ 🔊 📷 🏠 🚶
House 🔦♿🏠♿ Garden 🔦 ➡️ ♿

Find out more: 01342 323029 or
standen@nationaltrust.org.uk

Standen House		M	T	W	T	F	S	S
House								
11 Jan–2 Feb	11–3:30	·	·	·	·	·	S	S
3 Feb–1 Nov	11–4:30*	M	T	W	T	F	S	S
2 Nov–27 Nov	Tour**	M	T	W	T	F	·	·
28 Nov–31 Dec†	11–4:30*	M	T	W	T	F	S	S
Garden, café and shop								
Open all year	10–5††	M	T	W	T	F	S	S

*November and December: closes 3:30. **Admission by tour only; last tour 2:30. †Closed 24 and 25 December. ††January, November and December: close 4.

Stoneacre

Otham, Maidstone, Kent ME15 8RS 1928

Medieval farmhouse sitting within a hidden horticultural haven, orchard, meadows and woodland. Home to famous designer and critic Aymer Vallance. **Note**: open weekends and Bank Holidays, 14 March to 1 November, 11 to 5.

Find out more: 01580 710701 or
stoneacre@nationaltrust.org.uk

Uppark House and Garden

South Harting, Petersfield,
West Sussex GU31 5QR

1954

Parking: 300 yards.

High on its vantage point on the South Downs ridge, Uppark has views as far south as the Solent. Outside, the intimate garden is being gradually restored to its historical design, with plenty of space in the adjacent meadow to play and relax. Filled with purchases from the Grand Tour, Uppark's Georgian interiors illustrate the comfort of life 'upstairs' in contrast to the 'downstairs' world of its servants. Highlights include one of the best examples of an 18th-century British doll's house in the country. **Note**: due to conservation work, access to some areas may be limited (please check before visiting).

Eat, shop, stay: café (licensed) serving breakfast, lunches and afternoon tea. Shop selling books, plants, local food and much more. Second-hand bookshop.

Things to see and do: Indoors Rare 18th-century British doll's house. **Outdoors** Weekly garden tours (April to October). Open-air theatre and music in the summer. Harting Down, Hinton Ampner and Petworth House nearby. **Dogs**: welcome on short leads in grounds.

Access:
House **Garden**

Find out more: 01730 825415 or uppark@nationaltrust.org.uk

Uppark House		M	T	W	T	F	S	S
House (ground floor only)								
29 Feb–1 Nov	11:30–4	**M**	**T**	**W**	**T**	**F**	**S**	**S**
Servants' quarters								
Open all year	11:30–4	**M**	**T**	**W**	**T**	**F**	**S**	**S**
Garden, shop and café*								
Open all year	10–5	**M**	**T**	**W**	**T**	**F**	**S**	**S**

*1 January to 2 February and 2 November to 31 December: close at 4. Everything closed 24 and 25 December.

Perfectly proportioned, Uppark House and Garden, West Sussex, commands far-reaching southerly views

Wakehurst

Ardingly, Haywards Heath,
West Sussex RH17 6TN

🏠 ♣ 🎣 🌳 🔔 ☕ 1964

Parking: 50 yards.

Wakehurst, Kew's wild botanic garden
in Sussex, has more than 202 hectares
(500 acres) of beautiful ornamental gardens,
woodlands and a nature reserve. Internationally
significant for collections, scientific research
and plant conservation, you can also visit
Kew's unique Millennium Seed Bank, where
science and horticulture work side by side.
Note: funded and managed by the
Royal Botanic Gardens, Kew.
Parking charges apply (including members).

Eat, shop, stay: Seed Café serving cakes,
sandwiches and soup. Redwoods Coffee
Shop serving hot drinks and snacks. Stables
Restaurant offering hot and cold food.
Gift shop. Plant centre (not National Trust).

Things to see and do: free daily guided tours.
Seasonal festival programme, open-air theatre,
lantern trail. Courses. Events all year.
Natural play areas for families. Kingfisher
and badger-watching (charges apply).
Dogs: assistance dogs only.

Access: 🅿️ 🚻 🚾 ♿ 🚼
Buildings ♿ 🚼 🚻 ♿ **Grounds** ➡️ 🚾 ♿

Find out more: 01444 894066 or
wakehurst@kew.org   kew.org

Wakehurst		M	T	W	T	F	S	S
Garden*								
1 Jan–28 Feb	10–4:30	M	T	W	T	F	S	S
1 Mar–31 Oct	10–6	M	T	W	T	F	S	S
1 Nov–31 Dec**	10–4:30	M	T	W	T	F	S	S

*Mansion and Millennium Seed Bank: close one hour
earlier. Shop and catering closing times may vary.
Shop: closed Easter Sunday. UK National Trust members
free (reciprocal agreements made between the Trust
and other parties do not apply). Mansion occasionally
closes for private events (please check before you visit).
**Closed 24 and 25 December.

The White Cliffs of Dover

Langdon Cliffs, Dover, Kent

🏠 🎣 🏛 ☕ 1968

Satnav: use CT15 5NA. **Parking**: on site,
limited (please check before visiting Sundays
and Bank Holidays, April to October).

There can be no doubt that The White Cliffs
of Dover are one of this country's most
spectacular natural features and have been
a symbol of hope for generations. You can
appreciate their beauty through the seasons
by taking one of the country's most dramatic
clifftop walks, which offer unrivalled views
of the English Channel while savouring the
rare flora and fauna found only on this chalk
grassland. You can also learn more about the
fascinating military history of The White Cliffs
by taking a torchlit tour of Fan Bay Deep
Shelter, a labyrinth of forgotten Second World
War tunnels. **Note**: nearest toilets at White
Cliffs. Age restrictions apply at Fan Bay.

Eat, shop, stay: shop selling gifts and
outdoor goods. Coffee shop serving lunches,
homemade cakes and cream teas. Both
with unrivalled views of the Port of Dover.
Homemade cakes, sandwiches and loose-leaf
tea available in lighthouse tea-room.

Things to see and do: Indoors Pick up a ticket for a guided tour of the Lighthouse and Fan Bay Deep Shelter. **Outdoors** Natural play area. Spectacular viewpoints. Waymarked trail to South Foreland Lighthouse.
Dogs: welcome on leads. Please be aware of livestock and cliff edges.

Access: 🅿️♿🎫🖼️♿🎧📷🌀 **Visitor Centre** ♿♿
Fan Bay Deep Shelter 🔦 **Countryside** ➡️♿

Find out more: 01304 202756 or whitecliffs@nationaltrust.org.uk

The White Cliffs of Dover, Kent: the striking stretch of cliffs, above, and labyrinthine Fan Bay Deep Shelter, opposite

The White Cliffs		M	T	W	T	F	S	S
Visitor Centre, shop and kiosk								
1 Jan–2 Feb	10–4	**M**	**T**	**W**	**T**	**F**	**S**	**S**
3 Feb–1 Nov	10–5*	**M**	**T**	**W**	**T**	**F**	**S**	**S**
2 Nov–31 Dec**	10–4	**M**	**T**	**W**	**T**	**F**	**S**	**S**
Fan Bay Deep Shelter								
27 Mar–1 Nov	11–3	**M**	·	·	·	**F**	**S**	**S**

*6 July to 6 September: open to 5:30.
**Closed 24 and 25 December.

Winkworth Arboretum

Hascombe Road, Godalming, Surrey GU8 4AD

⊞ ⊞ 1952

Parking: 100 yards.

The National Trust's only arboretum was born from one man's vision and passion. Dr Wilfrid Fox used the wooded valley and its lakes as a canvas for 'painting a picture' with trees. The fruits of his labour are an award-winning collection of more than 1,000 varieties of trees and shrubs set in the picturesque Surrey Hills, offering stunning combinations of colour every season. Famous for vibrant autumnal foliage and carpets of bluebells in spring, the azaleas, magnolias and snowdrops make Winkworth worth visiting all year round for beautiful scenery, picnics and events for all ages.
Note: some steep slopes; banks of lake and wetlands only partially fenced.

Eat, shop, stay: cosy tea-room offering freshly baked scones, cakes and light lunches with small shop section.

Things to see and do: events suitable for all ages, including regular guided walks. Discover our Tree Adventure, natural play area and viewing platform, or relax in the boathouse and enjoy lakeside views. **Dogs**: welcome on leads.

Access: 🅿️🏔️♿🚻♿ **Grounds** ♿➡️

Find out more: 01483 208477 or winkwortharboretum@nationaltrust.org.uk

Winkworth Arboretum		M	T	W	T	F	S	S
1 Jan–31 Jan	10–4	M	T	W	T	F	S	S
1 Feb–31 Mar	10–5	M	T	W	T	F	S	S
1 Apr–31 Oct	10–6	M	T	W	T	F	S	S
1 Nov–31 Dec*	10–4	M	T	W	T	F	S	S

Tea-room closes 30 minutes earlier than arboretum. Car-park gates locked at closing time. *Closed 24 and 25 December.

The boathouse at Winkworth Arboretum, Surrey, below, and hunting for Easter eggs, above

Woolbeding Gardens

Midhurst, West Sussex GU29 9RR

✿ 1957

Parking: none available. Access by park-and-ride minibus from Midhurst (booking essential).

Bordering the River Rother, Woolbeding Gardens is a horticultural haven where modern yet romantic planting meets sophisticated colour palettes. Elegant garden rooms and meticulous borders merge with a wooded landscape that conceals dramatic architectural follies. Ever-changing, from the seasons to the planting, every moment offers something new and picturesque. **Note**: all visits must be booked. Access by park-and-ride minibus from Midhurst.

Eat, shop, stay: Orchard Café serving barista-style coffee, speciality teas, and a selection of tempting treats. Shop selling gardening books, gifts and plants.

The summerhouse at Woolbeding Gardens, West Sussex, left, and one of the elegant garden rooms, above

Things to see and do: introductory talks and specialist Gardeners' Workshops. See glimpses of the Heatherwick Glasshouse and surrounding Silk Route garden under construction (opening in 2021). **Dogs**: assistance dogs only.

Access: 🅿️♿🚻🍼♿
Reception ♿♿ **Garden** ♿➡️♿

Find out more: 0344 249 1895 or woolbedinggardens@nationaltrust.org.uk

Woolbeding Gardens		M	T	W	T	F	S	S
23 Apr–19 Jun*	10:30–5				T	F		
24 Jun–28 Aug	10:30–5			W	T	F		
3 Sep–25 Sep	10:30–5				T	F		

*Closed 8 May. Advance booking essential.
Access by park-and-ride minibus only from Midhurst.

Additional countryside car parks in Kent, Surrey and Sussex

Surrey
Black Down	GU27 3BJ
Harewoods	RH1 5PW
Holmwood Common	RH5 4NX
Hydon's Ball and Heath	GU8 4BB
Limpsfield Common	RH8 0TW
Witley and Milford Commons	GU8 5QA

Kent
Oldbury Hill	TN15 0ET
One Tree Hill	TN15 0SN
Toys Hill	TN16 1QG

East Sussex
Crowlink	BN20 0AY

West Sussex
Lavington Common	GU28 0QL
Woolbeding Countryside	GU29 9RR

Flying high at Osterley Park and House, London

London

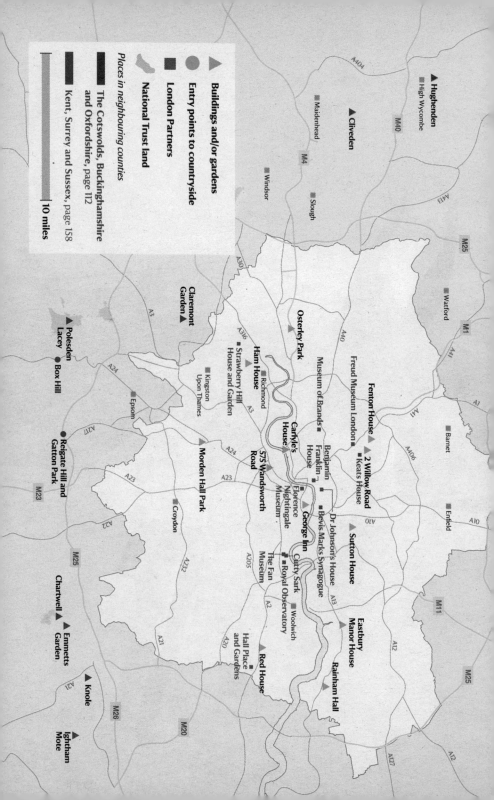

Places in neighbouring counties

Kent, Surrey and Sussex, page 158

The Cotswolds, Buckinghamshire and Oxfordshire, page 112

National Trust land

London Partners

Entry points to countryside

Buildings and/or gardens

10 miles

▲ Hughenden
■ High Wycombe

■ Maidenhead

▲ Cliveden

M40

M4

■ Windsor

■ Slough

M25

■ Watford

M1

M41

▲ Claremont Garden

A3

A30

▲ Polesden Lacey

● Box Hill

A24

A306

▲ Osterley Park

A40

Freud Museum London

Fenton House ▲

▲ 2 Willow Road

■ Keats House

Museum of Brands ■

Strawberry Hill House and Garden ■

Ham House ▲

■ Richmond

A3

■ Kingston Upon Thames

Carlyle's House ▲

Benjamin Franklin House ■

Dr Johnson's House ▲

■ Bevis Marks Synagogue

▲ Sutton House

A1

■ Barnet

A406

A41

A10

■ Enfield

M11

M25

A12

■ Epsom

A24

▲ Morden Hall Park

A23

575 Wandsworth Road ▲

A23

Florence Nightingale Museum ■

● George Inn

The Fan Museum ■

■ Cutty Sark

■ Royal Observatory

■ Woolwich

▲ Eastbury Manor House

▲ Rainham Hall

A13

● Reigate Hill and Gatton Park

M23

■ Croydon

A232

A2

A205

A20

Hall Place and Gardens

▲ Red House

M25

▲ Chartwell

▲ Emmetts Garden

A21

A20

M26

M20

▲ Knole

● Ightham Mote

A21

A27

Carlyle's House

24 Cheyne Row, Chelsea, London
SW3 5HL [1936]

Home of Victorian writer Thomas Carlyle and
his amusing wife Jane; friends included Ruskin,
Dickens and Thackeray. Small walled garden.
Note: open 29 February to 1 November,
Wednesday to Sunday, 11 to 5, and
Bank Holiday Mondays.

Find out more: 020 7352 7087 or
carlyleshouse@nationaltrust.org.uk

Eastbury Manor House

Eastbury Square, Barking IG11 9SN

🏠 ✤ 🔔 🍽 [1918]

Parking: on adjacent streets (free but limited).

Barely altered since it was built circa 1573,
this Grade I-listed Elizabethan gentry house
features soaring chimneys, early 17th-century
wall-paintings and an original turret staircase.

Outside there is a cobbled courtyard and
peaceful walled garden with bee boles to
explore. **Note**: managed by London Borough
of Barking and Dagenham. Some rooms
are closed occasionally for functions.
Special events and activities are charged
at an additional cost.

Eat, shop, stay: garden tea-room
(not National Trust) serving drinks, afternoon
tea, sandwiches, snacks and light meals.
Shop (not National Trust) selling Tudor
pottery, toys, books and souvenirs.

Things to see and do: Indoors Exhibitions,
guided tours and trails. Talks, workshops,
family days, events and holiday activities.
Outdoors Theatre, trails, re-enactments
and exhibitions. Special events and family
activities. **Dogs**: welcome on leads in
grounds only.

Access: 🅿️♿🚻🏠🎦🚪🅰️
Building 🏠♿🔼🛗🐕♿

Find out more: 020 8227 2942 or
eastburymanor@nationaltrust.org.uk

Eastbury Manor House		M	T	W	T	F	S	S
13 Feb–18 Dec	10–4	·	·	·	**T**	**F**	·	·
22 Mar–13 Dec	11–4	·	·	·	·	·	·	**S**

House occasionally used for private bookings.
Tours available on request until 2.

**Dressing up at Eastbury Manor House, Barking,
which has barely altered since about 1573**

Fenton House and Garden

Hampstead Grove, Hampstead,
London NW3 6SP

🏠 ✤ T 1952

Parking: none on site.

This 1686 house, with views across London from Hampstead's Holly Hill, is filled with world-class collections of ceramics, paintings, textiles and musical instruments. The ever-changing horticultural gem that is the garden includes an orchard, kitchen garden, rose garden, terraces and lawns, and never fails to delight.

Eat, shop, stay: small retail area selling local and National Trust items, garden plants and produce.

Inside Fenton House and Garden, Hampstead, above, and the horticultural gem of a garden, left

Things to see and do: **Indoors** Collections talks, exhibitions and music. **Outdoors** Garden tours and events, including Apple Weekend. Keats House, Freud Museum (National Trust Partners) and 2 Willow Road nearby. **Dogs**: assistance dogs only.

Access: 🏠 ♿ ⊡ ⊘ Building ♿ ♿ 🚶 Grounds ♿

Find out more: 020 7435 3471 or fentonhouse@nationaltrust.org.uk

Fenton House		M	T	W	T	F	S	S
29 Feb–1 Nov	11–5			W	T	F	S	S

Open Bank Holidays and selected dates in December.

George Inn

The George Inn Yard, 77 Borough High Street, Southwark, London SE1 1NH 1937

This public house, dating from the 17th century, is London's last remaining galleried inn. **Note**: leased to a private company. No table bookings (call for details). Open every day all year. Closed 25 and 26 December.

Find out more: 020 7407 2056 or georgeinn@nationaltrust.org.uk

Ham House and Garden

Ham Street, Ham, Richmond TW10 7RS

🏛️ ♿ ⬆️ 🍴 1948

Satnav: takes you to stables on nearby Ham Street, carry straight on past these to car park.
Parking: none on site, nearest 380 yards (not National Trust) and on street.

Beautifully situated on the banks of the Thames, Ham is truly one of London's treasures. You can step back in time, walking on the original marble floors while admiring the lavish furnishings, cabinets and artwork collected by the Duke and Duchess of Lauderdale and enjoyed by Charles II during his visits here. The re-imagining of the 17th-century garden is quite wonderful. Containing a large walled kitchen garden, lavender parterre, woodland wilderness garden, two wildflower meadows and boasting an annual display of spring bulbs, the garden was designed to impress.

Eat, shop, stay: café serving a selection of hot and cold lunches, drinks, cakes and dishes made from seasonal ingredients. Picnics welcome. Shop selling gifts for all occasions, as well as seasonal garden produce. Second-hand bookshop.

Things to see and do: Indoors 'Pop-Up Talks' (volunteer dependent). Family Discovery Bags. **Outdoors** Garden history and architecture tours (volunteer dependent). Extra family-friendly activities at weekends and during school holidays. **Dogs**: welcome on short leads.

Access: 🅿️♿🐕♿📷🎨🖼️ House ♿♿🚻♿ Café ♿♿🚻♿ Gardens ♿♿♿➡️♿♿

Find out more: 020 8940 1950 or hamhouse@nationaltrust.org.uk

Ham House		M	T	W	T	F	S	S
House								
Open all year*	12–4	M	T	W	T	F	S	S
Garden, café and shop								
Open all year	10–5**	M	T	W	T	F	S	S

*Selected rooms closed, January to March, November and December. **1 January to 1 February and 1 November to 31 December: closes at 4. Closed 24 and 25 December.

An opulent room at Ham House and Garden, Richmond, below, and the north front, above

Morden Hall Park

Morden Hall Road, Morden, London SM4 5JD

🏛️ ♿ ✿ 🎣 👕 🍴 1941

Parking: 25 yards, next to garden centre.

Step into this 50-hectare (125-acre) oasis and you'll soon forget you're in bustling South London. Once a private country estate, the grounds were gifted to the National Trust to become a park for all people, and have been a local treasure ever since. Peaceful tree-lined riverside paths lead to wide open meadows and a collection of historic buildings which hint at an industrial past. The 1920s rose garden is a delight for the senses in summer and a perfect picnic spot, while a stroll on the immersive wetland boardwalk gives a rare glimpse into the secretive world of waterbirds.
Note: parking for visitors to Morden Hall Park only, five-hour maximum stay (including members). Admission charges apply to some events (including members).

Eat, shop, stay: garden centre offers expert advice and sells peat-free plants grown in National Trust nurseries. The Potting Shed Café in the former kitchen garden serves hearty fare, while the Stableyard Café offers light refreshments at weekends. Second-hand bookshop with period features.

The garden centre at Morden Hall Park, Morden

Things to see and do: **Indoors** Regular exhibitions in the Stableyard Gallery and permanent display in the Snuff Mill.
Outdoors Open-air theatre and cinema during the summer. Family events at Easter, half terms and Christmas. Natural play area.
Dogs: welcome on leads around buildings, rose garden, playground and wetland boardwalk. Within sight elsewhere.

Access: 🅿️♿🚻🏠♿📷♿ Snuff Mill ♿🚹♿
Café and garden centre ♿♿ Parkland ♿♿➡️♿

Find out more: 020 8545 6850 or mordenhallpark@nationaltrust.org.uk

Morden Hall Park
Open every day all year

Potting Shed Café: open 8 to 6. Garden centre: open Monday to Saturday, 9 to 6; Sunday, 10 to 4. Rose garden and Stableyard: open 8 to 6. 1 November to 1 March: all buildings and gardens close one hour earlier, no change to garden centre Sunday opening.

With a natural play area, opposite, riverside paths, below, and meadows, it is easy to forget Morden Hall Park is in London

Osterley Park and House

Isleworth, London

🏠 ❖ ♿ 🍽 1949

Satnav: enter Jersey Road and TW7 4RD.
Parking: 400 yards.

A suburban palace caught between town and country, Osterley Park and House is one of the last surviving country estates in London. Past fields and grazing cattle, just around the lake the magnificent house awaits, presented as it would have been when it was redesigned by Robert Adam in the late 18th century for the Child family. A place for welcoming friends and clients, fashioned for show and entertaining, the lavish state apartments tell the story of a party palace. Recently returned family portraits and furniture now add a personal touch to grand rooms. Elegant pleasure gardens and hundreds of acres of parkland are perfect for whiling away a peaceful afternoon.

Eat, shop, stay: Stables Café, serving fresh seasonal dishes and homemade cakes (indoor and outdoor seating), and Brewhouse Café (open seasonally). Gift shop, second-hand bookshop and plant sales in the Stables courtyard. Free Wi-Fi. Picnics welcome in the park and gardens.

Things to see and do: **Indoors** Events and family activities all year. **Outdoors** You can stroll through colourful formal gardens, with herbaceous borders, ornamental vegetable beds and an established winter garden. With meadows, woodland and a natural play trail with rope swings and stepping stones, you can let your imagination (and the children's) run wild. Why not enjoy a game of table tennis on the front lawn or a walk around the estate, with impressive views across Middle Lake towards the 18th-century house?

Family-friendly multipurpose pathways are perfect for cycling, with trail maps and suggested routes available. **Dogs**: welcome on leads (designated off-lead area), excluding house and – March to October – gardens.

Access: 🅿️ 🚻 ♿ 🚪 🔊 📷 🎧 📱 👓 House ♿ ♿
Shop and bookshop ♿ **Garden** ♿ ➡️ 🚫 ♿

Find out more: 020 8232 5050 or osterley@nationaltrust.org.uk
Jersey Road, Isleworth, London TW7 4RB

Osterley Park	
Open every day all year	10–5*

*House: open 11 to 12 for guided tours (places limited), freeflow 12 to 4, last entry 3:30. November and December: selected rooms open for exhibition, 11 to 4. House occasionally closed for filming. 1 January to 23 February and 9 November to 31 December: closes 4. Everything closed 25 December.

Magnificent Osterley Park and House in Isleworth, this page and opposite, offers grand interiors, elegant pleasure gardens and vast stretches of parkland to explore

Rainham Hall

The Broadway, Rainham, London RM13 9YN

🏚 ✣ 1949

Parking: 300 yards (not National Trust).

Built in 1729 for an enterprising merchant, Rainham Hall (above) has been home to nearly 50 different inhabitants, including a scientist-vicar and historians. The current exhibition 'The Denney Edition: celebrating an icon of 20th-century style' is inspired by *Vogue* photographer Anthony Denney, who lived at the Hall in the 1960s.

Eat, shop, stay: the Stables Café serves seasonally inspired light lunches, freshly baked scones, cakes, barista coffee, teas and soft drinks. Gifts, guidebooks and postcards available.

Things to see and do: **Indoors** Exciting exhibition programme continues. Regular events, including family activities and seasonal festivities. **Outdoors** Almost 1½-hectare (3-acre) community garden.
Dogs: assistance dogs only.

Access: 🖼🦽🏷🎨 House 🦽🚻
Café 🦽♿⬆ Garden 🦽♿➡

Find out more: 01708 525579 or rainhamhall@nationaltrust.org.uk

Rainham Hall		M	T	W	T	F	S	S
Hall								
1 Feb–20 Dec	10:30–4:30	·	·	W	T	F	S	S
Gardens and Stables Café								
2 Jan–29 Mar*	10–4:30	·	·	W	T	F	S	S
1 Apr–27 Sep	10–4:30	M	T	W	T	F	S	S
30 Sep–31 Dec*	10–4:30	·	·	W	T	F	S	S

Open Bank Holiday Mondays. Everything closed 24 to 26 December. *Close dusk if earlier.

Red House

Bexleyheath, London

🏚 ✣ 2003

Satnav: use DA6 8HL – Danson Park car park.
Parking: at Danson Park, just over ½ mile. Charge at weekends and Bank Holidays (including members).

The only house commissioned, created and lived in by William Morris, founder of the Arts and Crafts movement, Red House (below) is a building of extraordinary architectural and social significance. An ongoing conservation project is revealing Red House's secrets, including original pre-Raphaelite wall-paintings and Morris's first decorative schemes.

Eat, shop, stay: William Morris shop housed in our Grade II*-listed Coach House. Café in original kitchen serving light lunches and cakes. Picnics welcome in the orchard.

Things to see and do: **Indoors** Award-winning film *A Poem of a House*. Exhibition of Philip Webb's personal effects. Children's trails (school holidays). Guided tours.
Outdoors Garden tours. Lawn games.
Dogs: assistance dogs only.

Access: 📷🦽🏷🖼🎨 Building 🦽 Grounds 🦽➡

Find out more: 020 8303 6359 or redhouse@nationaltrust.org.uk
Red House Lane, Bexleyheath, London DA6 8JF

Red House		M	T	W	T	F	S	S
29 Feb–1 Nov	11–5	·	·	W	T	F	S	S
6 Nov–20 Dec	11–4:30	·	·	·	·	F	S	S

Admission by guided tour only at 11, 11:30, 12, 12:30 and 1 (booking recommended); freeflow 1:30 to 5 (4:30 in November and December). Last admission 45 minutes before closing. Tea-room: last serving 4:30 (4 in November and December). Open Bank Holiday Mondays.

Parking is free for members, but don't forget to scan your card in the car park when you visit

Sutton House and Breaker's Yard

2 and 4 Homerton High Street, Hackney, London E9 6JQ

🏠 ❀ 🔔 ⛲ 1938

Parking: none on site and very limited nearby, not National Trust (charge including members).

For nearly 500 years Sutton House (above) has reflected and adapted to the world around it; its identity ranging from a country house to an East London squat. Today it continues to reflect Hackney, hosting hundreds of visits from community and school groups, as well as events and weddings all year.

Eat, shop, stay: treat yourself to tea and cake in the courtyard, bookshop or among upcycled vehicles of the Breaker's Yard garden.

Things to see and do: **Indoors** New family adventures or exhibition every Easter, summer, Halloween and Christmas. Annual summer exhibition created with artists and local community. **Outdoors** Breaker's Yard playground. **Dogs**: assistance dogs only.

Access: 🏛♿🚻🏠🖼📷⛲.😊🅿 **Building** ♿♿

Find out more: 020 8986 2264 or suttonhouse@nationaltrust.org.uk

Sutton House		M	T	W	T	F	S	S
8 Apr–19 Apr	12–4:30	·	·	W	T	F	S	S
22 Jul–30 Aug	12–4:30	·	·	W	T	F	S	S
21 Oct–25 Oct	12–4:30	·	·	W	T	F	S	S
21 Nov–20 Dec	12–4:30	·	·	W	T	F	S	S

Special interest house tours available all year (booking essential). Open Bank Holiday Mondays.

575 Wandsworth Road

575 Wandsworth Road, Lambeth, London SW8 3JD

🏠 2010

Parking: none on site.

Khadambi Asalache (1935–2006) turned this modest Grade II-listed Georgian terraced house into a work of art. Featuring hand-carved fretwork throughout, the house and collections continue to inspire all who visit. Please wear or bring socks as no outdoor shoes are allowed in the house. **Note**: sorry no toilets or café. Access by booked guided tour only (charge including members).

Access: House ♿🚻🏠

Find out more: 0344 249 1895 (bookings) or 575wandsworthroad@nationaltrust.org.uk

575 Wandsworth Road		M	T	W	T	F	S	S
6 Mar–7 Nov	Tour*	·	·	·	·	F	S	·

*Access by guided tour only (approximately one hour) for up to six people (booking essential, places extremely limited, tickets released in February, May and August).

575 Wandsworth Road, Lambeth: intricate fretwork

2 Willow Road

Hampstead, London NW3 1TH

🏠 ⊤ 1994

Innovative 2 Willow Road in Hampstead

Parking: very limited, metered on-street parking nearby (not National Trust).

This late 1930s house, an architect's vision of the future, paints a vivid picture of the creative and social circles in which Ernö and Ursula Goldfinger moved. Today you can explore the intimate and evocative interiors, innovative designs, intriguing personal possessions and impressive 20th-century art collection.
Note: sorry no toilet.

Eat, shop, stay: a small table in the entrance hall has property-related items available for sale.

Things to see and do: events, including late openings and tours. Fenton House nearby, as well as Keats House and the Freud Museum (both London partners).
Dogs: assistance dogs only.

Access: 🅿️ 🔄 🎞️ 🖼️ 🔊 📷 🖼️ **Building** ♿ 🚶

Find out more: 020 7435 6166 or 2willowroad@nationaltrust.org.uk

2 Willow Road		M	T	W	T	F	S	S
29 Feb–1 Nov	11–5*		·	·	**W**	**T**	**F**	**S**	**S**

*Entry by one-hour guided tour only at 11, 12, 1 and 2 (places limited, tickets available on day at door only). Wednesday to Friday tours at 11 occasionally booked by groups. 3 to 5, self-guided viewing (timed entry when busy). Open Bank Holidays.

National
Trust
Partner

London partners

'National Trust Partner' is an exciting venture between the National Trust and a selection of small, independent heritage attractions and museums within London. The Partnership aims to bring enhanced benefits to National Trust members living in London or for those visiting the capital for a day out, helping to provide increased opportunities to explore our rich and diverse heritage.

Entry charges: 50 per cent discount for members on presentation of a valid membership card. For full visiting information (and access), please see individual National Trust Partner websites.

Benjamin Franklin House

The world's only remaining home of Benjamin Franklin, featuring a unique 'Historical Experience'.

Underground: Charing Cross or Embankment.
Train: Charing Cross.

Find out more: 020 7925 1405 or benjaminfranklinhouse.org

Cutty Sark

Nineteenth-century tea clipper, meticulously preserved to tell the stories of life on board, now with free audio tour.

Overground: Cutty Sark (DLR).
Train: Greenwich or Maze Hill.
River: Greenwich Pier.

Find out more: 020 8312 6608 or bookings@rmg.co.uk   rmg.co.uk/cuttysark

Bevis Marks Synagogue

Dated 1701, Britain's oldest surviving synagogue contains Cromwellian and Queen Anne furniture.

Underground: Liverpool Street or Aldgate.
Train: Liverpool Street.

Find out more: 020 7621 1188 or bevismarks.org.uk

Dr Johnson's House

Late 17th-century town house, once home to lexicographer and wit Samuel Johnson.

Underground: Chancery Lane or Blackfriars.
Train: Blackfriars.

Find out more: 020 7353 3745 or drjohnsonshouse.org

The Fan Museum

Unique collection of more than 6,000 fans, housed in elegant Georgian buildings.

Overground: Cutty Sark (DLR).
Train: Greenwich.

Find out more: 020 8305 1441 or thefanmuseum.org.uk

Freud Museum London

See Freud's study and the original psychoanalytic couch on which Freud's patients told him their dreams.

Underground: Finchley Road.
Overground: Finchley Road & Frognal.

Find out more: 020 7435 2002 or freud.org.uk

Florence Nightingale Museum

Celebrate the life of this healthcare pioneer, female icon, the founder of modern nursing and trailblazer during her bicentenary year, #Nightingale2020.

Underground: Waterloo or Westminster.
Overground: Waterloo. **Train**: Waterloo.

Find out more: 020 7188 4400 or florence-nightingale.co.uk

Hall Place and Gardens

Stunning Tudor house with magnificent gardens.

Train: Bexley.

Find out more: 01322 526574 or hallplace.org.uk

Keats House

Elegant Regency villa where the Romantic poet John Keats wrote his best-loved poems.

Underground: Hampstead or Belsize Park.
Overground: Hampstead Heath.

Find out more: 020 7332 3868 or keatshouse@cityoflondon.gov.uk

Royal Observatory

Stand on the world's Prime Meridian, take an awe-inspiring journey through space and discover the home of Greenwich Mean Time.

Overground: Cutty Sark (DLR).
Train: Greenwich or Maze Hill.
River: Greenwich Pier.

Find out more: 020 8312 6608 or bookings@rmg.co.uk rmg.co.uk/royalobservatory

Museum of Brands

Nostalgic experience of consumer culture: journey from Victorian times to your childhood.

Underground: Ladbroke Grove.

Find out more: 020 7243 9611 or museumofbrands.com

Strawberry Hill House and Garden

Horace Walpole's beautifully restored 18th-century Gothic castle and garden near the Thames in Twickenham.

Train: Strawberry Hill and Twickenham.

Find out more: 020 8744 1241 or strawberryhillhouse.org.uk

East of England

Legend

▲ Buildings and/or gardens

● Entry points to coast and countryside

National Trust land

Places in neighbouring counties

The Cotswolds, Buckinghamshire and Oxfordshire, page 112

London, page 202

East Midlands, page 252

|— 10 miles —|

M181

A15
A631
A1103
A46
A15
A158

Tattershall Castle ▲

A16
A52
A17

Belton House ▲
A52
A16
A151

Woolsthorpe Manor ▲
A606
A1
A16
A15

A47
King's Lynn
A17
A1101

Brancaster Estate ●

Sheringham Park
West Runton and Beeston Regis Heath
Blakeney ▲
Cromer
Felbrigg Hall ▲

Blickling Estate ▲
A140

Horsey Windpump ▲

A47
Swaffham
NORWICH
A47
A146
Great Yarmouth ▲
Elizabethan House Museum
A146

Peckover House ▲
PETERBOROUGH
A47
A134
A10
A1065

Oxburgh Hall ▲

Darrow Wood ●
A143

A43
A605
A6116

Lyveden ▲
A1(M)
A14

Ramsey Abbey Gatehouse ▲
A141

A6
A14

Houghton Mill ▲
A1

Wicken Fen ●
Newmarket
A11
A134

A1066

A143
A140

Dunwich Heath ●

A12

Willington Dovecote and Stables ▲
A428
A14
CAMBRIDGE

Anglesey Abbey ▲
Bury St Edmunds
Theatre Royal ▲
Ickworth ▲

Lavenham Guildhall ▲
Kyson Hill ▲
Sutton Hoo ●

BEDFORD
A6

Wimpole Estate ▲
A505
A505
A10

Melford Hall ▲
A134
IPSWICH
A14
Orford Ness ●

M1
A421
A1(M)

Sundon Hills Country Park ●
Sharpenhoe ●
M11
A131

Pin Mill ▲
A12

Ascott ▲
Totternhoe Knolls ●
A602
Luton
Shaw's Corner ▲

Paycocke's House ▲
Flatford ▲
A120
Bourne Mill ▲
Colchester
A133

Pitstone Windmill ▲
Dunstable Downs ●
HERTFORD

Hatfield Forest ●
A120

Grange Barn ▲
Copt Hall Marshes ●

Ashridge Estate ▲

Coombe Hill ●
Whipsnade Tree Cathedral
Morven Park ●
A10
M25
CHELMSFORD
A414
A12
Northey Island ●
A130

M40
A41
A13
M1
A406
A406
A127

Danbury Commons and Blakes Wood ●

M4

Eastbury Manor House ▲
Rainham Hall ▲
A127
A13

Rayleigh Mount ●

M3

M26
M20
M2

Anglesey Abbey, Gardens and Lode Mill

Quy Road, Lode, Cambridge,
Cambridgeshire CB25 9EJ

🏠🖼️❖ 1966

Parking: 50 yards (2-metre height restrictions in some areas of car park).

This welcoming and elegant house and its gardens have something new to offer each season. You can discover Lord Fairhaven's extensive collection and find out how we care for it, then explore the domestic wing to see how the staff serving him ran his household like clockwork. The nationally celebrated gardens, with sweeping avenues, classical statuary and flower borders, offer captivating views, vibrant colours and delicious scents throughout the year. Children can play, explore and discover nature in the Wildlife Discovery Area. A visit to the historic working watermill on beautiful Quy Water will complete your day.

Anglesey Abbey, Gardens and Lode Mill in Cambridgeshire: the elegant Abbey, below, and Mill, above

Eat, shop, stay: Redwoods restaurant serving sandwiches, hot meals, teas, cakes, hot drinks. Light refreshments and snacks in gardens during peak times. Shop and plant centre selling local products and gifts. Freshly milled wholemeal flour available from the historic watermill. Second-hand bookshop.

Things to see and do: Indoors Hands-on activities and demonstrations in the house. **Outdoors** Self-led family activities. Weekday garden tours. **Dogs**: assistance dogs only. Printed and downloadable dog walk in local area available.

Access: 🅿️♿🚻♿♿🚼📷🖥️🔆⚲♿
Abbey and Mill ♿♿🚶 Domestic wing ♿🚶
Grounds ♿➡️♿♿

Ethereal silver birch trees, above, and the library, below, at Anglesey Abbey, Gardens and Lode Mill

Find out more: 01223 810080 or
angleseyabbey@nationaltrust.org.uk

Anglesey Abbey		M	T	W	T	F	S	S
Garden, restaurant, shop and plant centre								
1 Jan–29 Mar	9:30–4:30*	M	T	W	T	F	S	S
30 Mar–25 Oct	9:30–5:30*	M	T	W	T	F	S	S
26 Oct–31 Dec	9:30–4:30*	M	T	W	T	F	S	S
House								
1 Jan–29 Mar	11–4**	M	T	W	T	F	S	S
30 Mar–25 Oct	11–5**	M	T	W	T	F	S	S
26 Oct–31 Dec	11–4**	M	T	W	T	F	S	S
Lode Mill†								
Open all year	10:30–3:30		T	W	T	F	S	S

*Shop and plant centre: open at 10. **House: tour available
most days at 10:15. Last entry one hour before closing.
†Lode Mill: occasionally opens Mondays.
Everything closed 24 to 26 December.

Ashridge Estate

near Berkhamsted, Hertfordshire

[⚌] [blank] [blank] 1926

Satnav: use HP4 1LT for the visitor centre and Bridgewater Monument.
Parking: at visitor centre, Ivinghoe Beacon and many other parts of estate.

This special place has been enjoyed for centuries by everyone from pilgrims to picnickers. With its rich wildlife, diverse habitats and varied history, there is plenty to uncover at Ashridge. From the scent of the bluebells in spring, glorious birdsong and spectacular views from the chalk downland of the Ivinghoe Hills in summer, the rutting fallow deer in autumn and crisp walks on swathes of open common in winter, Ashridge has a landscape for every season. Waymarked trails and walks leaflets available from the visitor centre. Wildwood Den natural play area for children. Climb the Bridgewater Monument for fantastic views. **Note**: toilets available only when café open.

Eat, shop, stay: shop offering an ever-changing array of local and seasonal gifts, plants, maps and books. The Brownlow Café (concession) serves homemade meals and snacks to eat in the outdoor courtyard.

Things to see and do: events and children's activities throughout the year, including trails, guided walks and workshops. Nearby Pitstone Windmill is open Sundays and Bank Holidays from 3 May to 31 August. **Dogs**: under close control at all times for the safety of wildlife and visitors.

Access: [icons]
Visitor centre [icon] Grounds [icons]

Find out more: 01442 851227 or ashridge@nationaltrust.org.uk

Ashridge Estate		M	T	W	T	F	S	S
Estate								
Open all year	Dawn–dusk	M	T	W	T	F	S	S
Visitor centre, Brownlow Café and shop								
Open all year	10–4*	M	T	W	T	F	S	S
Bridgewater Monument (weather dependent)**								
28 Mar–25 Oct	11–4	.	.	.	.	.	S	S

*Visitor centre, café and shop: 1 March to 31 October, open to 5; closed 24 and 25 December; café: March to October, open 8 to 5; November to February, 8 to 4.
**Bridgewater Monument: open daily, school holidays.

Ashridge Estate, Hertfordshire, has been enjoyed for centuries by everyone from pilgrims to picnickers

Blakeney National Nature Reserve

near Morston, Norfolk

🏠🏛️♿🚂♿🐾♿ 1912

Satnav: use NR25 7BH for Morston Quay or NR25 7NE for Blakeney Quay.
Parking: at Morston Quay, Blakeney Quay and Green Way Stiffkey Saltmarshes.

At the heart of the Norfolk Coast Area of Outstanding Natural Beauty, Blakeney National Nature Reserve boasts wide open spaces and uninterrupted views of the beautiful North Norfolk coastline. The 4-mile long shingle spit of Blakeney Point offers protection for Blakeney Harbour and provides a perfect habitat for the vast array of resident and migratory wildlife. Spectacular displays of the summer-breeding tern colony and winter-breeding grey seals will delight visitors all year round. Great for walkers, sightseers and wildlife enthusiasts alike, the internationally important reserve guarantees an inspiring and memorable visit no matter the season. **Note**: nearest toilets at Morston Quay and Blakeney Quay.

Eat, shop, stay: takeaway snacks, drinks and treats available from our refreshment kiosk at Morston Quay. Nearby pubs and hotels (not National Trust) offering locally themed menus. Our holiday cottage, a simple lodge by Blakeney village, offers a romantic getaway for two.

Blakeney National Nature Reserve, Norfolk, above and below, lies within an Area of Outstanding Natural Beauty

Things to see and do: information centres at Morston Quay and Lifeboat House on Blakeney Point. Extensive coastal walks on the Norfolk Coast Path. Guided walks available. Ferry trips (not National Trust) to Blakeney Point. **Dogs**: welcome under close control. Seasonal restriction applies at Blakeney Point, 1 April to 15 August.

Access: ♿🚻🅿️🚌♿
Information centre ♿♿ Lifeboat House ♿♿

Find out more: 01263 740241 or blakeneypoint@nationaltrust.org.uk

Blakeney		M	T	W	T	F	S	S
Refreshment kiosk (Morston Quay)								
4 Jan–9 Feb	11–2	·	·	·	·	·	S	S
15 Feb–23 Feb	11–3	M	T	W	T	F	S	S
29 Feb–1 Nov	10–4	M	T	W	T	F	S	S
7 Nov–13 Dec	11–2	·	·	·	·	·	S	S
19 Dec–31 Dec*	11–2	M	T	W	T	F	S	S
Lifeboat House (Blakeney Point)								
1 Apr–1 Nov	Dawn–dusk	M	T	W	T	F	S	S

*Closed 25 December. Morston Information Centre and refreshment kiosk: opening times may be extended depending on tides. Nature Reserve open all year.

Blickling Estate

Blickling, Aylsham, Norfolk NR11 6NF

🏠✝🍷♿🦽🚶 1940

Parking: 400 yards.

You'll never forget your first sight of Blickling, as the breathtaking Jacobean mansion comes into view, flanked by ancient yew hedging and encircled by its historic park. This 1,933-hectare (4,700-acre) gift to the nation was bequeathed by its visionary owner, Lord Lothian, whose role was pivotal in creating the 1937 Act of Parliament that allowed whole estates to be left to the National Trust without incurring death duties. Your support is helping to tackle some of the crucial conservation work needed to protect the most significant library held by the National Trust and the Long Gallery that houses it. You may see this work happening as part of your visit. **Note**: additional charges apply for some special events and experiences.

Breathtaking Blickling Estate in Norfolk, above and below

Eat, shop, stay: three cafés and a pub offering bed and breakfast (not National Trust). Large second-hand bookshop, stamp shop with extensive stock for collectors (donations welcome), shop, plant shop and Loft Gallery. Nine holiday cottages on the estate.

Things to see and do: Indoors 400 years of history brought to life through art, personal interpretation, family trails and living history performances. RAF museum with personal stories of those who served here during the Second World War.

Outdoors The formal garden, with its parterre and double borders, inspired by three centuries of history, also has a productive walled garden. Park offers guided walks and talks, cycling, running and walking trails (free guides). Pyramid mausoleum. Permit fishing (June to March). Seasonal cycle hire. Changing programme throughout the year including Easter fun, magnificent bluebells, summer open-air music and winter lighting. Felbrigg Hall and Sheringham Park nearby.
Dogs: welcome under close control in park and outside Farmyard café. Assistance dogs only elsewhere.

Access: 🅿 ♿ 🚻 🔄 🎟 🚗
House 🚶 ♿ 🛗 👥 ♿   Garden ♿ ➡ 🚲 ♿

There are free guides available to help visitors enjoy the various cycling, running and walking trails at Blickling Estate

Find out more: 01263 738030 or blickling@nationaltrust.org.uk

Blickling Estate		M	T	W	T	F	S	S
House*								
1 Jan–8 Mar	11–3:30	M	T	W	T	F	S	S
9 Mar–1 Nov	12–5	M	T	W	T	F	S	S
2 Nov–29 Nov	11–3:30	M	T	W	T	F	S	S
30 Nov–20 Dec	11:30–6:30	M	T	W	T	F	S	S
21 Dec–31 Dec	11–3:30	M	T	W	T	F	S	S
Garden, shops and cafés								
1 Jan–8 Mar	10:30–4	M	T	W	T	F	S	S
9 Mar–1 Nov	10–5:30	M	T	W	T	F	S	S
2 Nov–29 Nov	10:30–4	M	T	W	T	F	S	S
30 Nov–20 Dec	11–7	M	T	W	T	F	S	S
21 Dec–31 Dec**	10:30–4	M	T	W	T	F	S	S
Park								
Open all year	Dawn–dusk	M	T	W	T	F	S	S

*Last entry to house one hour before closing.
**Closed 24 and 25 December. Fishing all year, except 16 March to 15 June inclusive.

Places may occasionally close for events or bad weather, check at nationaltrust.org.uk

Bourne Mill

Bourne Road, Colchester, Essex CO2 8RT

🏠 1936

Bourne Mill in Essex was originally built for banquets

Parking: on site (very limited), or on street.

Built for banquets and converted into a mill in the 17th century, Bourne Mill still has a working waterwheel. The surrounding pond, wetlands and woods are home to a variety of wildlife, including birds, bats, waterfowl and many insects, which provide plenty of scope for family fun.

Eat, shop, stay: light refreshments available. Pond-side seating area and shop selling a range of National Trust products.

Things to see and do: **Indoors** Discover how the mill works. Watch the waterwheel turn. **Outdoors** Explore the wildlife area, try your hand at pond dipping and '50 things' activities. **Dogs**: welcome on leads.

Access: 🅿️🚻🖐️🔦📷📖🎵
Building 🔣🔣 Grounds 🔣🔣

Find out more: 01206 549799 or bournemill@nationaltrust.org.uk

Bourne Mill		M	T	W	T	F	S	S
15 Feb–23 Feb	10–3:30	M	T	W	T	F	S	S
29 Feb–29 Mar	10–3:30	·	·	·	·	·	S	S
30 Mar–1 Nov	10–3:30	M	T	W	T	F	S	S

Brancaster Estate

near Brancaster, Norfolk

🏠🏖️🏛️🐾🛏️ 1923

Satnav: use PE31 8AX (Beach Road); PE31 8BW (Brancaster Staithe).
Parking: Beach Road, Brancaster (not National Trust), charge including members. Limited parking at Harbour Way, Brancaster Staithe. Both subject to tidal flooding.

The Brancaster Estate comprises the beautiful endless sandy Brancaster Beach (below), perfect for summer sandcastles and winter walks, the intriguing Branodunum Roman Fort site and the traditional fishing harbour of Brancaster Staithe. The area is rich in wildlife and offers a memorable visit regardless of the time of year. **Note**: beach car park (not National Trust). Toilets at beach and harbour. Parking charges apply at Brancaster Beach (including members). Weekly and seasonal passes available.

Eat, shop, stay: stay at Brancaster Activity Centre, perfect for a large group and family getaways. Self-catering accommodation sleeping up to 48 in dorm-style bedrooms with en-suite facilities.

Things to see and do: Norfolk Coast Path and coastline to explore. Panoramic views of the salt marsh across to Brancaster Harbour and Scolt Head Island National Nature Reserve. **Dogs**: welcome under close control. Small seasonal restriction zone on beach, May to September.

Access: 🚻

Find out more: 01263 740241 or brancaster@nationaltrust.org.uk

Copt Hall Marshes

near Little Wigborough, Essex 1989

Working farm on the remote and beautiful Blackwater Estuary – a fantastic birdwatching spot, important for overwintering species. **Note**: for satnav use CO5 7RD. St Nicholas Church not National Trust.

Find out more: 01245 227662 or copthall@nationaltrust.org.uk

Danbury Commons and Blakes Wood

near Danbury, Essex 1953

Varied countryside, ranging from the lowland heath of Danbury Common to ancient woodland with stunning spring flowers at Blakes Wood. **Note**: sorry no toilets. Satnav – for Danbury Commons use CM3 4JH and for Blakes Wood use CM3 4AU. Danbury Commons main car park closes dusk. Bicknacre Road car park locked at dusk.

Find out more: 01245 227662 or danbury@nationaltrust.org.uk

Darrow Wood

near Harleston, Norfolk 1990

Darrow Wood is a small, hedge-enclosed, lightly wooded pasture field containing earthworks, including remains of a compact motte-and-bailey castle. **Note**: for satnav use IP20 0AY, Darrow Green Road. Very limited roadside parking, then public footpath to Omega entrance sign (218 yards). Sorry no toilet.

Find out more: 01728 648020 (Dunwich Heath) or darrowwood@nationaltrust.org.uk

Dunstable Downs and the Whipsnade Estate

near Dunstable, Bedfordshire

🏛♿🐾🍴 1928

Satnav: use LU6 2GY. **Parking**: at Dunstable Downs, off B4541, and Bison Hill off the B4540.

The Downs have so much to offer all year round. As well as being the best kite-flying and picnicking site for miles around, Dunstable Downs are a haven for plants and wildlife, including orchids, butterflies, birds and much more. Enjoy the ever-changing view from the Chilterns Gateway Centre with a refreshing drink or delicious meal. **Note**: Chilterns Gateway Centre is owned by Central Bedfordshire Council and managed by the National Trust.

Eat, shop, stay: shop selling a wide range of gifts, toys, maps, books and local, seasonal products. The View Café serves a range of delicious lunches, snacks, hot and cold drinks and offers the option to eat in or take away. Picnics welcome.

Things to see and do: perfect for playing, kite-flying and picnics. There are several walking trails, all offering views across Aylesbury Vale. Natural play area within Chute Wood. Various activities available. **Dogs**: welcome on leads in car parks, in the centre and around livestock.

Access: [icons] **Dunstable Downs** [icons] Chilterns Gateway Centre [icons]

Find out more: 01582 500920 or dunstabledowns@nationaltrust.org.uk

Dunstable Downs		M	T	W	T	F	S	S
Chilterns Gateway Centre								
1 Jan–16 Feb	10–4	M	T	W	T	F	S	S
17 Feb–30 Jun	9–5	M	T	W	T	F	S	S
1 Jul–31 Aug	9–6	M	T	W	T	F	S	S
1 Sep–31 Oct	9–5	M	T	W	T	F	S	S
1 Nov–31 Dec*	10–4	M	T	W	T	F	S	S

*Closed 24 and 25 December. Hot food served up to 60 minutes before Centre closes. Entry to main car park closes 30 minutes after Centre closes.

Ever-changing views from Dunstable Downs and the Whipsnade Estate in Bedfordshire, above and below

Dunwich Heath and Beach

near Saxmundham, Suffolk

 1968

Be at one with nature at Dunwich Heath and Beach, Suffolk

Satnav: use IP17 3DJ. **Parking**: on site.

Dunwich Heath has been in the care of the National Trust for more than 50 years. A precious landscape on the Suffolk coast, Dunwich Heath offers a true sense of being at one with nature. Located in the middle of an Area of Outstanding Natural Beauty, there is an abundance of wildlife, including rare birds such as the Dartford warbler and the mysterious nightjar, as well as herds of red deer. The network of footpaths allows you to immerse yourself in nature and explore different habitats, including heather heath, gorse tracks, open grassland, woodland, shingle beach and sandy cliffs.

Access: [icons] Grounds [icons]

Find out more: 01728 648501 or
dunwichheath@nationaltrust.org.uk

Dunwich Heath		M	T	W	T	F	S	S
Tea-room and shop								
4 Jan–16 Feb	10–3	·	·	·	·	·	S	S
17 Feb–29 Feb	10–4	M	T	W	T	F	S	S
1 Mar–24 Jul	10–5	M	T	W	T	F	S	S
25 Jul–30 Aug	9:30–5	M	T	W	T	F	S	S
31 Aug–31 Oct	10–5	M	T	W	T	F	S	S
1 Nov–20 Dec	10–3	·	·	·	·	·	S	S
26 Dec–31 Dec	10–3	M	T	W	·	·	S	S

Open 1 January, 10 to 3.

Dunwich Heath and Beach, above and top

Eat, shop, stay: clifftop tea-room offering
food made from ethically sourced ingredients.
Enjoy a light lunch or afternoon tea with freshly
baked scones and cakes. Gift shop selling
selected National Trust bestsellers and items
to help you explore Dunwich Heath.
Holiday apartments available.

Things to see and do: self-guided walking
trails, mobility vehicles and accessible route,
nature-inspired events, summer weekly
bird-ringing demonstration. Children's
activities including trails, bug-hunting,
den-building and geocaching. Food themed
events. **Dogs**: welcome on leads March to end
of August. 'Woof' walk and beach unrestricted.

Elizabethan House Museum

4 South Quay, Great Yarmouth,
Norfolk NR30 2QH [1943]

A 16th-century quayside home, set out to
reflect day-to-day domestic life from Tudor to
Victorian times. **Note**: managed by Norfolk
Museums Service. Open 1 April to 1 November,
weekdays and Sundays, 10 to 4.

Find out more: 01493 855746 or
elizabethanhouse@nationaltrust.org.uk

Felbrigg Hall, Gardens and Estate

Felbrigg, near Cromer, Norfolk

🏠✝✿🐾🏡 1969

Satnav: use NR11 8PP. **Parking**: 100 yards. Electric vehicle charging point in main car park.

Atmospheric Felbrigg is a place of tranquillity. The Hall, which still contains its original and extensive collection, reflects the people who shaped it. A home to many generations, it has more than 400 years of family stories to be discovered. Set in extensive parkland, with a working walled garden and dove-house, orangery, lake, ancient woodland and miles of estate walks, all framed by big Norfolk skies, Felbrigg is the perfect place to escape and relax at any time of year. **Note**: additional charges apply for some special events and experiences, as well as the Attics and Cellars Tour (including members).

Felbrigg Hall, Gardens and Estate, Norfolk, above and left

Eat, shop, stay: Squire's Pantry serving a selection of sandwiches, light meals, snacks, cakes and drinks. Jester's refreshment kiosk is open at peak times. Shop and second-hand bookshop selling a selection of gifts and plants. Eight beautiful holiday cottages on the estate.

Things to see and do: **Indoors** Introductory talks and tours of attics and cellars on most days (call to confirm on day of visit). Children's trails. **Outdoors** Events (see website for details). Tracker Packs for children.
Dogs: welcome in tea-room and wider estate (on leads where signed or livestock present).

Access: 🅿️♿🏢🚻👁️🐕📖
Hall 🏠♿ Gardens 🏠➡️🚬♿

Find out more: 01263 837444 or felbrigg@nationaltrust.org.uk
Felbrigg, near Cromer, Norfolk NR11 8PR

Felbrigg Hall		M	T	W	T	F	S	S
House and gardens								
15 Feb–29 Mar	11–3	M	T	W	T	F	S	S
30 Mar–1 Nov	12–5*	M	T	W	T	F	S	S
House**								
7 Nov–20 Dec	11–3	.	.	.	.	.	S	S
Gardens								
2 Nov–20 Dec	11–3	M	T	W	T	F	S	S
Shop and tea-room								
1 Jan–29 Mar	10–4	M	T	W	T	F	S	S
30 Mar–1 Nov	10–5	M	T	W	T	F	S	S
2 Nov–31 Dec	10–4	M	T	W	T	F	S	S
Parkland								
Open all year	Dawn–dusk	M	T	W	T	F	S	S

House and gardens: last entry one hour before closing; 25 October to 1 November, close at 4. *Gardens: 30 March to 1 November, open 11. **House: 7 November to 20 December, selected show rooms only open. Closed 24, 25 and 26 December.

Flatford

East Bergholt, Suffolk CO7 6UL

🏠 ⛵ 1943

Parking: 100 yards.

Flatford lies at the heart of the Dedham Vale Area of Outstanding Natural Beauty. This charming hamlet was the inspiration for some of John Constable's most famous paintings, including *The Hay Wain*, *Boat Building* and *Flatford Mill*. The fascinating exhibition gives you an insight into Constable's life and career while Bridge Cottage tells the story of the people who lived and worked at Flatford. You can explore the beautiful countryside on one of the circular walks or hire a boat and row along the River Stour. A visit to Flatford is a chance to walk in Constable's footsteps. **Note**: no public access inside Flatford Mill, Valley Farm and Willy Lott's House. £3.50 charge for guided tour (including members).

Eat, shop, stay: riverside tea-room serving a tempting range of homemade cakes and light lunches. The gift shop offers quality gifts, souvenirs and Constable merchandise.

Things to see and do: volunteer guides offer short walking tours of the views which inspired John Constable (April to October only). Waymarked circular walks and family trails around Flatford. **Dogs**: welcome, but please keep dogs on leads near livestock.

Access: 🅿 🐕 ♿ 📷 ♿ 🅰 ⚑ ∴ ⊘
Bridge Cottage ♿ ♿ **Grounds** ♿ ♿ ♿

Find out more: 01206 298260 or flatford@nationaltrust.org.uk

Flatford		M	T	W	T	F	S	S
1 Jan–16 Feb	10–4	·	·	W	T	F	S	S
17 Feb–23 Feb	10–4	M	T	W	T	F	S	S
26 Feb–29 Mar	10–4	·	·	W	T	F	S	S
30 Mar–27 Sep	10–5	M	T	W	T	F	S	S
28 Sep–1 Nov	10–4	M	T	W	T	F	S	S
4 Nov–20 Dec	10–4	·	·	W	T	F	S	S
21 Dec–31 Dec*	10–4	M	T	W	T	F	S	S

*Closed 25 December.

The River Stour gently meanders through Flatford in Suffolk, below, while a girl enjoys a boating trip, above

Grange Barn

Grange Hill, Coggeshall, Colchester, Essex CO6 1RE

🏠 🍴 1989

Parking: on site.

One of Europe's oldest timber-framed buildings, Grange Barn stands as a lasting reminder of the once-powerful Coggeshall Abbey. With oak pillars soaring up to a cathedral-like roof, bearing the weight of centuries, it was saved and restored in the 1980s.

Eat, shop, stay: honey from Grange Barn's beehives to buy (in season), as well as souvenirs, second-hand books and ice cream. Coffee shop at nearby Paycocke's House and Garden. Picnics welcome.

Things to see and do: exhibition on the life and work of local woodcarver Bryan Saunders. Various events during the year. Great for picnics and access to local walks.
Dogs: welcome on leads in grounds.

Access: 📘🖼 Building 🏚 Grounds 🏔

Find out more: 01376 562226 or grangebarn@nationaltrust.org.uk

Grange Barn		M	T	W	T	F	S	S
15 Feb–23 Feb	10–4	M	T	W	T	F	S	S
24 Feb–29 Mar	10–4	M			·	F	S	S
30 Mar–1 Nov	10–5*	M	T	W	T	F	S	S

*28 September to 1 November: closes at 4. Closes occasionally for private events (check before visiting).

Hatfield Forest National Nature Reserve

near Bishop's Stortford, Essex

🏠 🏛 ♿ ⛵ 🍴 1924

Satnav: use CM22 6NE. **Parking**: on site (extremely limited in winter).

When Henry I established a Royal Hunting Forest here in 1100, he could little have guessed that almost a millennium later it would be the best survivor of its kind in the world. The forest has been a Site of Special Scientific Interest since the 1950s, due to its breadth of habitats and wildlife. Explore the wide open plains (below), grazed by Red Poll cattle, or enjoy the shade of the coppice woodland. With more than 405 hectares (1,000 acres), there are many places for imaginative play or quiet relaxation. **Note**: to protect the forest, the best time to visit is May to September.

Eat, shop, stay: outdoor café (external seating only) serving hot food and cold refreshments, ice cream and drinks. Shop selling gifts, guidebooks and maps.

Things to see and do: you can enjoy open-air theatre, WoodFest and other events. Rowing boat hire and family activities in the summer holidays. **Dogs**: on leads near livestock, in the lake area and woodland. Always under close control.

Access: 📘🖼🏚🖼🚻🔲
Shell House 🏔🏚 Forest ➡🦽♿

Find out more: 01279 874040 (Infoline).
01279 870678 or
hatfieldforest@nationaltrust.org.uk

Hatfield Forest		M	T	W	T	F	S	S
Car parks								
4 Jan–5 Apr*	10–3	·	·	·	·	·	S	S
6 Apr–4 Oct	9–4:30	M	T	W	T	F	S	S
10 Oct–20 Dec*	10–3	·	·	·	·	·	S	S
Café and shop								
1 Jan–29 Mar	9–3	·	·	W	T	F	S	S
1 Apr–4 Oct	9–5	M	T	W	T	F	S	S
7 Oct–24 Dec	9–3	·	·	W	T	F	S	S
30 Dec–31 Dec	9–3	·	·	W	T	·	·	·

*Space limited. Car parks open weather permitting.

Horsey Windpump

Horsey, Great Yarmouth, Norfolk NR29 4EE

⚡🏠🚂🐾🛏️ 1948

Parking: on site.

Restored and standing proud over the Broadland landscape, Horsey Windpump is complete with winding cap and patent sails. Explore this historic building and discover its fascinating story and the connection between man and nature. There are fantastic views over Horsey Mere and beyond from the top. **Note**: surrounded by Horsey Estate – managed by the Buxton family.

Eat, shop, stay: shop and tea-room (next to Horsey Windpump) serving snacks, drinks and small range of gifts. Converted barn holiday cottages in village. Perfectly placed for exploring the Broads and Norfolk coast.

Things to see and do: walking routes to Horsey Mere and the beach. Boat trips (not National Trust) across Horsey Mere (April to September). Guided walks at nearby Heigham Holmes. **Dogs**: welcome on leads.

Access: 🅿️♿🎦🎧📷
Windpump 🚶♿♿ Grounds ♿➡️

Find out more: 01263 740241 or horseywindpump@nationaltrust.org.uk

Horsey Windpump		M	T	W	T	F	S	S
Windpump, shop and tea-room								
7 Mar–29 Mar	11–4:30	·	·	·	·	·	S	S
4 Apr–30 Sep	10–5	M	T	W	T	F	S	S
1 Oct–1 Nov	11–4	M	T	W	T	F	S	S
7 Nov–29 Nov	11–3:30	·	·	·	·	·	S	S
Shop and tea-room								
15 Feb–23 Feb	11–3:30	M	T	W	T	F	S	S
26 Dec–31 Dec	11–3:30	M	T	W	T	·	S	S

Car park and toilets open all year, dawn to dusk.

Houghton Mill and Waterclose Meadows

Houghton, near Huntingdon, Cambridgeshire PE28 2AZ

🏠♿🅰️🔔 1939

Parking: on site.

Historic mill in an inspiring riverside setting surrounded by meadow walks. All the family can enjoy hands-on activities in the oldest working watermill on the Great Ouse. As well as seeing milling demonstrations, you can buy flour, ground in the traditional way on our French burr millstones.

Eat, shop, stay: riverside tea-room serving snacks, cakes and scones made with our traditional stoneground flour. Shop selling freshly ground flour and gifts. Tranquil riverside camp/caravan site with luxury camping pods.

Things to see and do: Indoors Milling demonstrations on Sundays. Baking days. Family events. **Outdoors** Open-air theatre, activities and summer holiday events. Access to surrounding meadows via public footpaths. **Dogs**: assistance dogs only in mill; all dogs welcome in grounds on leads.

Access: 🅿️♿🎦🎧📷📷📷📷
Mill ♿♿ Tea-room ♿ Grounds ➡️

Find out more: 01480 499990 (mill). 01480 499996 (campsite) or houghtonmill@nationaltrust.org.uk

Houghton Mill		M	T	W	T	F	S	S
Mill								
14 Mar–1 Nov	11–5	·	·	·	·	·	S	S
16 Mar–20 May	1–5	M	T	W	·	·	·	·
25 May–28 Aug	1–5	M	T	W	T	F	·	·
31 Aug–28 Oct	1–5	M	T	W	·	·	·	·
Tea-room								
10 Jan–13 Mar	10:30–3:30	·	·	·	·	F	S	S
14 Mar–1 Nov	10:30–5	M	T	W	T	F	S	S
6 Nov–20 Dec	10:30–3:30	·	·	·	·	F	S	S

Mill: open Bank Holiday Mondays and Good Friday, 11 to 5. Waterclose Meadows Caravan and Campsite: open March to November (01480 499996). Car park and riverside: close 8, or dusk if earlier.

Ickworth

The Rotunda, Horringer, Bury St Edmunds,
Suffolk IP29 5QE

🏛️ ✝️ ♣️ 🖼️ 🏕️ 1956

Satnav: may not direct you to main entrance.
Access to Ickworth is through Horringer village.
Parking: on site.

An Italianate palace in the heart of an ancient
deer park. Formal gardens, pleasure grounds,
rolling Suffolk landscape and woodlands invite
gentle strolls, long walks, runs, bike rides and
picnics. The Italianate Garden mirrors the
architecture of the house and celebrates the
Hervey family's passion for Italy, while also
encasing an idiosyncratic Victorian stumpery.
The Rotunda is home to one of the finest silver
collections in Europe, family portraits by
Gainsborough and Reynolds, works by Titian
and Velázquez, and Neo-classical sculpture.

The servants' quarters recreate domestic
service through the stories and memories
of those who lived here. **Note**: extensive
conservation works all year.

Eat, shop, stay: West Wing Café (lunch 12 to
2:30). Porter's Lodge Café (dog-friendly).
Squash Court Café. Gift shop and plant
and garden shop. Second-hand books.
Five holiday cottages. Hotel accommodation
at The Ickworth.

Clinging on for dear life at Ickworth in Suffolk, below, and the elegant staircase from the Museum Landing, above

Exploring Ickworth's parkland, above, and a detail from a lavishly decorated tureen, below

Things to see and do: **Indoors** New house exhibition. Tours daily. Living history. Children's crafts. **Outdoors** Family church. Open-air art installation, theatre and cinema. Family activities and autumn Wood Fair. Speciality walks. All-weather multi-use trail. **Dogs**: welcome on leads. Assistance dogs only in the Italianate Garden.

Access: 🅿️ 🅳 ♿ 👓 ♿ 🦽 🎧 🖼️ ⚟ ••
House 🏛️♿🔢🚻♿ West Wing 🏛️♿🔢🚹♿
Garden/parkland 🏛️➡️🚗♿

Find out more: 01284 735270 or ickworth@nationaltrust.org.uk

Ickworth		M	T	W	T	F	S	S
House*								
1 Jan–1 Mar	11–3†	M	T	W	T	F	S	S
2 Mar–1 Nov**	11–4†	M	T	W	T	F	S	S
2 Nov–31 Dec	11–3†	M	T	W	T	F	S	S
Gift shop, West Wing and Porter's Lodge cafés								
1 Jan–1 Mar	10:30–4††	M	T	W	T	F	S	S
2 Mar–1 Nov	10:30–5††	M	T	W	T	F	S	S
2 Nov–31 Dec	10:30–4††	M	T	W	T	F	S	S
Plant and garden shop								
1 Jan–1 Mar	12–3	M	T	W	T	F	S	S
2 Mar–1 Nov	11–5	M	T	W	T	F	S	S
2 Nov–31 Dec	12–3	M	T	W	T	F	S	S
Italianate Garden								
Open all year	10:30–5	M	T	W	T	F	S	S

*House: access limited due to conservation work.
**Daily tours: 11 to 12. †House: last entry 45 minutes before closing. ††Porter's Lodge Café: opens 10. Italianate Garden, plant and garden shop and Porter's Lodge Café: may close earlier in winter and adverse weather. Everything closed 24 and 25 December.

Kyson Hill

Broomheath, Woodbridge, Suffolk 1934

Petite Kyson Hill, with its grassy slopes, specimen trees and estuarine views, is a favourite destination for walking and relaxation. **Note**: sorry no toilet. Broomheath public car park, 546 yards (not National Trust). For satnav use IP12 4DL. OS map reference is 197/212:TM264478.

Find out more: 01394 389700 (Sutton Hoo) or kysonhill@nationaltrust.org.uk

Lavenham Guildhall

Market Place, Lavenham, Sudbury,
Suffolk CO10 9QZ

🏠 ✿ 1951

Parking: in village (free) – not National Trust.
Nearest car parks at Prentice Street (200 yards,
24 spaces), use CO10 9RD, and main car park
at Church Street (800 yards, 86 spaces),
use CO10 9SA.

The Guildhall of Corpus Christi is a remarkable
testament to the last 500 years of village life.
This complex of timber-framed buildings
provides an atmospheric backdrop to the
stories of the people who shaped and
influenced its fortunes and, ultimately, the
village of Lavenham we see today. Sometimes
sad, sometimes uplifting, their tales are
poignant and life-affirming. From religious
guild to workhouse, family home to nightclub,
there is more than meets the eye. Don't miss
the annual exhibition curated by the local
community and take the opportunity to
explore Lavenham village, known for its
beautiful timber-framed buildings and
impressive church.

**Timber-framed Lavenham Guildhall in Suffolk, above and
below, has played a key role in village life for 500 years**

Eat, shop, stay: tea-room serving light lunches,
cream teas and hot and cold drinks. Shop
selling local gifts, souvenirs, books and plants.

Things to see and do: **Indoors** Trails for all the
family and dressing-up costumes. Changing
exhibitions. **Outdoors** Small courtyard garden
and 'Swift' wildlife garden. Guided walks and
talks throughout the year. **Dogs**: welcome on
leads in the garden.

Access: 🅿️♿🚶🎫🏠🕙♿ ·· ◎
Guildhall ♿ **Garden** ♿ ♿

Find out more: 01787 247646 or
lavenhamguildhall@nationaltrust.org.uk

Lavenham Guildhall		M	T	W	T	F	S	S
3 Jan–10 Feb	10-3:30	M	·	·	·	F	S	S
14 Feb–24 Feb	10-3:30	M	T	W	T	F	S	S
28 Feb–2 Nov	10-5*	M	T	W	T	F	S	S
6 Nov–21 Dec†	10-3:30	M	·	·	·	F	S	S

*26 October to 2 November: open 10 to 3:30; tea-room
last orders 15 minutes before closing. †Christmas Fair: early
December (parts of museum closed).

Melford Hall

Long Melford, Sudbury, Suffolk CO10 9AA

🏠 ✳ 👪 1960

Parking: on site.

Melford Hall is a family home that has suffered its fair share of trials and tribulations, from being ransacked during the Civil War to being devastated by fire in 1942. It is thanks to the many generations who have called it home and left their mark, that it continues to survive. It is their stories, and those of the Hyde Parker family who currently live there – ranging from naval exploits to visits from their cousin Beatrix Potter – that make this family home such an intriguing place to explore.

Eat, shop, stay: Old Kitchen Café serving light lunches, sandwiches and cream teas with seating for 45 in Park and Courtyard rooms (additional tables outdoors). Gate Lodge shop selling souvenirs, gifts, books, souvenir story books and plants.

Things to see and do: **Indoors** Introductory tours and talks. Spot-it quiz for children under eight. **Outdoors** Garden tours and games. Walks, talks and family events. **Dogs**: welcome on leads in car park and park walk only.

Access: 🅿 👜 ♨ 🎧 🔊 🚶 🏛 🖼 🚪 Building 🔧🔧🔧🔧 Grounds 🔧🔧

Find out more: 01787 376395 (Infoline). 01787 379228 or melford@nationaltrust.org.uk

Melford Hall		M	T	W	T	F	S	S
1 Apr–1 Nov	12–5*			W	T	F	S	S

*House: 12 to 1 entry by short tour only (places limited); freeflow from 1. Open Bank Holiday Mondays and Good Friday.

Exuberant borders (and children) in the garden at Melford Hall in Suffolk, below, and the library, above

Morven Park

near Potters Bar, Hertfordshire 1928

The site of the original Toll Bar, these 8 hectares (20 acres) of parkland were created 150 years ago. **Note**: sorry no toilet or on-site parking. For satnav use EN6 1HS.

Find out more: 01582 873663 or morvenpark@nationaltrust.org.uk

Northey Island

near Maldon, Essex 1978

A peaceful retreat in the Blackwater Estuary, important for overwintering birds, Northey is also the oldest recorded battlefield in Britain. **Note**: for satnav use CM9 6PP (CM9 5JQ for parking). Access by tidal causeway, please telephone in advance to check tide times and arrange permit.

Find out more: 01621 853142 or northeyisland@nationaltrust.org.uk

Orford Ness National Nature Reserve

Orford Quay, Orford, Woodbridge, Suffolk IP12 2NU

🏠🏊🚴🌳 1993

Orford Ness National Nature Reserve in Suffolk, above and left, is wild, remote, exposed and totally captivating

Parking: at Riverside car park, Quay Street, not National Trust (charge including members), 150 yards to Trust Orford Quay office to buy ferry ticket.

Suffolk's secret coast – wild, remote, exposed. Known as the 'Island', only reached by National Trust ferry, the Ness contains the ruined remnants of a disturbing past. Ranked among the most important shingle features in the world, rare and fragile wildlife thrives where weapons, including atomic bombs, were tested and perfected. **Note**: limited tickets. Steep, slippery steps, long distances. Hazardous debris. Limited access: 'pagodas' only on tours. Charge for ferry crossing (including members).

Eat, shop, stay: shops, cafés and pubs in village (none National Trust). Fresh fish available at quay. Local smokehouses.

Things to see and do: trails lead through coastal grazing marsh and vegetated shingle habitats to the sea, taking in ex-military testing areas, buildings, displays and wildlife.

A little egret, above, and delicate sea thrift, below, at Orford Ness National Nature Reserve

Dogs: assistance dogs only.

Access: 🅿️🚻♿ Buildings 🚶♿ Trails ♿➡️

Find out more: 01728 648024 (Infoline). 01394 450900 or orfordness@nationaltrust.org.uk

Orford Ness		M	T	W	T	F	S	S
11 Apr–20 Jun	10–2	·	·	·	·	·		S
23 Jun–26 Sep	10–2		T	W	T	F		S
3 Oct–31 Oct	10–2	·	·	·	·	·		S

Access by National Trust ferry from Orford Quay – boats depart every 20 minutes, 10 to 2 only, returning regularly (last ferry 5). Tickets limited, only available on day. Main visitor trail (Red Route) always available, other routes open seasonally. Also open Good Friday, May Bank Holiday and Bank Holiday Sundays and Mondays (except 25 and 28 December and 1 and 2 January 2021).

Oxburgh Hall

Oxborough, near Swaffham, Norfolk PE33 9PS

🏠✝️❀🛏️🚵🍴 1952

Parking: on site.

Built 500 years ago by the still-resident Bedingfeld family, Oxburgh has endured turbulent times. Just like the 6th Baronet, we're now embarking on an ambitious project to restore the roof, windows and chimneys. You can experience Oxburgh's tale of endurance and see the restoration work as we erect the most complicated scaffold we've ever attempted. Why not sign a tile and become part of Oxburgh's story? Outside you can catch reflections in the moat, relax in the wildlife-rich seasonal garden, and explore the acres of woodland, streams and parkland. **Note**: major conservation works all year.

Eat, shop, stay: tea-room in Old Kitchen and Servants' Hall. The Pantry serves snacks on the go, muddy boots welcome! Picnics welcome in the grounds or area by car park.

Shop selling gifts, games and local products. Plant sales. Second-hand bookshop. Holiday cottage.

Things to see and do: Indoors Gatehouse experience and introductory talks most days, March to October. **Outdoors** Garden tours most days, March to October. Winter snowdrop walks. Family activities, including woodland den-building area. Year-round events. **Dogs:** welcome on leads in garden, estate, cafés and shop. Assistance dogs only in house.

Access: 🅿️🚻♿🅿️🖼️📷📖🚮
Hall 🔥♿🚶♿ Chapel ♿ Garden ♿➡️♿

Find out more: 01366 328258 or oxburghhall@nationaltrust.org.uk

Oxburgh Hall		M	T	W	T	F	S	S
House								
15 Feb–1 Nov	11–5*	M	T	W	T	F	S	S
2 Nov–21 Dec	11–4**	M	·	·	T	F	S	S
Garden, shop and tea-room								
4 Jan–14 Feb	10:30–4	M	·	·	·	F	S	S
15 Feb–1 Nov	10:30–5	M	T	W	T	F	S	S
2 Nov–31 Dec	10:30–4†	M	T	W	T	F	S	S

*Freeflow 11 to 3:45; tours from 3:45. **House: access by tours only (places limited). †Everything closed 24 to 26 December.

Oxburgh Hall in Norfolk: still very much a family home

Paycocke's House and Garden

25 West Street, Coggeshall, Colchester, Essex CO6 1NS

🏠♿ 1924

Parking: at Coggeshall Grange Barn, less than ½ mile.

Set in an ancient village full of listed buildings, this exquisitely carved half-timbered Tudor cloth merchant's house (above) offers five centuries of craftsmanship and conservation. Follow the many changes and see how the house was saved from demolition and restored to its former glory, then enjoy the tranquil cottage garden.

Eat, shop, stay: coffee shop serving cream teas, coffee, cakes and soft drinks (courtyard and garden). Picnics welcome. Shop selling gifts and local products. Plants for sale at our garden stall. Second-hand bookshop.

Things to see and do: Indoors Events all year. Children's dressing-up costumes. **Outdoors** Garden games. Why not combine with visit to nearby Grange Barn and enjoy the circular walk? **Dogs:** welcome in garden only on a lead; assistance dogs only in house.

Access: 🅿️🚻♿🅿️📷📖🚮
Building 🔥 Garden 🔥♿

Find out more: 01376 561305 or paycockes@nationaltrust.org.uk

Paycocke's House		M	T	W	T	F	S	S
15 Feb–23 Feb	10–4	M	T	W	T	F	S	S
24 Feb–29 Mar	10–4	M	·	·	T	F	S	S
30 Mar–27 Sep	10–5	M	T	W	T	F	S	S
28 Sep–1 Nov	10–4	M	T	W	T	F	S	S
28 Nov–29 Nov	10–3	·	·	·	·	·	S	S

Peckover House and Garden

near Wisbech, Cambridgeshire

🏠♿🐕🔔🍴 1943

Satnav: use PE13 1RG or PE13 2RA for nearest car parks. **Parking:** nearest at Chapel Road or Somers Road, 500 yards (not National Trust). Car parks occasionally used for town events and may not be in use – please check before journey.

While its riverside setting at Wisbech was popular among merchants, imposing Peckover House stood apart as an oasis of calm, reflecting the Quaker way of life. The Peckovers were bankers and added a specially designed wing to the house; an exhibition tells its story. The family also loved their garden, and you can discover its delights as you explore the unexpected 0.8 hectare (2 acres) of abundance.

Eat, shop, stay: the Reed Barn is the ideal place for a light lunch or afternoon tea. Browse our gift shop, second-hand bookshop and our plant trolley. Stay a little longer in one of our holiday cottages – Wainman House or Coach House Loft.

Things to see and do: Indoors Grand piano to play, behind-the-scenes tours, handling collection, children's trails and exhibitions. **Outdoors** Garden tours and croquet/lawn games (summer). Octavia Hill's Birthplace House opposite (not National Trust). **Dogs:** assistance dogs only.

Access: 🏠♿🚻🅿🖼🚻🚶
House 🅿♿ Garden 🅿➡♿

Visitors enjoying a garden tour at Peckover House and Garden in Cambridgeshire, above; the imposing Staircase Hall, right, and façade, below

Find out more: 01945 583463 or
peckover@nationaltrust.org.uk
North Brink, near Wisbech,
Cambridgeshire PE13 1JR

Peckover House		M	T	W	T	F	S	S
11 Jan–16 Feb*	12–4	·	·	·	·	·	S	S
22 Feb–3 Apr**	11–4	M	T	W	T	F	S	S
4 Apr–18 Oct†	11–5	M	T	W	T	F	S	S
19 Oct–1 Nov†	11–4	M	T	W	T	F	S	S
7 Nov–15 Nov†	11–4	·	·	·	·	·	S	S
12 Dec–20 Dec††	11–4	M	T	W	T	F	S	S

*Garden, tea-room and shop only open. **House: open by timed
tours only weekdays; freeflow at weekends. †House: open 12
to 4. ††Christmas celebration. Closed 15 May and 14 August.

Pin Mill

near Chelmondiston, Suffolk 1978

A woodland and heathland restoration site.
A number of footpaths from the village
with panoramic views over the River Orwell.
Note: for satnav use IP9 1JW. Parking in
Pin Mill village, not National Trust (charge
including members), or Chelmondiston.

Find out more: 01206 298260 or
pinmill@nationaltrust.org.uk

Ramsey Abbey Gatehouse

Hollow Lane, Ramsey, Huntingdon,
Cambridgeshire PE26 1DH 1952

This fascinating medieval gatehouse, along
with the Lady Chapel, are all that remain
of the great Benedictine abbey at Ramsey.
Note: on school grounds so no public access
except on open days. Gatehouse and Lady
Chapel open first Sunday of the month,
April to September, 1 to 5.

Find out more: 01480 499992 or
ramseyabbey@nationaltrust.org.uk

Rayleigh Mount

Rayleigh, Essex 1923

Medieval motte-and-bailey castle site, with
adjacent windmill housing historical exhibition.
Note: exhibition in windmill operated by
Rochford District Council. For satnav use
SS6 7ED. Parking at Bellingham Lane – adjacent
to main entrance (not National Trust).
Gates close 2 on Saturdays. Opening times
may vary, call 01268 775328 to check
before visiting.

Find out more: 01284 747500 or
rayleighmount@nationaltrust.org.uk

Sharpenhoe

near Streatley, Bedfordshire 1939

Managed as a nature reserve; archaeology,
geology and nature come together to provide
a stunning landscape. **Note**: sorry no toilets.
For satnav use LU3 3PR. Car park between
Sharpenhoe and Streatley.

Find out more: 01582 873663 or
sharpenhoe@nationaltrust.org.uk

Shaw's Corner

Ayot St Lawrence, near Welwyn,
Hertfordshire AL6 9BX

🏠❄️ 1944

Arts and Crafts-inspired Shaw's Corner in Hertfordshire

Satnav: some routes might take you
through a ford and an unsignposted route.
Parking: very limited (not suitable for
large vehicles).

George Bernard Shaw's peaceful, rural Arts
and Crafts-inspired home and garden show
what inspired this great playwright and social
activist. Pictures and sculpture reflect his
wide circle of influential friends and interests.
You can enjoy volunteer-led play readings
in the summer, guided tours and our annual
exhibition. **Note**: access roads are very narrow.

Eat, shop, stay: hot drinks and cakes served
from our vintage coffee van. Ice cream
and soft drinks available in the garden.
Shop offering a range of gifts and toys.
Second-hand bookshop.

Things to see and do: events, including
script-in-hand play readings.
Dogs: assistance dogs only.

Access: 🅿️🖥️🎦
House 🔊🔦🚻♿ Grounds 🔊♿♿

Find out more: 01438 821968 (Infoline).
01438 820307 or
shawscorner@nationaltrust.org.uk

Shaw's Corner			M	T	W	T	F	S	S
15 Feb–1 Nov	11–5			·	W	T	F	S	S
Open Bank Holiday Mondays.									

Sheringham Park

Upper Sheringham, Norfolk NR26 8TL

🏠🚲❄️🏊🚤♿ 1987

Parking: 60 yards. Two electric vehicle
charging points in car park.

Making use of the park's undulating landscape,
Humphry Repton created views of the North
Norfolk coast that can still be enjoyed today.
His 1812 design stated 'Sheringham Park had
more natural beauty and advantages than any
place he had ever seen'. The Upcher family
added an extensive rhododendron collection
to Repton's design, bringing an array of
colour to the wild garden in the spring.

Places may occasionally close for events or bad weather, check at nationaltrust.org.uk

A walk around the varying habitats of the 405-hectare (1,000-acre) estate may be interrupted by the drumming of a woodpecker, the song of skylarks or the sound of a steam train travelling through the park. **Note**: Sheringham Hall is privately occupied. April to September: limited access by written appointment with leaseholder.

Eat, shop, stay: gift shop selling guidebooks, local gifts and souvenirs. Peat-free plant sales. Courtyard Café serving soup, sandwiches, cake and ice cream. A range of gluten-free food also available. Picnics welcome. Five holiday cottages on site.

Things to see and do: self-guided trails and guided walks. Climb the gazebo tower to see coastal views enjoyed since Napoleonic times. Wide-ranging events programme for families and adults. Free children's Tracker Packs.

Humphry Repton-designed Sheringham Park in Norfolk, above and left

Dogs: welcome under close control. Please keep on leads near livestock and visitor facilities.

Access: ⬚⬚⬚⬚⬚⬚⬚⬚ Building ⬚⬚ Grounds ⬚⬚⬚⬚

Find out more: 01263 820550 or sheringhampark@nationaltrust.org.uk

Sheringham Park		M	T	W	T	F	S	S
Park								
Open all year	Dawn–dusk	M	T	W	T	F	S	S
Visitor centre and Courtyard Café								
2 Jan–14 Feb	10–4	·	·	·	T	F	S	S
15 Feb–1 Nov	10–5	M	T	W	T	F	S	S
5 Nov–20 Dec	10–4	·	·	·	T	F	S	S

Courtyard Café opens 8:45 and visitor centre 9:30 on Saturdays. Visitor centre and Courtyard Café: open 10 to 4, 1 January, and daily 27 to 31 December; open to 6, 23 to 25 May.

Sundon Hills Country Park

Upper Sundon, Bedfordshire 2000

Wildlife-rich chalk grassland, beech woodland, open meadows and a picnic site with views north towards the Greensand Ridge. **Note**: sorry no toilets. For satnav use LU3 3PE.

Find out more: 01582 873663 or sundonhills@nationaltrust.org.uk

Sutton Hoo

Sutton Hoo, Woodbridge, Suffolk IP12 3DJ

🏠 🏛 ♿ 🚻 🍽 1998

Parking: on site.

For 1,300 years Sutton Hoo's secrets were hidden deep within a burial mound until, in 1939, a discovery was made which changed history. From the sandy soil archaeologists unearthed the imprint of a 27-metre-long ship, its timbers long since rotted away. This was revealed to be the ship burial of an Anglo-Saxon king, complete with exquisite gold and silver treasures. A stunning full-size ship sculpture, newly designed exhibitions, breathtaking replicas, the atmospheric Royal Burial Ground and a 17-metre-high viewing tower offering stunning views over the landscape and River Deben, all bring this fascinating story to life. There is also a variety of walks on the estate, including two new routes.

Eat, shop, stay: Kings River café and Keepers' café serving hot meals, snacks and ice creams. Both cafés have views looking out towards the River Deben. Gift shop. Second-hand bookshop. Three spacious holiday apartments within Tranmer House, all with views across the estate.

Things to see and do: **Indoors** Exhibition highlighting the lives of the Anglo-Saxons and just how Sutton Hoo came to be such a significant place in English history: some original treasures, replicas, guest exhibitions, film, crafts and storytelling. Tranmer House, the former home of Edith Pretty, houses an exhibition exploring the people and stories behind the Sutton Hoo discovery and landscape, with archive images and footage, some original items, audio and talks. **Outdoors** Full-scale ship sculpture, viewing tower, walks, dye garden, children's trails and play area. **Dogs**: welcome on leads in reception, shop, café and walks.

One of the atmospheric burial mounds at Sutton Hoo in Suffolk, below. The Ship Sculpture, right, and visitors enjoying an Easter egg hunt, bottom right

Entry is still possible at most places up to 30 minutes before closing

Access: [accessibility icons]
Buildings [icons] Grounds [icons]

Find out more: 01394 389700 or
suttonhoo@nationaltrust.org.uk

Sutton Hoo		M	T	W	T	F	S	S
1 Jan–29 Feb	10–4	M	T	W	T	F	S	S
1 Mar–31 Oct	10–5	M	T	W	T	F	S	S
1 Nov–31 Dec*	10–4	M	T	W	T	F	S	S

*Closed 24 and 25 December.

Theatre Royal Bury St Edmunds

Westgate Street, Bury St Edmunds,
Suffolk IP33 1QR 1974

Last surviving Regency playhouse in Britain,
this Grade I-listed theatre offers a vibrant
drama, music, dance and comedy programme.
Note: managed by Bury St Edmunds Theatre
Management Ltd. Tours are free to National
Trust Members, admission charges apply to
shows. Guided tours available (call for details).

Find out more: 01284 769505 or
theatreroyal@nationaltrust.org.uk

Totternhoe Knolls

Castle Hill Road, Totternhoe,
Bedfordshire 2000

The dramatic earthworks of a Norman castle
rise from windswept chalk grassland habitat,
sitting high above the surrounding landscape.
Note: sorry no toilets. For satnav use LU6 1RG.

Find out more: 01582 873663 or
totternhoeknolls@nationaltrust.org.uk

West Runton and Beeston Regis Heath

near West Runton, Norfolk 1925

A lovely place to walk among heath and woods,
with fine views of the North Norfolk coast.
Note: sorry no toilets. For satnav
use NR27 9ND.

Find out more: 01263 820550 or
westrunton@nationaltrust.org.uk

Whipsnade Tree Cathedral

Whipsnade, Dunstable, Bedfordshire 1960

Peaceful place with trees planted in shape of
medieval cathedral. Created after the First
World War to commemorate fallen comrades.
Note: dogs allowed under control. Annual
service second Sunday, June. Car park open
9 to 4 (winter); 9 to 7 (summer). Satnav use
LU6 2LQ. Donations welcome. Open daily,
1 January to 28 March and 25 October to
31 December, 9 to 4; 29 March to
24 October, 9 to 7.

Find out more: 01582 872406 or
whipsnadetc@nationaltrust.org.uk

Wicken Fen National Nature Reserve

near Ely, Cambridgeshire

⊠ 🖭 🚻 1899

Satnav: use CB7 5XP. **Parking**: 120 yards.

With vast skies above flowering meadows, sedge and reedbeds, Wicken Fen reveals a lost fenland landscape. A wealth of wildlife lives in this important wetland, including rarities such as hen harriers and bitterns, numerous dragonflies, moths and wildfowl. Changing every season, the fen feels wild, although people have shaped it for centuries; see how they lived and worked in the fenman's yard and cottage. The Wicken Fen Vision, an ambitious landscape-scale conservation project, is opening new areas for wildlife and for exploration. Grazing herds of Highland cattle and Konik ponies help create a diverse range of new habitats. **Note**: some paths are seasonal. We are building a new elevated viewing facility (August and September). Charges apply for Wicken Lode boat trips (including members).

Eat, shop, stay: shop in the visitor centre selling wildlife and outdoor books, local food and crafts. Café serving light lunches and afternoon teas. Picnics welcome.

Things to see and do: explore the heart of the Fen on foot, via the Boardwalk and longer paths. Seasonal boat trips available. Cycle across the wider reserve; we hire bikes, or bring your own. **Dogs**: welcome on leads on reserve and in visitor centre.

Access: 🅿️ 🚻 ♿ 🏛️ 👶 📷 🔊 📖
Building ♿ Grounds ♿

Find out more: 01353 720274 or wickenfen@nationaltrust.org.uk

Wicken Fen		M	T	W	T	F	S	S
Reserve, visitor centre and shop								
Open all year*	10–5**	M	T	W	T	F	S	S
Café								
1 Jan–14 Feb	10–4:30	M	T	W	T	F	S	S
15 Feb–1 Nov	10–5	M	T	W	T	F	S	S
2 Nov–31 Dec	10–4:30	M	T	W	T	F	S	S

*Closed 25 December. **Access to reserve dawn to dusk; visitor centre closes dusk in winter.

Wicken Fen National Nature Reserve, Cambridgeshire, in winter, below, and a young visitor, right

Willington Dovecote and Stables

Willington, Church End, near Bedford, Bedfordshire MK44 3PX 1914

These stunning remnants of Gostwick's show farm stand like two ancient warriors, the only survivors from the battle with time. **Note**: open last Sunday of month April to September, 1 to 5. Dovecote and Stables can be viewed by appointment dependent on volunteer availability, contact Judy Endersby (01234 838278).

Find out more: 01480 499992 or willingtondovecote@nationaltrust.org.uk

Wimpole Estate

Arrington, Royston, Cambridgeshire SG8 0BW

🏠 ✝ 🏛 ♿ ❀ ♨ 🍴 | 1976 |

Satnav: follow the brown signs, entrance via A603. **Parking**: on site, 440 yards. Electric vehicle charging point in car park.

A unique working estate, with an impressive mansion at its heart. Discover Wimpole's acres of parkland, miles of walks, vibrant walled kitchen garden and Home Farm. Explore the Hall, where intimate rooms contrast with beautiful Georgian interiors. With its various owners driven by passion and purpose, Wimpole is both a place to escape to and a place to get involved. We continue the 3rd Earl of Hardwicke's passion for trail-blazing food production and design, celebrating the estate's past magnificence and echoing Elsie Bambridge's 20th-century revival. As owners changed, a roll-call of ingenious architects, artists and landscape designers shaped the estate. Wimpole is an 'all-year-round' place to visit, reflecting the changing seasons, with something to captivate and inspire all visitors.

Wimpole Estate in Cambridgeshire, clockwise from right, the house, walled garden and Breakfast Room

Eat, shop, stay: choose from the Old Rectory Restaurant, Farm Café and Stables Café, serving produce from the walled garden and Home Farm. Stable shop with gifts and plants, Wimpole rare-breed meat, flour, apple juice and eggs. Second-hand bookshop, toy shop.

Things to see and do: Indoors Explore the Hall at your own pace, from grand rooms upstairs to the basement. Pop into the Gardener's Cottage to uncover our garden history. **Outdoors** Seasonal spectaculars, including daffodils, spring blossom, summer parterre, herbaceous borders and autumn trees. Guided walks in the gardens and parkland. Daily farm activities: groom the donkey, meet the Shires and feed the pigs. Lambing time and Easter egg trail, history festival, open-air theatre, '50 things to do before you're 11¾' and Christmas events. Sporting activities, including running and walking groups, cycle and running trails. **Dogs**: welcome on leads in the park (livestock grazing). Assistance dogs elsewhere.

Access:

Hall

Farm

Gardens

Find out more: 01223 206000 or wimpole@nationaltrust.org.uk

Wimpole Estate		M	T	W	T	F	S	S
Hall								
15 Feb–1 Nov*	11–5	M	T	W	T	F	S	S
Home Farm and Farm Café								
4 Jan–9 Feb**	10:30–3:30	·	·	·	·	·	S	S
15 Feb–1 Nov	10:30–5	M	T	W	T	F	S	S
7 Nov–27 Dec**	10:30–3:30	·	·	·	·	·	S	S
Garden, Old Rectory Restaurant and stable block								
1 Jan–14 Feb	10–4	M	T	W	T	F	S	S
15 Feb–1 Nov	10–5	M	T	W	T	F	S	S
2 Nov–31 Dec	10–4	M	T	W	T	F	S	S
Visitor welcome								
1 Jan–14 Feb	9–4:30	M	T	W	T	F	S	S
15 Feb–1 Nov	8–5:30	M	T	W	T	F	S	S
2 Nov–31 Dec†	9–4:30	M	T	W	T	F	S	S
Park								
Open all year†	7–7	M	T	W	T	F	S	S

*Hall: open for tours November to February and Christmas weekends. **Home Farm: open daily, 1 to 3 January and 28 to 31 December, 10:30 to 3:30; open mid-week for tours, November to February. Estate: 24 December, closes 1; closed 25 December; †Visitor welcome and park: open 10 to 4, 26 December. Car park: open 7 to 7. Hall and farm: last entry one hour before closing.

East Midlands

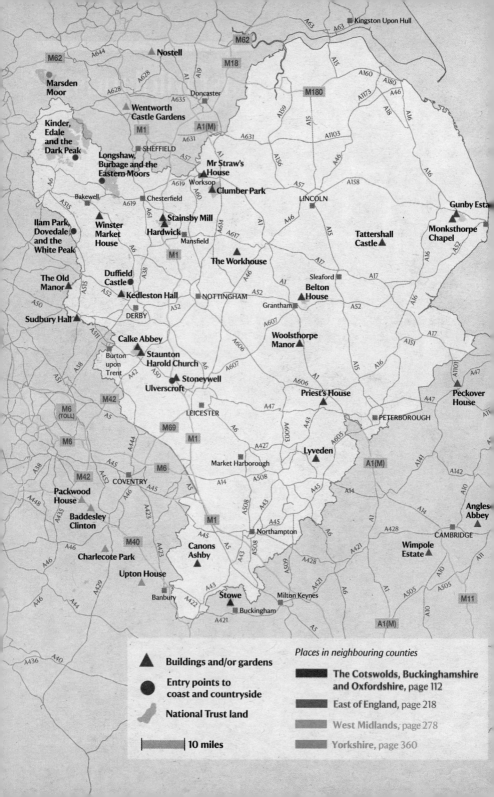

Kingston Upon Hull

M62

Nostell

Marsden Moor

Wentworth Castle Gardens

Doncaster

Kinder, Edale and the Dark Peak

M180

Longshaw, Burbage and the Eastern Moors

SHEFFIELD

Mr Straw's House

Bakewell

Worksop

Clumber Park

Chesterfield

Gunby Estate

Ilam Park, Dovedale and the White Peak

Winster Market House

Stainsby Mill

Hardwick

LINCOLN

Monksthorpe Chapel

Mansfield

Tattershall Castle

The Old Manor

The Workhouse

Duffield Castle

Sleaford

Belton House

Sudbury Hall

Kedleston Hall

NOTTINGHAM

DERBY

Grantham

Calke Abbey

Burton upon Trent

Staunton Harold Church

Woolsthorpe Manor

Stoneywell

Ulverscroft

Priest's House

Peckover House

LEICESTER

PETERBOROUGH

M69

M6 (TOLL)

M6

Lyveden

Market Harborough

Packwood House

Angles Abbey

COVENTRY

Baddesley Clinton

CAMBRIDGE

Northampton

Wimpole Estate

Charlecote Park

Canons Ashby

Upton House

Banbury

Stowe

Milton Keynes

Buckingham

Legend

▲ Buildings and/or gardens

● Entry points to coast and countryside

National Trust land

|———| 10 miles

Places in neighbouring counties

The Cotswolds, Buckinghamshire and Oxfordshire, page 112

East of England, page 218

West Midlands, page 278

Yorkshire, page 360

Belton House

near Grantham, Lincolnshire

🏛️ ✝️ ❖ ♿ 🔔 ☂️ 1984

Satnav: use NG32 2LW. **Parking**: on site.

Belton House sits elegantly in formal gardens with views across pleasure grounds and an ancient deer park. Although built on a relatively modest scale, it has a superlative collection of porcelain and silver, a world-renowned library, and an architectural finesse that reflects the wealth and education of generations of the Brownlow family. It's often cited as being the perfect example of an English country house. In more recent times, Belton has become a popular destination for generations of families, with a huge adventure playground and seasonal activities, so there is something to do all year round. **Note**: entry to the mansion is by timed ticket (available to book in advance).

Eat, shop, stay: enjoy lunch in Belton's newly refurbished Stables Café. Ride Play Café and Muddy Hands kiosk open daily for casual family dining. Large gift shop. Second-hand bookshop also offers seasonal plants.

Things to see and do: **Indoors** Learn more about Belton with themed interpretation and guided tours. The basement is open by guided tour all year. For young families, there's an indoor adventure play café (timed entry at busy times) and a discovery centre for weekend and school holiday activities. **Outdoors** Downloadable walks, seasonal trails and interpretation in the gardens and parkland. Events, including open-air cinema, theatre and autumn market. National Trust's largest outdoor adventure playground. Family-focused events during the school holidays. New Christmas lights event. Woolsthorpe Manor, home of Sir Isaac Newton, is nearby.
Dogs: welcome on leads in shops, parkland and courtyards. Pup and Saucer dog café.

Known for its superlative collections, Belton House in Lincolnshire also has so much to offer out of doors

Whether you are a lover of architecture or prefer horticulture, Belton House will delight, with interiors such as the Blue Bedroom, left, and Dutch Garden, above

Access: 🅿️🚽♿🔋🚻🧺📷🎧📹📱🚫
House ♿🚼🔗 Grounds 🚼➡️🔗♿

Find out more: 01476 566116 or belton@nationaltrust.org.uk
Belton, near Grantham, Lincolnshire NG32 2LS

Belton House		M	T	W	T	F	S	S
House*								
29 Feb–1 Nov	12:30–5	M	T	W		T	F	S	S
Shops, restaurant, Ride Play Café, adventure playground								
Open all year	9:30–5:30**	M	T	W	T*	F	S	S
Basement†								
Open all year	Tour	M	T	W		T	F	S	S

*Open daily by timed entry; last entry 4.
**Close at 4, November to February.
†Volunteer-led tours (subject to availability), 11 to 3; last winter tour at 2. Park and gardens: open as shops and restaurant. Bellmount Woods: open daily (access from separate car park). Everything closed 25 December.

Calke Abbey

Ticknall, Derby, Derbyshire DE73 7JF

🏠✝🌿♿⚡🚶🅿🍽 1985

Parking: on site.

Poised somewhere between gentle neglect and downright dereliction, Calke Abbey, the un-stately home, is unlike other great country estates. Entering along the Lime Tree Avenue offers views of the historic parkland, home to ancient oaks, secluded ponds and woodland walks. The National Nature Reserve awaits discovery, and Calke Explore provides the perfect base to begin exploring the wider estate. Peeling paintwork and abandoned rooms tell the story of a country house in decline, while a vast collection reveals the varied interests of a loving family who never threw anything away. The walled garden offers moments of reflection, including a domed orangery and faded glasshouses, and beds bursting with seasonal produce and colour echo the history of Calke's working garden.

Eat, shop, stay: breakfast and main meals served daily in the restaurant, and a choice of cafés and pop-up outlets serving light refreshments (weekends and peak times). Large gift shop, plant sales and second-hand bookshop. Five holiday cottages.

Things to see and do: **Indoors** 'HumanKind' explores Calke's stories of isolation, kindness and compassion with an immersive exhibition in the family apartments. Stableyards, garden outbuildings and underground tunnels hint at the lives of those who lived and worked at Calke. Family activities in Squirt's Stable every weekend and school holiday (February to October).

Curious contrasts between grandeur and dilapidation characterise Calke Abbey in Derbyshire, above and below

Outdoors 243 hectares (600 acres) of parkland to explore, featuring 'HumanKind' landscape rooms and waymarked walks, including the accessible, cycle-friendly Tramway Trail. Bird hides are perfect for spotting wildlife, with deer and lambing seasonal highlights. Outdoor play and events all year, including food fairs, open-air cinema and guided walks. Stoneywell nearby.
Dogs: welcome on leads in wider estate; in the garden (November to February).

Access:
House **Stables**
Grounds

Find out more: 01332 863822 or calkeabbey@nationaltrust.org.uk

Eclectic collections fill every corner of Calke Abbey, such as these natural history displays in the Saloon

Calke Abbey		M	T	W	T	F	S	S
Calke Park National Nature Reserve*								
Open all year	7:30–7	**M**	**T**	**W**	**T**	**F**	**S**	**S**
House**								
29 Feb–1 Nov	12:30–5	**M**	**T**	**W**	**T**	**F**	**S**	**S**
HumanKind exhibition								
29 Feb–1 Nov	11–4	**M**	**T**	**W**	**T**	**F**	**S**	**S**
Garden								
2 Jan–24 Dec	10–5†	**M**	**T**	**W**	**T**	**F**	**S**	**S**
Stables, restaurant and shop								
Open all year	10–5†	**M**	**T**	**W**	**T**	**F**	**S**	**S**

*Closes dusk, if earlier; closed 25 December.
**House: timed ticket required, available from the ticket office. †Garden, stables, restaurant and shop: close at 5 when house is open, March to October; at 4 all other times. Everything closed 25 December.

 Places may occasionally close for events or bad weather, check at nationaltrust.org.uk

Canons Ashby

near Daventry, Northamptonshire NN11 3SD

[icons] 1981

Parking: 200 yards.

Ancient and peaceful, Canons Ashby is far removed from today's bustling lifestyle. Medieval canons built their priory near the small village of Ashby, but the Dissolution left a curiously truncated church and the village was lost, leaving nothing but mounds in the landscape. Nearby, the Elizabethan Dryden family built their home, making few changes during their 450 years of occupation. Victorian Sir Henry Dryden's curiosity led him to record the detail of the mansion, its unusual blend of architectural styles, mysterious wall-paintings, plasterwork and fine furnishings. Outside, lush gardens, parkland and ancient church offer space for tranquil contemplation. **Note**: admission may be by timed tickets on busy days.

Elizabethan murals at Canons Ashby in Northamptonshire

Exploring the verdant gardens at Canons Ashby

Eat, shop, stay: Stables tea-room and pretty tea garden offering light meals and freshly baked treats. Coach House shop selling home and garden gifts and Canons Ashby home-grown plants. Well-stocked second-hand bookshop.

Things to see and do: Indoors Discovery trails for families in the house. **Outdoors** Parkland and garden walks all year. Family activities and trails available throughout the year. Garden games and natural play available. **Dogs**: welcome on leads in car park, paddock, tea garden and parkland.

Access: [icons] House [icons] Church [icons] Grounds [icons]

Find out more: 01327 861900 or canonsashby@nationaltrust.org.uk

Canons Ashby		M	T	W	T	F	S	S
House*								
3 Feb–29 Mar*	11–3	M	T	W	T	F	S	S
30 Mar–1 Nov	11:30–4	M	T	W	T	F	S	S
7 Nov–29 Nov*	11–3	·	·	·	·	·	S	S
30 Nov–22 Dec*	11–3	M	T	W	T	F	S	S
Tea-room, shop, gardens, priory church and parkland*								
1 Jan–2 Jan*	10–3	·	·	W	T	·	·	·
3 Feb–29 Mar*	10–3:30	M	T	W	T	F	S	S
30 Mar–1 Nov	10–5	M	T	W	T	F	S	S
2 Nov–22 Dec*	10–3:30	M	T	W	T	F	S	S
27 Dec–31 Dec*	10–3	M	T	W	T	·	·	S

*House and garden: some areas may close in winter for conservation work. House: last entry 2:30 in February, March, November and December and 3:30, April to October; closes dusk if earlier. Timed tickets may operate at certain times.

Clumber Park

Worksop, Nottinghamshire S80 3BE

✚ ✛ 🎦 🍸 1946

Parking: 250 yards.

Carved out of the ancient forest of Sherwood, a space of playfulness and pleasure on a grand scale was created by the Dukes of Newcastle. Clumber Park is true to its spirit as a place of recreation, with 20 miles of cycle routes and 1,537 hectares (3,800 acres) of parkland, woodland and heathland to explore. The beauty of the Gothic Revival chapel, with its original stained-glass windows, reveals a rich historic past. The Pleasure Grounds frame the magnificent lake, making a perfect place to stroll or picnic. The Walled Kitchen Garden, with its National Collection of Rhubarb, provides a variety of fruit and vegetables to the café, and there are colourful herbaceous borders during the summer.

Eat, shop, stay: café and garden tea-house serving hot meals, snacks, cream teas and a children's menu. Pizza oven (peak times). Large gift shop and plant sales, second-hand bookshop. Cycle hire, servicing and sales. Picnics welcome and designated barbecue site.

Clumber Park in Nottinghamshire, below and right

Inside the fascinating glasshouse at Clumber Park

Things to see and do: Indoors Year-round activities for all ages and interests, including art, history and wildlife exhibitions at the Discovery Centre. The glasshouse and Museum of Gardening Tools at the Walled Kitchen Garden and Clumber chapel – a cathedral in miniature. **Outdoors** Seasonal highlights include the spring bluebells, rhododendrons and apple blossom, late-summer-flowering heathers and autumn tree colour. During your visit, tick off some of the '50 things to do before you're 11¾'. There are many downloadable walks, woodland play areas, a cycle hire centre and many outdoor activities. **Dogs**: welcome. Indoor refreshment area for dog walkers. Downloadable guide.

Access: 🅿️ 🚻 ♿ 🚪 ♿ 🎦 🦽
Buildings ♿ ♿ **Grounds** 🦽 ➡️ ♿ ♿

Find out more: 01909 476592 or clumberpark@nationaltrust.org.uk

Clumber Park		M	T	W	T	F	S	S
Park								
Open all year	7–7	M	T	W	T	F	S	S
Visitor facilities, café, shop, kitchen garden, chapel*								
1 Jan–28 Mar	10–4**	M	T	W	T	F	S	S
29 Mar–24 Oct	10–5**	M	T	W	T	F	S	S
25 Oct–31 Dec	10–4**	M	T	W	T	F	S	S

Park: open until dusk in summer. 29 March to 25 October: visitor facilities (café, shop, kitchen garden, chapel, cycle hire centre, garden tea-house, Discovery Centre and woodland play park) close at 6 at weekends and Bank Holidays. Open daily, except 25 December.
*Chapel: 14 January to 17 March, closed for conservation.
**Café: opens at 9. Last cycle hire two hours before closing.

Duffield Castle

Duffield, Derbyshire 1899

Site of one of England's largest medieval castles – see its foundations, imagine the stories and enjoy the Derbyshire views.
Note: sorry no toilets. Steep steps. For satnav use DE56 4DW.

Find out more: 01332 842191 or duffieldcastle@nationaltrust.org.uk

Gunby Estate, Hall and Gardens

Gunby, Spilsby, Lincolnshire PE23 5SS

1944

Satnav: entrance is off roundabout (not beyond or before). **Parking:** on site.

The Massingberd family home from 1700 until 1967, Gunby Hall (above) still feels cherished and lived-in. Exploring three floors, you can easily imagine you'll bump into one of the family at any moment. Enjoy garden colour whatever the season: abundant spring flowers, summer roses, autumn borders and plentiful fruit and vegetables. **Note:** building works all year. Booking system may be operating from September (please call for details).

Eat, shop, stay: courtyard tea-room offering small selection of cakes and packaged sandwiches. Well-stocked second-hand bookshop. Small gift shop, seasonal plants and produce. Three holiday cottages.

Gunby Estate, Hall and Gardens in Lincolnshire

Things to see and do: events throughout year, from open-air theatre to Rose and Apple Days. Footpaths across wider park and estate: ask for directions and maps at admission.
Dogs: welcome on leads in the gardens, courtyard tea-room terrace and grounds.

Access: House Grounds

Find out more: 01754 890102 or gunbyhall@nationaltrust.org.uk

Gunby Estate		M	T	W	T	F	S	S
House								
1 Mar–1 Nov	11–5*	M	T	W	·	·	S	S
5 Dec–20 Dec	11–4	M	T	W	T	F	S	S
Gardens and tea-room								
1 Mar–1 Nov	11–5**	M	T	W	T	F	S	S
5 Dec–20 Dec	11–4	M	T	W	T	F	S	S

*House: last admission one hour before closing (on busy days entry may be by timed ticket); also open 8 May.
**Tea-room: last service 4:30.

Gunby Hall Estate: Monksthorpe Chapel

Monksthorpe, near Spilsby, Lincolnshire PE23 5PP 2000

Monksthorpe Chapel, dated 1701, was made to look like a barn to avoid detection and features a rare open-air baptistry. **Note:** Chapel open daily, 1 March to 1 November, 11 to 5. Grounds open every day all year, 11 to 5. Access by key, obtained from Gunby Hall tea-room (£20 refundable deposit required).

Find out more: 01754 890102 or monksthorpe@nationaltrust.org.uk

Hardwick

near Chesterfield, Derbyshire

🏠 ✿ 🛏 🚹 1959

Satnav: use S44 5RW.
Parking: 600-space car park.

Wending its way through parkland scattered with ancient oaks, Hardwick's steep drive offers tantalising glimpses of the hall's turrets, which bear the initials of an indomitable lady. Bess of Hardwick had the vision, the wealth and the sheer audacity to construct a house that still takes people's breath away today. Built as a testament to the wealth and taste of Bess, the house contains a collection of objects and textiles fine enough to grace any room in any palace in Europe. You can wander through the herb-scented gardens, with their seasonal delights and surprises, then explore the beautiful parkland and discover the duck decoy and ice house in the lower park. **Note**: Old Hall owned by the National Trust and administered by English Heritage (01246 850431).

Eat, shop, stay: Great Barn Restaurant serving hot meals, seasonal specials (made using garden produce) and cakes. Stables shop and garden shop with many plants propagated in Hardwick's nursery. Picnic areas. Three holiday cottages (sleeping two, six and 12).

Things to see and do: **Indoors** Seasonal events, including Easter and Christmas. **Outdoors** Open-air films during the summer and themed tours and talks. You can see the garden highlights, including the stumpery and herbaceous borders. There are also walking trails around the estate and surrounding countryside. Family woodland trail and fun family activities during all school holidays. Stainsby Mill is nearby. **Dogs**: welcome on leads in stableyard, park and car park.

Hardwick, Derbyshire, below: a testament to the wealth and taste of Bess of Hardwick. Enjoying an open-air film, above

Detail of the Flossie silk embroidery at Hardwick

Access: 🅿️♿🚻♿🔔🔄📷📹♿🅰️
Hall ♿♿♿ Restaurant ♿♿ Garden ➡️♿

Find out more: 01246 850430 or
hardwick@nationaltrust.org.uk
Doe Lea, near Chesterfield, Derbyshire S44 5QJ

Hardwick		M	T	W	T	F	S	S
Hall								
15 Feb–29 Mar	11–4	·	·	W	T	F	S	S
1 Apr–1 Nov*	11–5	·	·	W	T	F	S	S
21 Nov–20 Dec**	11–3	·	·	W	T	F	S	S
Garden								
1 Jan–29 Mar	10–5	M	T	W	T	F	S	S
30 Mar–1 Nov	9–6†	M	T	W	T	F	S	S
2 Nov–31 Dec	10–4	M	T	W	T	F	S	S
Restaurant and shop								
1 Jan–29 Mar	9–5††	M	T	W	T	F	S	S
30 Mar–1 Nov	9–6††	M	T	W	T	F	S	S
2 Nov–31 Dec	9–5††	M	T	W	T	F	S	S
Park								
Open all year		M	T	W	T	F	S	S

*Hall: also open Bank Holiday Mondays.
**Christmas opening: selected areas open.
†Garden: last entry at 5. ††Shop: opens at 10.
Closed 24 and 25 December.

Hardwick Estate: Stainsby Mill

Doe Lea, Chesterfield, Derbyshire S44 5RW

🏛️ 1976

Parking: limited on-road parking
(not National Trust).

A fully operational Victorian flour mill giving an insight into the workplace of a 19th-century miller. There has been a mill on this site for more than 100 years, providing flour for the local villages and the Hardwick Estate. Flour is ground regularly showing the cogs and machinery in action. **Note**: nearest toilets and refreshments at Hardwick Hall.

Hardwick Estate: Stainsby Mill in Derbyshire

Eat, shop, stay: you can learn more about the mill from our guides and pick up recipes to try at home. Restaurant and gift shop at nearby Hardwick.

Things to see and do: children's trail and activity sheets. Have a go at grinding flour on the hand quern. **Dogs**: welcome on leads at nearby Hardwick parkland.

Access: 🔄📹 Building ♿ Grounds ♿♿

Find out more: 01246 850430 or
stainsbymill@nationaltrust.org.uk

Stainsby Mill		M	T	W	T	F	S	S
15 Feb–22 May*	10–4	·	·	W	T	F	S	S
23 May–19 Jul*	10–5	·	·	W	T	F	S	S
22 Jul–31 Aug	10–5	M	T	W	T	F	S	S
2 Sep–1 Nov	10–4	·	·	W	T	F	S	S

*Open Bank Holiday Mondays, 10 to 4.

Ilam Park, Dovedale and the White Peak

Ilam, Ashbourne, Derbyshire

✝ 🏛 🎫 ♣ 🎎 🐕 🦴 | 1934

Satnav: use DE6 2AZ. **Parking**: at Ilam Park (119:132507) and Dovedale, not National Trust (charge including members).

The Stepping Stones at Dovedale lead to a riverside walk through the National Nature Reserve full of caves and pinnacles, rich in wildlife and fossils. A 1½-mile walk across fields links Dovedale and Ilam Park, a tranquil parkland nestled beneath steep-sided hills on the River Manifold. The park is dotted with majestic mature trees and offers views of the church, the rugged backdrop of Thorpe Cloud and Bunster Hill. A 1-mile circular parkland route makes this a popular choice for families and dog walkers. The Church of the Holy Cross contains stories of St Bertram, buried within. **Note**: Ilam Hall is let to the Youth Hostel Association. Dovedale car park is privately owned and there is also a charge for toilets.

Eat, shop, stay: tea-room at Ilam Park, with views towards Dovedale. Peak season accessible grab-and-go in stableyard. Shops at Ilam Park and Dovedale Barn offering maps, gifts and information. Stay at Ilam bunkhouse or at one of two holiday cottages at Wetton Mill.

Ilam Park, Dovedale and the White Peak, Derbyshire: rugged Thorpe Cloud, below, and chatting with a ranger

Things to see and do: circular parkland walk, stroll by the river or beneath the lime trees on Paradise Walk. Free Monday and Friday walks all year (no booking needed). Family holiday fun. **Dogs**: welcome on leads – seasonal access.

Access: 🅿️ 🚻 ♿ 🚼 📷 📶 Tea-room 🪑
Shop and visitor centre ♿ ♿ ♿ Ilam Park ♿ ➡️ ♿

Find out more: 01335 350503 or peakdistrict@nationaltrust.org.uk

Ilam Park			M	T	W	T	F	S	S
Dovedale Barn									
4 Apr–27 Sep	10:30–4:30		M	T	W	T	F	S	S
Tea-room and shop*									
1 Jan–14 Feb	10:30–4		M	T	W	T	F	S	S
15 Feb–1 Nov	10:30–5		M	T	W	T	F	S	S
2 Nov–31 Dec	10:30–4		M	T	W	T	F	S	S

*Shop: opens 11. Tea-room and shop: closed 24 and 25 December. Ilam bunkhouse: open all year (0344 335 1296). Darfar and Redhurst holiday cottages: available to let all year (0344 800 2070). Ilam Hall: available for overnight accommodation via the Youth Hostel Association (01335 350212).

Kedleston Hall

near Derby, Derbyshire

1987

Satnav: for main entrance use DE22 5JD.
Parking: 200 yards.

Be inspired by a true 'temple of the arts' – as envisioned by celebrated architect Robert Adam. Experience the grandeur of this lavishly decorated 1760s show palace in Derbyshire, lived in over the centuries by the Curzon family, and explore the Eastern Museum of objects. Collected by Lord Curzon during his time as Viceroy of India, these represent the rich diversity of cultures and communities across South Asia. The mansion is set in 332 hectares (820 acres) of landscape parkland and Pleasure Grounds, which can be explored on foot all year. The parkland is popular for dog walks, picnics and orienteering. **Note**: the medieval All Saint's Church is managed by the Churches Conservation Trust, not open daily.

Eat, shop, stay: Old Kitchen restaurant serves breakfasts, hot and cold lunches, cakes (indoor and outdoor seating). Refreshment kiosk at peak times. Gift shop, plant sales and second-hand bookshop. Luxury Park House holiday cottage sits on the edge of Kedleston Park.

Enjoying the garden at Kedleston Hall in Derbyshire, above, and a detail of the ornate state bed, below

Things to see and do: **Indoors** Explore the striking State Floor. Visit the Eastern Museum and find a book in the second-hand bookshop. **Outdoors** Waymarked walks, orienteering, tours and school holiday activities.
Dogs: welcome on leads in the parkland, gardens and outdoor seating areas. Water bowls available.

Access:
Ground floor **State Floor**
Grounds

Find out more: 01332 842191 or
kedlestonhall@nationaltrust.org.uk
Quarndon, near Derby, Derbyshire DE22 5JH

Kedleston Hall		M	T	W	T	F	S	S
Hall								
15 Feb–29 Mar	11–3:30	M	T	W	T	·	S	S
30 Mar–4 Oct*	11–4	M	T	W	T	·	S	S
5 Oct–1 Nov	11–3:30	M	T	W	T	·	S	S
6 Nov–28 Dec†	11–3:30	M	·	·	·	F	S	S
Park and Pleasure Grounds								
1 Jan–14 Feb	9:30–4	M	T	W	T	F	S	S
15 Feb–1 Mar	9:30–5	M	T	W	T	F	S	S
2 Mar–1 Nov	9:30–6	M	T	W	T	F	S	S
2 Nov–31 Dec	9:30–4	M	T	W	T	F	S	S
Restaurant and shop								
1 Jan–14 Feb	10–3:30	M	T	W	T	F	S	S
15 Feb–1 Mar	10–4	M	T	W	T	F	S	S
2 Mar–1 Nov	10–5	M	T	W	T	F	S	S
2 Nov–31 Dec	10–3:30	M	T	W	T	F	S	S

*Hall open Good Friday. †Hall: some parts closed for conservation work. Everything closed 25 December and occasionally for events.

Kinder, Edale and the Dark Peak

near Hope Valley, Derbyshire

🏚 🚻 🅿 🐕 1936

Parking: at Mam Nick National Trust car park (110:SK124832). Also non-National Trust parking at Edale, Castleton, Bowden Bridge, Hayfield, Sett Valley, Hayfield and Upper Derwent Valley (charge including members).

The Dark Peak, including Kinder, the Vale of Edale and along the Snake moors to the Derwent edges, offers exhilarating walks across heather moors, high gritstone edges and monumental windswept tors. Stories and wild nature abound amid the ancient peat bogs and quiet wooded cloughs. You can follow the route of the 1932 Mass Trespass onto Kinder Scout National Nature Reserve, retracing the steps of those early champions of access to wild places. Alternatively, a short walk up the steps of Mam Tor rewards you with panoramic views from this ancient hilltop fortress.
Note: nearest toilets in villages and visitor centres (not National Trust) at Ladybower Reservoir, Edale and Castleton.

Kinder, Edale and the Dark Peak in Derbyshire: Mam Tor, above, and dramatic Kinder Scout, below

Eat, shop, stay: Dalehead Bunkhouse offers group accommodation in a stone-built farmhouse deep in the Edale Valley.

Things to see and do: downloadable walking and cycling routes. **Dogs**: welcome on leads – seasonal access.

Find out more: 01433 670368 or peakdistrict@nationaltrust.org.uk

---

Kinder, Edale and the Dark Peak

Welcome shelters open all year: Lee Barn (110:SK096855), Dalehead (110: SK101843) and Edale End (SK161864) in the Edale Valley; South Head (SK060854) above Hayfield; Grindle Barns above Ladybower Reservoir (SK189895). Mam Nick car park (SK123832) and Dalehead Bunkhouse (0344 335 1296) open all year.

Longshaw, Burbage and the Eastern Moors

near Sheffield, Derbyshire

🏠🏛️💺♿♿ 1931

Satnav: use S11 7TZ (follow brown signs).
Parking: at Woodcroft car park (110: 266800), Wooden Pole and Haywood for Longshaw and at Curbar Gap, Birchen Edge and Shillito Wood for the Eastern Moors. Additional car parks at Surprise View and Burbage, not National Trust (charge including members).

A countryside haven on Sheffield's doorstep, Longshaw, Burbage and the Eastern Moors has a network of footpaths and bridleways you can explore within a typical Peak District landscape of skies and silhouettes. Here you'll find long views, with scooping shapes of rocks and hills and gorges where water tumbles through ancient woods and over mossy boulders. A diverse range of wildlife lives peacefully here among abandoned millstones and packhorse routes of the past. The designed landscape around Longshaw Lodge, a former grouse-shooting estate, offers a warm and friendly starting point for your adventure.
Note: National Trust/RSPB manage Eastern Moors for Peak District National Park; Burbage for Sheffield County Council.

Kite-flying at Longshaw, Burbage and the Eastern Moors in Derbyshire, above, and exploring the family trail, below

Eat, shop, stay: Longshaw café serving fresh seasonal snacks and dishes. The shop and welcome building sell outdoor and wildlife-themed products, maps and guides. White Edge Lodge, an old gamekeeper's house, is available as holiday accommodation.

Things to see and do: woodland and moorland paths, natural play, bridleways and waymarked walks. Kitchen garden behind café. Regular trails, outdoor activities, including Trust10 and nature conservation events. Free guided walks (Wednesdays and Sundays).
Dogs: welcome on leads – seasonal access.

Access: 🅿♿♿♿♿♿ Café and shop ♿♿
Moorland Discovery Centre ♿ Grounds ♿♿

Find out more: 01433 631757 (Longshaw). 0114 289 1543 (Eastern Moors) or peakdistrict@nationaltrust.org.uk

Longshaw		M	T	W	T	F	S	S
Tea-room and shop								
1 Jan–14 Feb	10:30–4	M	T	W	T	F	S	S
15 Feb–1 Nov	10–5	M	T	W	T	F	S	S
2 Nov–31 Dec	10:30–4	M	T	W	T	F	S	S

Closed 24 and 25 December. Tea-room building works planned for part of the year with temporary catering available. White Edge Lodge: available as holiday cottage all year (0344 800 2070). Longshaw Lodge: not open to public.

Lyveden

Harley Way, near Oundle,
Northamptonshire PE8 5AT

🏠🏛️✳️♿ 1922

Parking: 100 yards.

Deep in Northamptonshire lies a mysterious garden. Begun by Sir Thomas Tresham in 1595 but never completed, the house stands as testament to his Catholicism. Persecuted for his religious beliefs, Sir Thomas sought solace in the creation of his garden. New facilities opening in spring reveal the intriguing story behind Lyveden and provide the opportunity for lunch or cake in our new café. For the first time you can discover the wonder of this Elizabethan garden in the order originally intended, as grass paths, viewing mounts and moats lead you upwards from manor house to the symbolic garden lodge.
Note: opening times early in the year vary due to construction work.

Eat, shop, stay: new café (opening spring) serving sandwiches, soups, light meals and cakes. Ice cream available from the café and seasonally from the kiosk at the cottage. Picnics welcome. Small range of gifts, plants and souvenirs available at visitor reception.

Things to see and do: Indoors New interpretation spaces to explore in the manor from spring. **Outdoors** Family activities all year. New routes offer alternative views of the garden and space to breathe.
Dogs: welcome on leads. Assistance dogs only in manor and café.

Access: 🅿️♿🔖🚻📷🚸🐕♿
Manor 🏠 Lodge 🏠 Grounds ➡️

Find out more: 01832 205158 or
lyveden@nationaltrust.org.uk

Lyveden		M	T	W	T	F	S	S
18 May–25 Oct	10:30–5*	M	T	W	T	F	S	S
26 Oct–31 Dec	10:30–3:30	M	T	W	T	F	S	S

*Tea-room: last orders 4. Last audio guide issued one hour before closing. Everything closed 25 and 26 December. Due to new facilities opening in spring, opening times may change (please check before visiting).

Both eerie and intriguing, the Elizabethan lodge at Lyveden, Northamptonshire, is filled with religious symbols

Mr Straw's House

5–7 Blyth Grove, Worksop,
Nottinghamshire S81 0JG

🏠 ♿ 1990

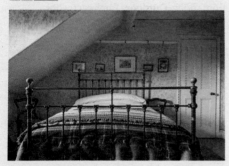

Mr Straw's House in Nottinghamshire: frozen in time

Parking: on site, in orchard opposite property.

Within the Sanderson-papered walls of this
middle-class home, the family lived thriftily,
installing few modern conveniences since 1923.
A large and intriguing collection of everyday
objects and personal papers has survived
alongside traces of the occasional indulgence.
The lovingly tended garden and orchard
include a cacti collection and fruit trees.
Note: entrance is by timed ticket only
(these must be bought in advance).

Eat, shop, stay: small shop selling a range
of souvenirs, plants, jam, books and gifts.
Small tea-room.

Things to see and do: changing displays,
family activities, events and guided town
walks all year. **Dogs**: assistance dogs only.

Access: 🚻 ♿ 🚗 🅿️ Gardens 🏛️
Warwick Villa, 5 Blyth Grove 🏛️ 👥
Endcliffe Villa, 7 Blyth Grove 🏛️ 👥

Find out more: 01909 482380 or
mrstrawshouse@nationaltrust.org.uk

Mr Straw's House		M	T	W	T	F	S	S
3 Mar–31 Oct*	Tour		**T**	**W**	**T**	**F**	**S**	·

*Admission by timed ticket (please telephone in advance
to book). Last timed ticket at 4. Guided tours 10 to 12:30,
freeflow from 12:30. Closed Good Friday.

The Old Manor

Norbury, Ashbourne, Derbyshire
DE6 2ED 1987

An idyllic medieval hall featuring a rare king
post and well-preserved Tudor door, set within
beautiful gardens and peaceful countryside.
Note: parking limited (cars only). Open Friday,
20 March to 23 October, 11 to 1, and Saturday,
21 March to 24 October, 1 to 3. Next to
National Trust holiday house, please
respect the occupants' privacy.

Find out more: 01283 585337 or
oldmanor@nationaltrust.org.uk

Priest's House, Easton on the Hill

38 West Street, Easton on the Hill, near
Stamford, Northamptonshire PE9 3LS 1966

Delightful small late 15th-century building,
with interesting local architecture and museum
exploring Easton on the Hill's industrial and
mining heritage. **Note**: open daily, 10 to 5.
Unmanned. Access from neighbouring
keyholders listed on property noticeboard.
Staffed on Sunday afternoons during June,
July and August. Closed 25 and 26 December.

Find out more: 01832 205158 or
priestshouse2@nationaltrust.org.uk

Staunton Harold Church

Staunton Harold Estate, Ashby-de-la-Zouch,
Leicestershire LE65 1RW 1954

A rare and imposing church built in 1653, with
a landscape lake and rolling wooded hills as its
backdrop. **Note**: nearest toilet 500 yards
(not National Trust). Parking not National

Trust; Staunton Harold Estate (charge including members). Open weekends, 4 April to 1 November, and Wednesday to Sunday, 3 June to 30 August, 12:30 to 4. Also open Good Friday and Bank Holidays. Services are normally held Easter to December, first and third Sundays.

Find out more: 01332 863822 or stauntonharold@nationaltrust.org.uk

---

Stoneywell

Whitcroft's Lane, Ulverscroft, Leicestershire LE67 9QE

🏠 ✳️ 2012

Parking: for booked visitors only.

Zigzagging from its rocky outcrop, Stoneywell is the realisation of one man's Arts and Crafts vision within a family home. Original furniture and family treasures fill the cottage's quirky rooms and, outside, every turn conjures childhood memories of holiday excitement – one way to the fort, another to the woods beyond. **Note**: booking essential (including members).

Eat, shop, stay: Stables tea-room (for booked visitors only) serving light lunches, homemade cakes, cream teas, scones and ice cream. Small range of gifts, seasonal plants and second-hand books. Picnics welcome in grounds.

Things to see and do: **Indoors** Guided tours, events and family activities reveal stories of life at Stoneywell. **Outdoors** Seasonal highlights, including daffodils, bluebells and extensive collection of rhododendrons.
Dogs: assistance dogs only.

Access: 🅿️🚌🎫🚪🅰️📷🚹♿🖐 ⬛🖐
Stables 🅰️🚹 Cottage 🅰️🚹 Gardens 🅰️➡️

Find out more: 01530 248040 (Infoline). 01530 248048 (bookings) or stoneywell@nationaltrust.org.uk

Stoneywell		M	T	W	T	F	S	S
1 Feb–30 Nov	Tour	**M**	**T**	**W**	**T**	**F**	**S**	**S**

Emerging organically from its rocky outcrop, Stoneywell in Leicestershire is an Arts and Crafts triumph

Sudbury Hall and the National Trust Museum of Childhood

Sudbury, Ashbourne, Derbyshire DE6 5HT

🏠 ✤ 🔔 🍸 1967

Parking: 500 yards.

A complete day out, with two unique experiences in one location. The Hall has one of the most surprising, light and beautiful long galleries in England and is the result of George Vernon's aspirations to create a perfect new home. Enjoy the way the magnificent interiors, including exuberant plasterwork and Grinling Gibbons woodcarving, breathe the spirit of the Restoration through their fineness, delicacy and touches of humour. The museum is a place of fun and fascination for all ages. You can discover about childhood from the Victorian period to the present day; send your little one up a chimney, play with our hands-on toys and games and experience the Victorian Schoolroom.

Sudbury Hall and the National Trust Museum of Childhood, Derbyshire: Victorian Schoolroom, left, and Hall, this page

Find out more: 01283 585337 or sudburyhall@nationaltrust.org.uk

Eat, shop, stay: tea-room serving light lunches and homemade cakes. Gift shop, plant sales, sweets, ice cream, toys and second-hand bookshop all situated in the stableyard area. Picnics welcome in the grounds.

Things to see and do: Indoors Hands-on toys in the museum and family activities at weekends and during most school holidays. Volunteer-led tours, subject to availability. **Outdoors** Trails and fun activities for all the family at weekends and during most school holidays. Spot wildlife by the lake. Younger visitors can have great adventures in the woodland play area. **Dogs**: welcome on leads in grounds; assistance dogs only indoors.

Access: 🏢♿🏠🅿️🚻♿🚮🚗♿🚫
Hall ♿🅿️ Museum ♿⬆️♿ Grounds ♿♿

Sudbury Hall	M	T	W	T	F	S	S
Hall, museum, tea-room and shop*							
3 Jan–10 Feb	11–4	**M**	·	·	·	**F**	**S**	**S**
14 Feb–2 Nov	11–5	**M**	**T**	**W**	**T**	**F**	**S**	**S**
6 Nov–16 Nov	11–4	**M**	·	·	·	**F**	**S**	**S**

*Hall: 11 to 12 access limited and by guided tour (subject to availability) – check before visiting for details. Tea-room and shop: open 10:30. Christmas opening from 20 November (please check website).

Tattershall Castle

Sleaford Road, Tattershall,
Lincolnshire LN4 4LR

[🏰][🏛][🔔][1925]

Parking: 150 yards from entrance. Height restrictions apply, maximum 2.4 metres.

Rising proudly from the flat Lincolnshire fens, Tattershall Castle was designed to display wealth, position and power. Built by Lord Ralph Cromwell, Treasurer of England, the Great Tower is one of the earliest and finest surviving examples of English medieval brickwork. Dramatically saved from being dismantled and exported, the castle and its huge Gothic fireplaces were restored from ruin by Lord Curzon of Kedleston between 1912 and 1914. Imagine the splendour of this once-palatial private residence as you wander through the vast echoing chambers. Ascend the spiral staircase from basement to battlements and take in spectacular views of the countryside. **Note**: access to the tower via a spiral staircase only (149 steps). Loose gravel paths throughout.

Eat, shop, stay: Guardhouse shop selling gifts, plants, souvenirs, second-hand books and a limited catering offer (hot and cold drinks, wrapped cakes and ice cream). Picnics welcome in the grounds.

Things to see and do: **Indoors** Multimedia guides (adult and family versions), children's trails, medieval games. **Outdoors** Year-round events for all ages and interests, including Easter egg hunt, re-enactment weekends, open-air theatre and Christmas events. **Dogs**: welcome on leads in the grounds.

Tattershall Castle in Lincolnshire, below and right, was designed to display wealth, position and power

Access: [access symbols] Castle [access symbol]

Find out more: 01526 342543 or tattershallcastle@nationaltrust.org.uk

Tattershall Castle		M	T	W	T	F	S	S
15 Feb–1 Nov	11–5	**M**	**T**	**W**	**T**	**F**	**S**	**S**
7 Nov–22 Nov	11–3*	·	·	·	·	·	**S**	**S**

Last entry one hour before closing. Last multimedia guide issued one hour before closing. Great Tower: some rooms may close occasionally for weddings. *May close earlier due to light levels.

Ulverscroft Nature Reserve

near Copt Oak, Loughborough, Leicestershire 1945

Nestled in the ancient Charnwood Forest, the heathland and woodland habitats of Ulverscroft support a rich variety of wildlife. **Note**: assistance dogs only. Sorry no toilet. For satnav use LE67 9QE. Limited parking along Whitcroft's Lane, adjacent to the reserve. Access by permit only from The Secretary, Leicestershire and Rutland Wildlife Trust, The Old Mill, 9 Soar Lane, Leicester, LE3 5DE (0116 262 9968). Please allow a week to receive permit.

Find out more: 01332 863822 or ulverscroftreserve@nationaltrust.org.uk

Winster Market House

Main Street, Winster, Matlock, Derbyshire DE4 2DJ 1906

A small listed 16th-century Market House with displays upstairs – the first Derbyshire place acquired by the National Trust, costing £50. **Note**: Winster Market House is unstaffed. Open daily, 14 April to 1 November, 11 to 5.

Find out more: 01335 350503 or winstermarkethouse@nationaltrust.org.uk

Woolsthorpe Manor

Water Lane, Woolsthorpe by Colsterworth,
near Grantham, Lincolnshire NG33 5PD

🏚️ ✳️ 1943

Parking: 50 yards.

The world changed here. Isaac Newton,
scientist, mathematician, thinker, craftsman,
was born and grew up at Woolsthorpe Manor,
doing much of his most important scientific
work before he was 26. Sent home from
Cambridge by the plague during 1665–7, he
experimented obsessively, laying foundations
for a groundbreaking scientific revolution. Here
he split sunlight into colours with a prism and
an apple fell from a tree to inspire his theory of
gravity. Newton's genius still resonates through
our world and for more than 300 years people
have come to walk in his footsteps and be
inspired by his story. **Note**: potential building
works and changes to opening hours
(please check before you visit).

**Woolsthorpe Manor in Lincolnshire, the relatively modest
birthplace of Isaac Newton, left, witnessed world-changing
experiments and discoveries. Newton's 'Principia', above,
is one of the most important works in the history of science**

Eat, shop, stay: Science Café. Shop with
Newton-inspired gifts and souvenirs.

Things to see and do: **Indoors** Explore the
Manor, access via timed entry. Hands-on
Science Centre. Family activities. Pop-up
science. Talks. Evening events. **Outdoors**
The gravity-inspiring apple tree. Orchard.
Stargazing. **Dogs**: assistance dogs only.

Access: 🅿️ 🚻 ♿ 🔊 📷 ♿ House 🔊 ♿ 🚻 ♿
Science Centre 🔊 ♿ ♿ Grounds 🔊 ➡️ ♿

Find out more: 01476 860338 or
woolsthorpemanor@nationaltrust.org.uk

Woolsthorpe Manor				M	T	W	T	F	S	S
15 Feb–1 Nov*	11–5			M	T	W	T	F	S	S

*Café: open 11 to 4:30. House: timed entry.
May close early due to low light levels.

The Workhouse, Southwell

Southwell, Nottinghamshire

🏠♿ 2002

Two views of The Workhouse, Southwell, Nottinghamshire

Satnav: use NG25 0QB. **Parking**: 200 yards.

Walking up the paupers' path towards The Workhouse, it is easy to imagine how the Victorian poor might have felt as they sought refuge here. This austere building, the most complete workhouse in existence, was built in 1824 as a place of last resort for the destitute. Its architecture was influenced by prison design, and its harsh regime became a blueprint for workhouses throughout the country. The stories of people who lived and worked here over the years help tell the history of the building's evolution and prompt reflection on how society has tackled social welfare through time.

Eat, shop, stay: café offering hot drinks, soup, sandwiches, cakes and snacks. Shop selling gifts, ice cream and traditional toys. Picnic benches in the garden.

Things to see and do: Indoors Newly conserved 1871 Firbeck Infirmary building. Seasonal programming updates our story through art, music, photography and innovative technology. Living history days, family events and exhibitions. **Outdoors** Victorian kitchen garden. **Dogs**: welcome on leads in front field.

Access: 🅿🚻♿🏢🗼🅿🖼️📷🚻♿🅿🖼️
Workhouse 🚻♿👪♿ Firbeck 🚻♿🛗
Grounds ♿➡️♿

Find out more: 01636 817260 or theworkhouse@nationaltrust.org.uk
Upton Road, Southwell, Nottinghamshire NG25 0PT

The Workhouse		M	T	W	T	F	S	S
Workhouse								
8 Feb–1 Nov*	12–5	M	T	W	T	F	S	S
Infirmary								
8 Feb–1 Nov	10:30–5	M	T	W	T	F	S	S

*Workhouse: open Bank Holidays from 11. Café: open 10:30 to 4. Guided tour of the outside and other buildings at 11 (places limited, book on arrival only). Last admission to site one hour before closing; may close earlier due to light levels.

Swinging high at Brockhampton,
Herefordshire

M56

M6

Little
Moreton
Hall

Congleton

Crewe

STOKE-ON-TRENT

Biddulph
Grange Garden

Ilam Park,
Dovedale
and the
White Peak

Bakewell

Chesterfield

Hardwi

Mansfie

M1

Wrexham

Erddig

M6

A534

A525

A50

A51

Chirk
Castle

Oswestry

Downs Banks

Stone

Kedleston Hall

DERBY

Sudbury Hall

Calke Abbey

Welshpool

Powis
Castle

Shrewsbury

Town Walls
Tower

Attingham
Park

Cronkhill

Benthall
Hall

Sunnycroft

Stafford

Shugborough
Estate

M54

M6
(TOLL)

Moseley
Old Hall

Letocetum
Roman Baths

Tamworth

M42

M69

Wilderhope
Manor

Morville
Hall

Wightwick
Manor

WOLVERHAMPTON

The Museum of Jewellery Quarter

Bridgnorth

Soho House

Aston Hall

Carding
Mill Valley

Wenlock
Edge

Dudmaston

Roundhouse

BIRMINGHAM

Blakesley Hall

Kinver Edge

Coffin Works
Museum

Moseley Road Baths
Birmingham Back to Backs

M6

Clent Hills

Sarehole Mill

COVENTRY

Knowles Mill

Kidderminster

M42

Packwood
House

M45

Croft
Castle

Berrington
Hall

Leominster

Hawford Dovecote

The Firs

Wichenford
Dovecote

Hanbury
Hall

Rosedene

Baddesley
Clinton

Warwick

Coughton
Court

A46

Charlecote
Park

Farnborough
Hall

Ca
As

Cwmmau
Farmhouse

Brockhampton

WORCESTER

Greyfriars'
House

Kinwarton
Dovecote

Stratford upon Avon

Upton
House

Banbury

The Weir
Garden

HEREFORD

Croome

Middle Littleton
Tithe Barn

Evesham

Hidcote

The Fleece Inn

M50

M5

Snowshill
Manor

Stow-on-
the-Wold

Chipping Norton

M40

Legend

- ▲ Buildings and/or gardens
- ● Entry points to countryside
- ■ Birmingham Partners
- National Trust land
- |——————| 10 miles

Places in neighbouring counties

The Cotswolds, Buckinghamshire and Oxfordshire, page 112

East Midlands, page 252

North West, page 314

Wales, page 396

Attingham Park

Atcham, Shrewsbury, Shropshire SY4 4TP

🏠♿👪☕ 1947

Parking: 25 to 200 yards.

Attingham inspires a sense of beauty, space and awe. From the moment you enter the gates, views open across the 200-year-old parkland to the Shropshire Hills and the impressive mansion emerges against silhouettes of cedar trees. The house, which sits at the heart of the Lord Berwick's estate, is an example of classical design and Italian influence. Outside, cattle graze and fallow deer roam, woodland glades of historic trees offer peace and shade, while the red-brick organic walled garden is a place of order, productivity and horticulture. The accessible paths around the parkland are perfect for walks, running or exploring the 1,619-hectare (4,000-acre) estate. Full of life and locally loved, there's something for everyone all year round.

Eat, shop, stay: hot food, light meals and afternoon tea are available from the main café (open daily). Greedy Pig kiosk in the Field of Play. Stables shop selling walled-garden produce, plants and venison (in season). Second-hand bookshop. Ismore Coppice Campground nearby.

Attingham Park in Shropshire: the awe-inspiring centuries-old parkland, above, and discovering what life was like for servants in the kitchen, below

Find out more: 01743 708123 (Infoline). 01743 708162 or attingham@nationaltrust.org.uk

Attingham Park		M	T	W	T	F	S	S
Park, Field of Play, Carriage House Café and Stables shop*								
1 Jan–14 Feb	8–5**	M	T	W	T	F	S	S
15 Feb–3 Apr	8–6	M	T	W	T	F	S	S
4 Apr–22 May	8–6:30	M	T	W	T	F	S	S
23 May–6 Sep	8–7	M	T	W	T	F	S	S
7 Sep–1 Nov	8–6	M	T	W	T	F	S	S
2 Nov–31 Dec	8–5	M	T	W	T	F	S	S
Walled Garden								
Open all year	9–5**	M	T	W	T	F	S	S
Mansion								
10 Jan–9 Feb†	11–3	·	·	·	·	F	S	S
15 Feb–1 Nov††	11–4:30	M	T	W	T	F	S	S
28 Nov–24 Dec¹	10–3:30	M	T	W	T	F	S	S

*Carriage House Café opens 9 and Stables shop opens 10; both close one hour before park, except 28 November to 27 December, when close 4:30.**Dusk if earlier. †Entry by tour only. ††Entry by tour only weekdays, 24 February to 27 March, 11 to 3. ¹Entry by timed ticket. Mansion: opens 24 December, 10 to 12, and for Christmas events (selected evenings). Field of Play kiosk: open 4 April to 6 September from 11, weekends and daily during Shropshire school holidays (weather permitting). 24 December: everything closes 3; closed 25 December.

Things to see and do: **Indoors** Relaxed visit to three floors of the mansion, including basement servants' quarters (selected days). Daily themed tours. Attingham Christmas in December (booking essential). **Outdoors** Led walks and talks (selected days), run routes, Field of Play, natural play trail, river walks (1 to 4 miles), pleasure grounds, ice house, bothy and historic stables to explore. Seasonal spectaculars include snowdrops, bluebells, summer blossom and autumn tree colour. Year-round events for all ages and interests, including family trails, deer-park safaris, annual classic car rally and open-air film and theatre evenings. Sunnycroft is nearby in Wellington. **Dogs**: welcome (dog-walkers' guide available).

Letting off steam at Attingham Park, below, and plant-buying decision-making, above left

Attingham Park Estate: Cronkhill

near Atcham, Shrewsbury, Shropshire
SY5 6JP 1947

Delightful picturesque Italianate hillside villa designed by Regency architect John Nash, with beautiful views across the Attingham Estate. **Note**: house ground floor, garden and stables open as part of visit. Property contents belong to tenant. Open Friday and Sunday, 8 and 10 May, 3 and 5 July, as well as 11 and 13 September, 11 to 4 (admission by booked timed tickets).

Find out more: 01743 708162 or cronkhill@nationaltrust.org.uk

Attingham Park Estate: Town Walls Tower

Shrewsbury, Shropshire SY1 1TN 1930

This last remaining 14th-century watchtower sits on what were once the medieval fortified, defensive walls of Shrewsbury. **Note**: sorry no toilet or car parking and 40 extremely steep, narrow steps to top floor. Open weekends, 25 and 26 April, 6 and 7 June, 15 and 16 August, 3 and 4 October, 10:30 to 3:30 (admission by booked timed ticket).

Find out more: 01743 708162 or townwallstower@nationaltrust.org.uk

Baddesley Clinton

Rising Lane, Baddesley Clinton, Warwickshire B93 0DQ

🏠 ✝ ✿ ♨ 🍵 1980

Parking: 100 yards.

The magic of Baddesley Clinton comes from its secluded, timeless setting deep within its own parkland. From refuge to haven, this atmospheric moated manor house has been a sanctuary since the 15th century. Discover Baddesley's late medieval, Tudor and 20th-century histories and uncover its stories, from hiding persecuted Catholics in its priest's holes, to the history of the Ferrers family who lived at Baddesley for more than 500 years. The peaceful gardens include fish pools, walled garden and a lakeside walk, perfect for a tranquil stroll.

Eat, shop, stay: Barn Restaurant serving hot meals, drinks and snacks and The Stables offering light refreshments, hot drinks and ice cream. Picnics welcome. Shop selling seasonal gifts, local foods and plants. Second-hand bookshop.

The secluded, timeless setting of moated Baddesley Clinton in Warwickshire, right, creates a sense of magic

Entry is still possible at most places up to 30 minutes before closing

Exploring the courtyard at Baddesley Clinton, above, and inside the 15th-century house, opposite

Things to see and do: **Indoors** Discover Baddesley's story, from medieval farmstead to modest Georgian status symbol and Victorian retreat. Seasonal children's trails. House dressed for Christmas throughout December. **Outdoors** Children can discover the woodland play area on the estate. Outdoor games in school holidays. Welcome talks and garden tours, plus walking trails around the estate and surrounding countryside. Packwood House and Coughton Court are nearby. **Dogs**: welcome on leads in car park and estate public footpaths.

Access: [icons] Building [icons] Grounds [icons]

Find out more: 01564 783294 or baddesleyclinton@nationaltrust.org.uk

Baddesley Clinton		M	T	W	T	F	S	S
1 Jan–14 Feb	9–4*	M	T	W	T	F	S	S
15 Feb–1 Nov**	9–5*	M	T	W	T	F	S	S
2 Nov–31 Dec	9–4*	M	T	W	T	F	S	S

*House: opens 11, admission by timed ticket (not bookable); 6 January to 14 February, weekday admission by guided tour (not bookable). **10 to 13 April (Easter): admission by bookable tickets only, limited (including members). Closed 24 and 25 December.

Benthall Hall

Broseley, Shropshire TF12 5RX

[icons] 1958

Parking: 100 yards.

Within this fine stone house, discover the history of the Benthall family from the Saxon period to the present day. Outside, the garden includes a beautiful Restoration church, a restored plantsman's garden with pretty crocus displays in spring and autumn, and an old kitchen garden.

Eat, shop, stay: tea-room serving drinks, cakes and ice cream.

Things to see and do: **Indoors** Informative guides, children's trail. **Outdoors** Elizabethan skittle alley. Circular walks through the park and woodland. **Dogs**: welcome in park and woodland.

Access: [icons] House [icons] Church [icons]

Find out more: 01952 882159 or benthall@nationaltrust.org.uk

Benthall Hall		M	T	W	T	F	S	S
15 Feb–31 Oct*	1–5**			W	T	F	S	S

*Open Bank Holiday Mondays. **Garden: open 12:30 to 5:30. Tea-room: last orders 4:30.

Charming Benthall Hall in Shropshire

Berrington Hall

near Leominster, Herefordshire HR6 0DW

🏠♿🚲🌳👜🔔☕ 1957

Parking: 30 yards.

Standing proud and strong, this fine Georgian mansion sits within 'Capability' Brown's final garden and landscape. In the house are jewel-like interiors, designed by Henry Holland and home to the Harley, Rodney and Cawley families. Upstairs you can explore the life of Ann Bangham, wife of Thomas Harley, and see a dress fit for a king. Learn more about the Berrington Garden Project, nurture your mind and body with a walk round the lake and discover the story behind the eating apple, including the historic varieties still growing in Berrington's garden. **Note**: major restoration to mansion stonework and garden paths and walls.

Eat, shop, stay: shop selling gifts, local products and preserves made from our fruit. Tea-room serving lunches, afternoon tea and cakes, made using garden produce. Stables café, open on busy days selling 'grab and go' fare. Triumphal Arch holiday cottage for longer stays.

The west front of Berrington Hall in Herefordshire

The Business Room at Berrington Hall

Things to see and do: Indoors Exhibitions and costume collection. Trails, games and dressing up. Servants' quarters. **Outdoors** Picnic spaces and walled garden. Boating on the lake in August. Den-building and play area. Waymarked walks. **Dogs**: welcome on leads in parts of garden, courtyard, stables café, shop and parkland.

Access: 🅿️♿🚻♿♿♿📷🎵👁️
Mansion 🏠♿ Tea-room 🛗 Grounds ♿➡️🚶♿

Find out more: 01568 615721 or berrington@nationaltrust.org.uk

Berrington Hall		M	T	W	T	F	S	S
1 Jan	10–4	·	·	**W**	·	·	·	·
4 Jan–9 Feb	10–4	·	·	·	·	·	S	S
15 Feb–1 Nov	10–5	M	T	W	T	F	S	S
7 Nov–20 Dec	10–4	·	·	·	·	·	S	S
27 Dec–31 Dec	10–4	M	T	W	T	·	·	S

Mansion and shop open at 11. Last admission one hour before closing. Gardens, parkland and Stables café: open 5:30 to 8:30 on Saturdays only in August.

Biddulph Grange Garden

Grange Road, Biddulph, Staffordshire ST8 7SD

🏵 1988

Parking: 50 yards.

Biddulph Grange Garden is a remarkable survival, a formal Victorian horticultural masterpiece and a quirky, playful paradise full of intrigue and surprise. Created by its visionary owner, James Bateman, the garden and Geological Gallery express his attempts to reconcile his religious convictions with his passion for botany and geology. His plant and fossil collections come from all over the world – a visit takes you on a journey from an Italian terrace to an Egyptian pyramid, via a Himalayan glen and Chinese garden, hidden by tunnels, hedges and rockwork. The collection includes rhododendrons, Wellingtonias and the oldest golden larch in Britain. **Note**: there are 400 steps in the garden.

Eat, shop, stay: self-service tea-room (indoor and outdoor seating). Gift shop and plant centre selling a range of plants and trees, including species you will see growing in the garden. Picnic area in the paddock beside the car park.

Purple splendour at Biddulph Grange Garden

Things to see and do: **Indoors** Talks in the unique Geological Gallery. **Outdoors** Introductory talks about the garden. Activities and events for visitors of all ages throughout the year. **Dogs**: assistance dogs only.

Access: 🅿️♿🚻🏛️📷🛗 Garden ♿

Find out more: 01782 517999 or biddulphgrange@nationaltrust.org.uk

Biddulph Grange Garden		M	T	W	T	F	S	S
1 Jan–14 Feb	9:30–3:30	M	T	W	T	F	S	S
15 Feb–13 Mar	9:30–4:30	M	T	W	T	F	S	S
14 Mar–23 Oct	9:30–5:30	M	T	W	T	F	S	S
24 Oct–1 Nov	9:30–4:30	M	T	W	T	F	S	S
2 Nov–31 Dec	9:30–3:30	M	T	W	T	F	S	S

Closes dusk if earlier. Closed 25 and 26 December.

The Himalayan glen at Biddulph Grange Garden in Staffordshire gives visitors a taste of drama

Birmingham

Birmingham Back to Backs

55–63 Hurst Street/50–54 Inge Street,
Birmingham, West Midlands B5 4TE

🏛️ ♿ 2004

Parking: nearest at Arcadian Centre,
Bromsgrove Street (not National Trust).

Immerse yourself in the life of residents at
Birmingham's last surviving court of back
to backs. The evocative tour will give you an
insight into how people lived from the 1840s to
the 1970s. With privies, coal fires, candlelight
and cramped spaces, you'll get a real taste of
back-to-back life. **Note**: booking essential.
Eight flights of steep, winding stairs.
Ground-floor tours available. Sorry no café.

Eat, shop, stay: traditional sweetshop selling childhood favourites and a small gift shop. Vintage holiday cottages (booked via National Trust Holidays).

Things to see and do: events all year.

Access: 🦽🎧🖼️💷🚻 Building ♿🧗🚶

Find out more: 0121 666 7671 (booking line) or backtobacks@nationaltrust.org.uk

Birmingham Back to Backs		M	T	W	T	F	S	S
18 Jan–19 Dec	Tour		T	W	T	F	S	S

Admission by timed, guided tour only (booking essential). Closed 31 August to 3 September. Open Bank Holiday Mondays (but closed next day). Term-time tours from 1: Tuesday, Wednesday and Thursday. Last tour times vary in winter due to low light levels.

Clent Hills

near Romsley, Worcestershire

See page 295

Moseley Road Baths

497 Moseley Road, Balsall Heath, Birmingham B12 9BX

Swim in beauty – this internationally significant Grade II*-listed swimming pool has been open for community swimming since 1907. **Note**: run as a coalition, with Birmingham City Council, Historic England, World Monuments Fund and swimming managed by Moseley Road Baths Charitable Incorporated Organisation. **Standard swimming admission prices apply (including members)**. Please visit website for public swimming times, opening times and prices.

Find out more: 0121 439 0320 or moseleyroadbaths.org.uk

Setting the table period-style, opposite, at the Birmingham Back to Backs, West Midlands. Join the evocative tour and find out what life was like for the residents from the 1840s to the 1970s

Roundhouse

Sheepcote Street, Birmingham B16 8AE

🏛️ 2017

Parking: public car parks nearby, not National Trust (charge including members).

This unique horseshoe-shaped building (above), a curious survivor, lies at the heart of Birmingham's canals and is an ideal base from which to explore the city by foot, bike or boat. Join us for a tour telling the story of Roundhouse, celebrating Birmingham, to see things differently. **Note**: Roundhouse Birmingham, a partnership with Canal & River Trust, opens early May Bank Holiday. Admission charges apply for all tours and activities (including members).

Eat, shop, stay: café (not National Trust).

Things to see and do: tours and events all year. Water-based activity spring and summer (booking recommended). Self-guided walking tours. **Dogs**: welcome on leads.

Access: 🦽🦼🚻♿

Find out more: roundhouse@nationaltrust.org.uk

Roundhouse		M	T	W	T	F	S	S
8 May–31 Dec	10–4:30*		M	T	W	T	F	S	S

*Times may vary (please check before visiting).

National Trust
Partner

Birmingham partners

'National Trust Partner' is a new venture between the National Trust and a selection of small, independent heritage attractions and museums in Birmingham.

National Trust members will benefit from a 50 per cent discount on presentation of a valid membership card. For full visiting information and access, please see individual National Trust Partner websites.

Aston Hall

One of the last great Jacobean houses, the Hall was built by Sir Thomas Holte between 1618 and 1635. In 1858 it was opened by Queen Victoria as the first public museum in a country house.

Train: Aston or Witton

Find out more: 0121 348 8100 or bmag.enquiries@birminghammuseums.org.uk birminghammuseums.org.uk/aston

Blakesley Hall

One of Birmingham's finest timber-framed houses, Blakesley Hall was built in 1590 by merchant Richard Smalbroke and is a peaceful haven in this urban location.

Train: Stechford

Find out more: 0121 348 8120 or birminghammuseums.org.uk/blakesley

Coffin Works Museum

Newman Brothers produced the world's finest coffin fittings from 1894 until 1999. With everything preserved *in situ* when work stopped, this time capsule is now an award-winning museum. **Note**: run by Birmingham Conservation Trust.

Train: Birmingham New Street

Find out more: 0121 233 4785 or coffinworks.org

Sarehole Mill

The idyllic childhood haunt of J. R. R. Tolkien, Sarehole Mill is a unique setting where you can learn about the millers who once worked at this rural retreat.

Train: Hall Green

Find out more: 0121 348 8160 or birminghammuseums.org.uk/sarehole

The Museum of Jewellery Quarter

A remarkable time-capsule museum, where you can enjoy guided tours and demonstrations of traditional jewellery making.

Train: Jewellery Quarter

Find out more: 0121 348 8140 or birminghammuseums.org.uk/jewellery

Soho House

The elegant Georgian home of Birmingham's great industrial entrepreneur Matthew Boulton.

Train: Jewellery Quarter

Find out more: 0121 348 8150 or birminghammuseums.org.uk/soho

Brockhampton

Bringsty, near Bromyard,
Herefordshire WR6 5TB

🏠✝️♿✿♿🐕 1946

Parking: 100 yards and 1 mile.

More than 600 years ago the Dumbleton family built this moated manor house tucked away in a Herefordshire valley. Find out about the lives of the people who lived here and discover how what was once a grand medieval hall was slowly transformed into a modest home for farmers. In the wider estate there are walks through a farming landscape with parkland, hidden dingles, gushing streams and wild woodlands waiting to be discovered. Join us as we replant lost Victorian orchards and explore the origins of the humble apple in new outdoor 'orchard rooms', created in partnership with the local community.
Note: some walks include challenging terrain with steep slopes and muddy areas.

Eat, shop, stay: Old Apple Store tea-room serves light lunches, tea and cakes. Granary shop selling plants, gifts and local produce, with kiosk serving takeaway drinks and snacks. Second-hand bookshop. Three holiday cottages – sleeping three, five and 10.

Things to see and do: **Indoors** family activities and trails – historical demonstrations and conservation in action. **Outdoors** New 'orchard rooms', events, family trails and games. Natural play trail, orienteering and waymarked walks. Picnics welcome. **Dogs**: welcome on leads outdoors.

Access: 🅿️♿♿♿♿🏛️📷♿
Manor house ♿♿♿ Grounds ♿➡️♿

Find out more: 01885 482077 or brockhampton@nationaltrust.org.uk

Brockhampton		M	T	W	T	F	S	S
Estate								
Open all year	10–5	**M**	**T**	**W**	**T**	**F**	**S**	**S**
House, Granary shop and Old Apple Store tea-room								
4 Jan–9 Feb	10–3*	.	.	.	.	.	**S**	**S**
15 Feb–1 Nov	10–5*	**M**	**T**	**W**	**T**	**F**	**S**	**S**
7 Nov–27 Dec	10–3*	.	.	.	.	.	**S**	**S**

Everything closed 25 and 26 December.
*House and Granary shop open 11.

The pretty garden at Brockhampton in Herefordshire, below, and a view over the estate, above

Parking is free for members, but don't forget to scan your card in the car park when you visit

Carding Mill Valley and the Long Mynd

near Church Stretton, Shropshire

🏚️🖼️⛱️👣☂️ 1965

Satnav: use SY6 6JG. **Parking**: 50 yards.

At Carding Mill Valley you are suddenly in the heart of wild countryside (above). Here families can enjoy playing in the stream, a variety of walks and exploring. From the valley, head up to the top of the Long Mynd and be rewarded with views of Shropshire and beyond.

Eat, shop, stay: Chalet Pavilion tea-room and roof terrace in Carding Mill Valley serving hot lunches, afternoon teas, drinks and ice cream. Shop selling gifts, souvenirs, maps, pond nets.

Things to see and do: courses and family-friendly events all year. Free walks cards available in Carding Mill Valley.
Dogs: welcome on leads and under close control – seasonal access.

Access: 🅿️♿🪑🚻🛗🎧 **Building** 🏛️

Find out more: 01694 725000 or cardingmill@nationaltrust.org.uk

Carding Mill Valley		M	T	W	T	F	S	S
Tea-room								
1 Jan–14 Feb	10–4	M	T	W	T	F	S	S
15 Feb–1 Nov	10–5	M	T	W	T	F	S	S
2 Nov–31 Dec*	10–4	M	T	W	T	F	S	S
Shop								
1 Jan	11–4	·	·	W	·	·	·	·
4 Jan–9 Feb	10–4	·	·	·	·	·	S	S
15 Feb–1 Nov	11–5**	M	T	W	T	F	S	S
2 Nov–31 Dec*	11–4**	M	T	W	T	F	S	S

*Tea-room and shop: closed 25 December.
**Shop: opens 10 at weekends.

Charlecote Park

Wellesbourne, Warwick, Warwickshire CV35 9ER

🏚️✝️🖼️♿⛱️🚐 1946

Parking: 300 yards.

Charlecote Park was already in its middle age when Elizabeth I arrived 450 years ago, entering through the gatehouse and on to the welcoming red-brick mansion, just as you will today. A family home for more than eight centuries, it is a place of surprising treasures, with collections reflecting the tastes, lifestyle and varied fortunes of the Lucy family. Imagine the hum of activity of a working estate in the domestic 'below-stairs' spaces and in the laundry room and brewhouse in the courtyard. In the stables see the family's carriage collection, while in the parkland Jacob sheep and fallow deer roam across the 'Capability' Brown landscape, a haven for wildlife in which you can picnic and play, walk and wander.

Eat, shop, stay: variety of catering facilities, serving a range of meals and snacks. Servants' Hall shop and plant centre selling a range of Charlecote-specific, locally sourced produce and plants. Second-hand bookshop. Picnics welcome. Stay at Turret holiday flat (sleeps six).

Peaceful Charlecote Park in Warwickshire

Things to see and do: Indoors You can explore the three carriage houses, brewhouse, laundry and tack room and learn more in the introductory gatehouse timeline room. Visit the new livestock interpretation area in The Spinney. The house is festively decorated during December. **Outdoors** Why not take a walk through the wider parkland? Guided walks, talks and seasonal trails for all ages. **Dogs**: welcome on leads (designated areas).

Access: 🅿️♿🚻♿🔊♿📷🎧🚪🅰️◉
Building ♿♿♿ **Grounds** ♿➡️♿♿

Find out more: 01789 470277 or charlecotepark@nationaltrust.org.uk

Charlecote Park		M	T	W	T	F	S	S
Park, garden, cafés, shop and plant centre*								
1 Jan–14 Feb	9–4**	M	T	W	T	F	S	S
15 Feb–1 Nov	9–5**	M	T	W	T	F	S	S
2 Nov–31 Dec	9–4**	M	T	W	T	F	S	S
House†								
1 Jan–5 Jan	11–3:30			W	T	F	S	S
15 Feb–1 Nov††	11–3:30	M	T	W	T	F	S	S
7 Nov–22 Nov	11–3:30						S	S
28 Nov–31 Dec	11–3:30	M	T	W	T	F	S	S

*Shop and plant centre: open 10. **Park/garden: close dusk if earlier. †House: timed ticket admission; building works may impact access. ††House: Wednesday access by taster tours only (limited availability). Everything closed 25 December.

Charlecote Park: ornately carved chair in the Billiard Room, opposite, and discovering the garden, below

Clent Hills

near Romsley, Worcestershire

🏛️♿ 1959

Satnav: use B62 0NL for Nimmings Wood entrance. **Parking**: at Nimmings Wood; additional parking at Adam's Hill and Walton Hill. Please note the gates at Nimmings Wood are locked daily with no out-of-hours service – vehicles cannot be retrieved once the gates are locked.

Set on the edge of Birmingham and the Black Country, this green oasis with panoramic views (above) is the perfect place for a refreshing walk or a picnic on a sunny day. Families can create their own adventures – building dens, hunting for geocaches or simply getting closer to nature. **Note**: nearest facilities at Nimmings Wood entrance.

Eat, shop, stay: popular café at Nimmings Wood car park (not National Trust) serving freshly prepared food with locally sourced ingredients, drinks, ice cream and homemade cakes (sorry no cards).

Things to see and do: events all year, including guided rambles and family activities. Natural play area and play trails. **Dogs**: welcome, but must be on a lead on the easy access path, natural play and café areas.

Access: 🅿️♿🎧➡️

Find out more: 01562 887912 or clenthills@nationaltrust.org.uk

Clent Hills

Nimmings Wood car park: open 9 to 5, 1 March to 31 October; to 4 at all other times. Café open 10 to 4. Everything closed 25 December.

Coughton Court

Alcester, Warwickshire B49 5JA

🏠✝♿🏚🍴 1946

Parking: 150 yards.

Coughton has been home to the Throckmorton family for more than 600 years. Facing persecution for their Catholic faith, they were willing to risk everything. You can discover their story and find out about a family's struggles, perseverance and intrigues, including their link to the infamous Gunpowder Plot. Coughton is very much a family home with an intimate feel. The Throckmorton family still live here and they created and manage the gardens, including a riverside walk, bog garden and beautiful display of roses in the walled garden. **Note**: picnics welcome in the three fenced picnic areas only (none in the formal gardens please).

Eat, shop, stay: Coughton Café serving lunch, cakes and teas. Drinks and ice cream available from the Stableyard Coffee Bar during busy periods. Coach House shop selling local food and seasonal gifts. Throckmorton family plant sales. Second-hand bookshop. Three picnic areas.

Things to see and do: **Indoors** Children's trail. Paintings guide. **Outdoors** Wide selection of talks. Walking trails around the surrounding countryside. Woodland play, children's play house and outdoor games. **Dogs**: welcome on leads in car park and public footpaths.

Access: 🅿♿🚻♿♿🎦📷🎧⬤
House 🔲♿♿ **Grounds** 🔲➡♿

Find out more: 01789 400777 or coughtoncourt@nationaltrust.org.uk

Coughton Court		M	T	W	T	F	S	S
House, shop, café and grounds*								
29 Feb–29 Mar**	11–4	·	·	·	T	F	S	S
1 Apr–5 Jul	11–5	·	·	W	T	F	S	S
7 Jul–6 Sep	11–5	·	T	W	T	F	S	S
9 Sep–4 Oct	11–5	·	·	W	T	F	S	S
8 Oct–1 Nov	11–4	·	·	·	T	F	S	S

*Walled garden: opens at 12. **Grounds closed. Open Bank Holiday Mondays. Everything closed for private Throckmorton family days on 16 May, 25 July, 19 and 20 September. House admission by timed ticket (not bookable).

Coughton Court, Warwickshire, clockwise from above: the drawing room, parkland and beautiful walled garden

Croft Castle and Parkland

near Leominster, Herefordshire

🏠🏰✝🏛⚙🏊🐾🖼🍽 1957

Satnav: use HR6 0BL. **Parking**: 100 yards.

This intimate house became the Croft family home before the Domesday Book. Its walls conceal a rich and turbulent history, with many compelling 20th-century stories to uncover. The interiors, styled by Thomas Farnolls Pritchard, also tell an 18th- and 19th-century tale. You can take your dog for a stroll to the Iron Age hill fort, exploring the historic parkland with ancient trees along the way, and discover new views and walks in Fishpool Valley as we continue our restoration project. Croft Castle is a place to immerse yourself in 1,000 years of power, politics and pleasure.

Eat, shop, stay: tea-room (licensed) serving food made using garden produce – hot lunches, cakes and ice cream. Children's lunchboxes and half portions. Shop selling gifts, plants, home and garden products. Second-hand bookshop. Picnic area. Garden and Ambrey holiday cottages for a longer stay.

Things to see and do: **Indoors** Games, interactive memorabilia and dressing up. **Outdoors** Family activities, living history, open-air theatre, seasonal events. Natural and castle-inspired play areas. Walks, dog-walking, information barn and orienteering. **Dogs**: welcome on leads in garden, parkland, shop and glazed area of tea-room.

Access: 🅿️♿🚻🚼🦽👓🖐🎫
Castle 🔦♿♿ **Grounds** ♿➡🦽♿

Find out more: 01568 780246 or croftcastle@nationaltrust.org.uk Yarpole, near Leominster, Herefordshire HR6 9PW

Croft Castle		M	T	W	T	F	S	S
Castle, tea-room, garden, shop and parkland								
4 Jan–9 Feb	10–4*	·	·	·	·	·	S	S
15 Feb–1 Nov	10–5*	M	T	W	T	F	S	S
7 Nov–20 Dec	10–4*	·	·	·	·	·	S	S
Tea-room, garden, shop and parkland								
27 Dec–31 Dec	10–4*	M	T	W	·	·	·	·

Tea-room, garden, shop and parkland: also open 1 January, 10 to 4. *Castle and shop: open 11. Play area: open as parkland.

Croft Castle and Parkland, Herefordshire, above and below

Croome

near High Green, Worcester,
Worcestershire WR8 9DW

🏠 ✝ ♣ ♨ 🔔 | 1996 |

Satnav: follow signs from main road,
not satnav. **Parking**: on site.

There's more than meets the eye at Croome.
A secret wartime airbase, now a visitor centre
and museum, was once a hub of activity for
thousands of people. Outside is the grandest
of English landscapes, 'Capability' Brown's
masterful first commission, with commanding
views over the Malverns. The parkland, nearly
lost but now restored, is great for walks and
adventures with a surprise around every
corner. At the heart of the park lies Croome
Court, once home to the Earls of Coventry.
The 6th Earl was an 18th-century trendsetter,
and today Croome follows his lead, using
artists and craftspeople to tell the story of its
eclectic past in inventive ways. Explore four
floors of the mansion, perfect for making new
discoveries. **Note**: walled gardens, privately
owned (admission charge towards their
restoration, including members), open days
throughout the year.

The imposing mansion at Croome in Worcestershire

Eat, shop, stay: restaurant, gift shop, Gardener's Bothy plant shop and second-hand bookshop at the visitor centre. Tea-room serving light lunches in Croome Court's basement.

Things to see and do: **Indoors** Contemporary exhibitions, including select pieces from the collection and creative installations. All four floors of the house are open, some areas by guided tour. RAF Defford Museum at the visitor centre. **Outdoors** Acres of parkland to explore. Regular guided tours of the park and outer eye-catcher open days. Special family trails around park every school holiday. RAF-themed playground, natural play area and bird hide close to the visitor centre. Walled gardens to explore. **Dogs**: welcome on leads in garden and wider estate.

Croome: the Chinese Bridge, left, and the Rotunda, above, within 'Capability' Brown's masterful first commission

Access: 🅿️♿🚾🏛️🔲🎫👁️ 🖼️
House 🔲🏛️♿ Park ▶️🚶♿

Find out more: 01905 371006 or croome@nationaltrust.org.uk

Croome		M	T	W	T	F	S	S
House								
1 Jan–14 Feb	11–4	M	T	W	T	F	S	S
15 Feb–1 Nov	11–4:30	M	T	W	T	F	S	S
2 Nov–31 Dec*	11–4	M	T	W	T	F	S	S
Park, restaurant, shop and RAF Museum								
1 Jan–14 Feb	10–4	M	T	W	T	F	S	S
15 Feb–1 Nov	10–5	M	T	W	T	F	S	S
2 Nov–31 Dec*	10–4	M	T	W	T	F	S	S

*Everything closed 24 and 25 December.

Cwmmau Farmhouse

Brilley, Whitney-on-Wye,
Herefordshire HR3 6JP 1965

A charming 17th-century timbered farmhouse
with many original features and stunning
views across Herefordshire. **Note**: open daily,
19 to 25 June, 11:30 to 4:30.

Find out more: 01568 780246 or
cwmmaufarmhouse@nationaltrust.org.uk

Downs Banks

Washdale Lane, Oulton Heath, near Stone,
Staffordshire 1950

A little wilderness of woodlands and heath,
with easy access walks, in the heart
of the Midlands. **Note**: sorry no toilets.
Some steep paths.

Find out more: 01889 880160 or
downsbanks@nationaltrust.org.uk

Steeped in history but shaped by modern
tastes, Dudmaston in Shropshire, this page and right,
offers something to appeal to every age group

Dudmaston

Quatt, near Bridgnorth, Shropshire WV15 6QN

🏠 ♿ 🍽️ 🅿️ 1978

Parking: Dudmaston Hall car park (seasonal)
and pay and display car parks in Comer Woods,
Hampton Loade and the Sawmill.

Stretching across 1,214 hectares (3,000 acres)
of ancient woodland and park, Dudmaston is a
working estate with a family home at its heart.
Steeped in history but shaped by modern
tastes and radical thinking, it is a delightful
collision of unexpected contrasts. From the
picturesque dingle, to the remarkable pieces
by Moore and Matisse in the galleries, art has
always found a home here. Discover modern
sculpture in the garden or find a tranquil
spot to take in the views over the pool.
Explore the wider estate all year, with walks
from Comer Woods, Hampton Loade and
Sawmill. **Note**: the family home of
Mr and Mrs Mark Hamilton-Russell.

Eat, shop, stay: Orchard Tea-room offering lunches and cakes and a seasonal ice-cream parlour. Food outlet in Comer Woods open weekends and school holidays. Gift shop selling locally sourced items and plants. Second-hand bookshop. Holiday cottage and bunkhouse for rent.

Things to see and do: **Indoors** Historical family rooms, as well as modern, Spanish and botanical art collections, with guided art tours. **Outdoors** Garden tours, woodland playground and year-round walking and cycling trails. **Dogs**: welcome on leads in dingle and orchard.

Access:
Building **Grounds**

Find out more: 01746 780866 or dudmaston@nationaltrust.org.uk

Dudmaston		M	T	W	T	F	S	S
Park, tea-room and shop								
15 Feb–23 Feb*	11–4	·	·	·	·	·	**S**	**S**
15 Mar–31 Mar	11–4:30	**M**	**T**	**W**	**T**	·	·	**S**
1 Apr–30 Sep**	11–5	**M**	**T**	**W**	**T**	·	·	**S**
1 Oct–29 Oct	11–4:30	**M**	**T**	**W**	**T**	·	·	**S**
1 Nov–29 Nov	11–4	·	·	·	·	·	**S**	**S**
Galleries								
15 Mar–31 Mar	12:30–4	**M**	**T**	**W**	**T**	·	·	**S**
1 Oct–29 Oct	12:30–4	**M**	**T**	**W**	**T**	·	·	**S**
Hall and galleries								
1 Apr–30 Sep	12:30–4:30	**M**	**T**	**W**	**T**	·	·	**S**
Garden								
15 Mar–29 Oct†	11:30–4:30	**M**	**T**	**W**	**T**	·	·	**S**

*Dingle walks only. **Open Bank Holiday 8 May.
†April to September: garden closes at 5.

Farnborough Hall

Farnborough, near Banbury, Warwickshire OX17 1DU 1960

Carolean house with exquisite plasterwork and grand stairway. Set in landscaped gardens with a mile-long terrace walk and parkland views. **Note**: occupied and administered by the Holbech family. Open Wednesday and Saturday, 1 April to 30 September, 2 to 5:30. Also open 24 and 25 May.

Find out more: 01295 670266 (option six) or farnboroughhall@nationaltrust.org.uk

The Firs – Birthplace of Edward Elgar

Crown East Lane, Lower Broadheath, Worcester, Worcestershire WR2 6RH

🏠 ❀ ☂ 2017

Parking: on site.

Family treasures tell the story of Sir Edward Elgar's humble beginnings in the family cottage. Learn more about Elgar's inspiration in the modern visitor centre (three exhibition spaces). Outside, the cottage garden is the perfect place to sit and reflect on the life of this great composer and his works.

Eat, shop, stay: tea-room with outdoor courtyard dining area serving soup, sandwiches, seasonal food, cakes and scones freshly baked throughout day. Shop selling gifts, plants, books and Elgar-related souvenirs. Second-hand bookshop. Picnics welcome.

Things to see and do: 'All you need to write a symphony' exhibition. Live music performances and lectures throughout the year. **Dogs**: welcome on leads; assistance dogs only in cottage and tea-room.

The Firs – Birthplace of Edward Elgar in Worcestershire

The Firs: a humble cottage yet birthplace of a great man

Access: 👁️‍🗨️ icons
Visitor centre 👥 icons
Cottage 👥 icons Garden 👥 icons

Find out more: 01905 333330 or thefirs@nationaltrust.org.uk

The Firs		M	T	W	T	F	S	S
1 Jan–10 Jan	10–4	M	T	W	T	F	S	S
11 Jan–16 Feb	10–4	.	.	.	.	.	S	S
17 Feb–30 Oct	10–5	M	T	W	T	F	S	S
31 Oct–20 Dec	10–4	.	.	.	.	.	S	S
21 Dec–31 Dec*	10–4	M	T	W	T	F	S	S

*Closed 24 and 25 December.

The Fleece Inn

Bretforton, near Evesham, Worcestershire WR11 7JE 1978

Medieval half-timbered longhouse, now a traditional village inn, with barn and orchard. Known for folk music, Morris dancing and asparagus. **Note**: open daily, 10 to 11 (reduced opening 25 December).

Find out more: 01386 831173 or fleeceinn@nationaltrust.org.uk

Greyfriars' House and Garden

Friar Street, Worcester,
Worcestershire WR1 2LZ

🏠❄🔔 1966

Parking: none on site, nearest at nearby St Martins Gate, King Street and Cathedral Plaza car parks, not National Trust (charge including members).

Set in the heart of historic Worcester, this timber-framed house, built in the 1490s, reflected the fortunes of its surroundings for centuries until it was rescued and carefully restored by the Matley-Moores. Now you can explore 500 years of history through the lens of an unusual brother and sister.

Eat, shop, stay: small café in house, leading onto garden terrace, serving sandwiches, cakes, scones, ice cream and drinks. Small gift shop and second-hand bookshop.

Things to see and do: **Indoors** Themed events throughout the year, including house tours. Children's trails. **Outdoors** Garden games and geocaching. **Dogs**: welcome in garden.

Access: 🏠📶 House 🔆🏛🎫🐾

Find out more: 01905 23571 or greyfriars@nationaltrust.org.uk

Greyfriars' House		M	T	W	T	F	S	S
11 Feb–29 Mar	11–4*	·		T	W	T	F	S	S
31 Mar–25 Oct	11–5*	·		T	W	T	F	S	S
27 Oct–13 Dec	11–4*	·		T	W	T	F	S	S

*House: taster tours only, 11 to 1, places allocated on arrival; freeflow from 1. Open Bank Holiday Mondays.

Hanbury Hall

School Road, Hanbury, Droitwich Spa, Worcestershire WR9 7EA

🏠❄🍴🛏🍷 1953

Parking: 150 yards.

Georgian Hanbury Hall in Worcestershire

A country retreat in the heart of Worcestershire. The house and garden, originally a stage-set for summer parties, offer a glimpse into life at the turn of the 18th century. Don't miss the original wall-paintings by Sir James Thornhill; full of drama and politics, they show the birth of Georgian society. The original formal gardens, designed by George London, have been faithfully recreated and complement the relaxed later gardens, with orangery, orchards and walled garden. If you venture further afield, our walks into the parkland will lead you into the remains of ancient forests and historic avenues.

Eat, shop, stay: choice of catering facilities, serving a range of meals, snacks and pre-bookable afternoon tea. Shop selling a range of locally sourced products and plants. Make Hanbury a home from home in one of two holiday cottages.

Live theatre, above and below, at Hanbury Hall

Hawford Dovecote

Hawford, Worcestershire WR3 7SG 1973

Picturesque dovecote, which has survived virtually unaltered since the late 16th century, retaining many nesting boxes. **Note**: sorry no toilets or tea-room. Please park carefully to one side of Chatley Lane without obstructing any private access. Open daily, dawn to dusk.

Find out more: 01527 821214 or hawforddovecote@nationaltrust.org.uk

Kinver Edge and the Rock Houses

near Stourbridge, Staffordshire

1917

Kinver Edge and the Rock Houses, Staffordshire: two views

Things to see and do: spend perfect days picnicking and playing on sweeping lawns, surrounded by rolling Worcestershire countryside. For those seeking a more adventurous day, enjoy estate walks or 10k runs through the parkland. **Dogs**: welcome on leads in the parkland and in stableyard.

Access: 🅿️🅿️♿🧺📷🏞️📶🚽
Building 🅰️🅰️♿ Grounds 🅰️🅰️➡️🦽

Find out more: 01527 821214 or hanburyhall@nationaltrust.org.uk

Hanbury Hall	
Open every day all year*	9–5**

*Closed 22 and 23 January; 24 and 25 December.
**Closes dusk if earlier. Shop: opens 10. House: opens at 11; last entry depends on dusk (check on arrival).

Satnav: use DY7 6DL for Rock Houses.
Parking: for the Rock Houses park in lay-by on Compton Road or in the overflow car park on Kingsford Lane. For the wider countryside, either park in lay-by on Comber Road or in the car park with toilets on Kingsford Lane.

At the Holy Austin Rock Houses discover surprisingly cosy homes carved into the rock of an imposing sandstone ridge. Walks in the surrounding countryside of Kinver Edge cross open heathland, buzzing with wildlife, and woodland trails leading to further rock houses nestled among the trees. Dramatic views across three counties.

Eat, shop, stay: quirky tea-room inside a rock house with wood-burning stove, serving sandwiches, soup, cakes, scones and drinks. Seating outside with expansive views across surrounding countryside. Small shop and second-hand bookshop.

Things to see and do: Indoors Traditional toys, rag-rugging and free weekday tours (term-time). **Outdoors** Natural play-trail, woodland rock house and Iron Age hill fort. Family events all year. **Dogs**: welcome on leads in gardens of Rock Houses and countryside.

Access: ⓟ♿ **Restored Rock Houses** ♿ **Tea-room and toilets** ♿ **Gardens** ♿

Find out more: 01384 872553 or kinveredge@nationaltrust.org.uk Holy Austin Rock Houses, Compton Road, Kinver, near Stourbridge, Staffordshire DY7 6DL

Kinver Edge		M	T	W	T	F	S	S
4 Jan–9 Feb	11–3	.	.	.	.	.	S	S
15 Feb–1 Nov	11–4*	M	.	.	T	F	S	S
7 Nov–20 Dec	11–3	.	.	.	.	.	S	S

*Open every day during local school holidays.

Kinwarton Dovecote

Kinwarton, near Alcester,
Warwickshire B49 6HB 1958

Rare 14th-century circular dovecote with metre-thick walls, hundreds of nesting holes and original rotating ladder. **Note**: livestock may be grazing. Sorry no toilet. Limited parking (not National Trust). Open daily, 29 February to 1 November, 9 to 5.

Find out more: 01789 400777 or kinwartondovecote@nationaltrust.org.uk

Knowles Mill

Dowles Brook, Bewdley,
Worcestershire DY12 2LX 1938

Eighteenth-century mill retaining much of its machinery, including the frames of an overshot waterwheel. **Note**: Mill Cottage not open to visitors (please respect the resident's privacy). Sorry no toilets or tea-room. No parking at Mill Cottage. Open daily, dawn to dusk.

Find out more: 01527 821214 or knowlesmill@nationaltrust.org.uk

Letocetum Roman Baths and Museum

Watling Street, Wall, near Lichfield,
Staffordshire WS14 0AW 1934

Open-air remains of a once-important Roman staging post and settlement, including *mansio* (Roman inn) and bathhouse. **Note**: in the guardianship of English Heritage. Baths accessible all year. Museum open last weekend of month, March to October. Extra openings during August and for some Bank Holidays.

Find out more: 0370 333 1181 (English Heritage) or letocetum@nationaltrust.org.uk

Middle Littleton Tithe Barn

Middle Littleton, Evesham,
Worcestershire WR11 8LN 1975

Largest and finest restored 13th-century tithe barn in the country. **Note**: sorry no toilets. Open daily, 1 April to 31 October, 10 to 5.

Find out more: 01905 371006 or middlelittleton@nationaltrust.org.uk

Morville Hall

Morville, near Bridgnorth,
Shropshire WV16 5NB 1965

Elizabethan gem with a Georgian makeover.
Enchanting gardens spill down to the Mor
Brook against the backdrop of Shropshire hills.
Note: property contents are a mix of items
on loan and tenant's own. Open Friday and
Saturday, 15 and 16 May, 12 and 13 June,
10 and 11 July, 11 and 12 September, 12 to 5.
Dower House gardens opened independently
by Dr K. Swift on Sundays, Wednesdays and
Bank Holiday Mondays, 1 April to 30 September
(telephone 01746 714407 for details).

Find out more: 01746 780866 (Dudmaston
Hall) or morvillehall@nationaltrust.org.uk

Moseley Old Hall

Moseley Old Hall Lane, Fordhouses,
Wolverhampton, Staffordshire WV10 7HY

1962

Parking: on site.

This atmospheric farmhouse, built circa 1600,
holds many secrets. Charles II hid here after
escaping the 1651 Battle of Worcester. Inside,
a log fire crackles as 17th-century domestic life
surrounds you. Outside, explore the walled
garden, containing herbs and vegetables,
the orchard and knot garden. Beyond is
King's Walk Wood.

Moseley Old Hall, Staffordshire: a place of secrets

Eat, shop, stay: tea-room serving soup
and seasonal specials. Cakes and scones
baked all day. Accessible kiosk offering
range of takeaway refreshments and
ice cream. Shop selling gifts and plants.
Second-hand bookshop.

Things to see and do: Indoors Specialist
talks, tours and interactive demonstrations
recreating 17th-century life. **Outdoors** Seasonal
events, children's activities, two-level tree hide,
den-building, rope swings, trails. Wightwick
Manor nearby. **Dogs**: welcome on leads in
garden and grounds.

Access: [icons] Hall [icons]
Tea-room [icons] Garden and woodland [icons]

Find out more: 01902 782808 or
moseleyoldhall@nationaltrust.org.uk

Moseley Old Hall		M	T	W	T	F	S	S
10 Feb–28 Mar	10–4	M	T	W	T	F	S	S
29 Mar–30 Oct	10–5	M	T	W	T	F	S	S
31 Oct–21 Dec	10–4	M	·	·	·	F	S	S
27 Dec–31 Dec	10–3	M	T	W	T	·	·	S

House: opens 11; entry at very busy times by timed ticket;
February, March, November and December: access to top
floor may be limited for safety.

Packwood House

Packwood Lane, Lapworth,
Warwickshire B94 6AT

1941

Parking: 150 yards.

Surrounded by beautiful gardens and
countryside, Packwood was described by a
guest in the 1930s as 'a house to dream of,
a garden to dream in'. Lovingly restored at
the beginning of the 20th century by Graham
Baron Ash, you can discover the detail behind
the man, his passion for collecting and his
collection. The gardens include brightly
coloured, 'mingled style' herbaceous borders,
famous sculpted yews and an 18th-century
gentleman's kitchen garden.

**Packwood House, Warwickshire: exploring the grounds,
bottom right, and the lovingly restored house, top right**

Eat, shop, stay: Garden Kitchen café serving hot food, sandwiches and cakes. Catering trailer open during busy periods. Shop selling gifts, local foods and many plants (some grown on site). Picnics welcome by the lake, barnyard and picnic area by car park.

Things to see and do: **Indoors** Children's trail in the house. **Outdoors** Welcome and garden talks, countryside walks and natural play. Areas of the gardens may be closed (please call before travelling). **Dogs**: welcome in the barnyard, park footpaths and café terrace.

Access: ⬚⬚⬚⬚⬚⬚
House ⬚⬚⬚ **Grounds** ⬚⬚⬚

Find out more: 01564 782024 or packwood@nationaltrust.org.uk

Packwood House		M	T	W	T	F	S	S
1 Jan–14 Feb	9–4*	M	T	W	T	F	S	S
15 Feb–1 Nov	9–5**	M	T	W	T	F	S	S
2 Nov–31 Dec	9–4*	M	T	W	T	F	S	S

10 to 13 April (Easter): admission by bookable tickets only, limited (including members). House: admission by timed ticket (not bookable). *House and formal gardens: open 11, last entrance to house at 3. **House and formal gardens: open at 11. Closed 24 and 25 December.

Rosedene

Victoria Road, Dodford, near Bromsgrove, Worcestershire B61 9BU 1997

Restored 1840s cottage with an organic garden and orchard, illustrating the mid-19th-century Chartist movement. **Note**: available to hire as a 'back to basics' holiday cottage. Admission by guided tour on the first Sunday of month, March to December (booking essential).

Find out more: 01527 821214 or rosedene@nationaltrust.org.uk

Shugborough Estate

Milford, near Stafford, Staffordshire ST17 0UP

🏠🏛️🛗🌼🎣🐾 1966

Parking: 25 yards from reception.

Shaped by its illustrious and maritime history, Shugborough embodies utility, style, grandeur and comfort, a rich blend of landscape gardens and architecture. Join us on an exciting journey as the estate rejuvenates itself over the years and the stories and histories that led to it being described as a 'perfect paradise' are uncovered. You can explore the sweeping parkland, wander through a landscape peppered with monuments and discover the Park Farm, created at the cutting-edge of agricultural reforms. In the Georgian mansion, unearth prized treasures and experience life 'below stairs', then enter a world of glamour and royalty in the apartment of Patrick Lichfield, 5th Earl and fashion photographer.

Eat, shop, stay: delicious treats and meals on offer at the mansion tea-room and Park Farm Café. Why not visit the shop or plant centre and pick up the perfect gift or take home some produce from the walled garden?

Shugborough Estate in Staffordshire: the east front of the mansion, below, and Hadrian's Arch, above

Things to see and do: Indoors There are stories of adventure, travels and triumphs to discover in the mansion. **Outdoors** New estate walks to explore and wonderful views from the Triumphal Arch to enjoy plus explorers' wood natural play area for children. **Dogs**: welcome on leads in formal gardens and parkland.

Access: 🅿️♿🚌♿🚻♿🖼️♿
House 🖼️♿🚻♿ Grounds 🖼️➡️♿

Find out more: 01889 880160 or
shugborough@nationaltrust.org.uk

Discovering the parkland, above, and walled garden,
below, on the Shugborough Estate

Shugborough Estate		M	T	W	T	F	S	S
Park, gardens and Park Farm*								
1 Jan–14 Feb	9–4	M	T	W	T	F	S	S
15 Feb–23 Oct	9–6	M	T	W	T	F	S	S
24 Oct–31 Dec	9–4	M	T	W	T	F	S	S
Servants' quarters								
15 Feb–23 Oct	11–4:30	M	T	W	T	F	S	S
24 Oct–31 Dec	11–3:30	M	T	W	T	F	S	S
Mansion								
16 Mar–23 Oct	11–4:30	M	T	W	T	F	S	S
24 Oct–1 Nov	11–3:30	M	T	W	T	F	S	S
28 Nov–23 Dec	11–3:30	M	T	W	T	F	S	S
Lichfield apartment****								
16 Feb–15 Mar	11–4:30	M	T					S
16 Mar–23 Oct	11–4:30	M	T	W	T	F	S	S
24 Oct–1 Nov	11–3:30	M	T	W	T	F	S	S
Tea-room and shop								
1 Jan–14 Feb	10–4	M	T	W	T	F	S	S
15 Feb–23 Oct	10–5	M	T	W	T	F	S	S
24 Oct–31 Dec	10–4	M	T	W	T	F	S	S

*Walled garden and visitor reception: open as park,
gardens and Park Farm. **Lichfield apartment entry by
timed ticket only. Closed 25 December.

Sunnycroft

Wellington, near Telford, Shropshire

🏠❄️ 1999

Satnav: use TF1 2DP (exit seven from M54). **Parking**: 150 yards.

Hidden down an avenue of towering redwoods is this 'estate in miniature' sitting in the middle of suburbia. This rare survival of a Victorian red-brick villa (above), glasshouses and more, is a time capsule of a particular way of life. Sunnycroft is a family home that envelopes you in times past. **Note**: in February and March some parts of house may be closed due to rewiring.

Eat, shop, stay: small tea-room serving soup, sandwiches, cakes, scones, ice cream and drinks. Picnics welcome on lawn. Shop in the historic kitchen selling gifts, seasonal plants, produce and second-hand books.

Things to see and do: Indoors Introductory talks, guided tours, workshops, family activities and trails reveal stories of life at Sunnycroft. **Outdoors** Family trails, garden games and tours. Seasonal events. **Dogs**: welcome on leads in grounds only.

Access: 🅿️♿🚻🏠📷♿
Building ♿🏠 Grounds ♿♿➡️

Find out more: 01952 242884 or sunnycroft@nationaltrust.org.uk
200 Holyhead Road, Wellington, near Telford, Shropshire TF1 2DR

Sunnycroft		M	T	W	T	F	S	S
15 Feb–23 Feb	10:30–4	M	T	.	.	F	S	S
29 Feb–22 Mar	10:30–4	.	.	.	.	.	S	S
28 Mar–1 Nov	10:30–5	M	T	.	.	F	S	S
28 Nov–22 Dec	10:30–4	M	T	.	.	F	S	S

House: last admission one hour before closing.
Last service in tea-room 30 minutes before closing.

Upton House and Gardens

near Banbury, Warwickshire OX15 6HT

🏠❄️👜🔔☕ 1948

Satnav: on arrival follow brown signs to car park. **Parking**: 300 yards.

In 1927 Lord and Lady Bearsted extensively remodelled Upton House to create the perfect country residence for their family. Alongside spaces to showcase a world-class art and porcelain collection, including works by Bosch, Stubbs and El Greco, the gardens were altered to make the most of their position. Located on the edge of an ice-age valley, the gardens drop away from the south lawn down towards the Mirror Pool. They give you the opportunity to step away from busy lives as you meander past the borders, each of which has been planted to be at its seasonal best.
Note: steep paths and open water.

Eat, shop, stay: hot meals, sandwiches and cakes available from The Pavilion (licensed), made using seasonal produce from the gardens. Shop selling plants and mementoes of your visit. Second-hand bookshop. Two holiday cottages; one with 1930s décor and one overlooking the gardens.

Upton House and Gardens, Warwickshire, below and right

Things to see and do: Indoors World-class art and porcelain collection. Changing exhibitions and topical tours. Activities and workshops. **Outdoors** Woodland walk and quiet orchard. Seasonal planting schemes, garden chats and events. **Dogs**: assistance dogs only.

Access: ♿🅿️♿🌳♿💬🚪♪
House and gallery ♿♿♿ Grounds ♿♿♿

Find out more: 01295 670266 or uptonhouse@nationaltrust.org.uk

Upton House		M	T	W	T	F	S	S
House								
4 Jan–26 Jan	12–4	·	·	·	·	·	S	S
1 Feb–1 Nov	11–4	M	T	W	T	F	S	S
2 Nov–27 Nov	12–4	M	·	·	·	F	S	S
28 Nov–23 Dec	12–4	M	T	W	T	F	S	S
Gardens, café and shop*								
1 Jan–3 Jan	12–4	·	·	W	T	F	·	·
4 Jan–26 Jan	12–4	·	·	·	·	·	S	S
1 Feb–1 Nov	10:30–5**	M	T	W	T	F	S	S
2 Nov–27 Nov	12–4	M	·	·	·	F	S	S
28 Nov–23 Dec	12–5†	M	T	W	T	F	S	S
26 Dec–31 Dec	12–5	M	T	W	T	·	S	S

*November to March: gardens open by winter walk only.
**Gardens, café and shop open at 10 at weekends.
†Gardens close at 4 in December.

The Weir Garden

Swainshill, Hereford, Herefordshire HR4 7QF

🏛️❄️♿ 1959

Parking: on site.

Whatever the season, the natural beauty of this riverside garden is completely captivating. During spring, the ground beneath the ancient trees is carpeted with bulbs; then, in summer, a picnic by the river while watching the wildlife is irresistible. Autumn brings an abundance of seasonal produce in the walled garden.
Note: sturdy footwear recommended.

Eat, shop, stay: self-service tea and coffee available. Picnics welcome.

Things to see and do: events, including walks and talks. Historical secrets to discover, from giant fish to Roman remains. Natural play area and family trails during school holidays.
Dogs: assistance dogs only (dogs welcome in car park).

Access: ♿ Grounds ♿♿

Find out more: 01981 590509 or theweir@nationaltrust.org.uk

The Weir Garden		M	T	W	T	F	S	S
18 Jan–26 Jan	10:30–3:30	·	·	·	·	·	S	S
27 Jan–1 Nov	10:30–4:30	M	T	W	T	F	S	S
7 Nov–13 Dec	10:30–3:30	·	·	·	·	·	S	S

Spring at The Weir Garden in Herefordshire

Wenlock Edge

Shropshire 1981

A ribbon of ancient woodland along a narrow limestone escarpment, with flower-rich grasslands, old quarries, lime kilns and views across Shropshire. **Note**: some steep paths and steps. Nearest toilets in Much Wenlock. Satnav – use TF13 6AS for Much Wenlock and TF13 6DQ for Presthope car parks. Much Wenlock car park closes at dusk.

Find out more: 01694 725000 or wenlockedge@nationaltrust.org.uk

Wichenford Dovecote

Wichenford, Worcestershire WR6 6XY 1965

Small but striking 17th-century half-timbered dovecote at Wichenford Court.
Note: no access to Wichenford Court (privately owned). Sorry no toilet or tea-room. Please consider local residents when parking. Open every day all year, dawn to dusk.

Find out more: 01527 821214 or wichenforddovecote@nationaltrust.org.uk

Wightwick Manor and Gardens, West Midlands, this page and right: a place of social activism and astounding art

Wightwick Manor and Gardens

Bridgnorth Road, Wolverhampton, West Midlands WV6 8BN

1937

Parking: entrance off A454.

A place where liberal dreams for the future mix with a love for unfashionable art. The Mander family's political ideals inspired them to share their home and fill it with art for the nation to enjoy. Their belief in social activism, the right to roam, fairness for their employees and confronting fascism combines with a home bursting with works by the greatest artists of the pre-Raphaelites and Arts and Crafts movement. A house of colour and comfort; a garden of yew and roses; and a gallery of De Morgan treasures – the legacy of one remarkable family and their friends.

Eat, shop, stay: specialist shop selling William Morris and Arts and Crafts-inspired ranges with plant centre. Tea-room serving breakfast, light lunches, sandwiches and sweet treats.

Things to see and do: **Indoors** World-class art collection, specialist talks and tours available all year. Malthouse gallery with De Morgan Collection exhibition. **Outdoors** Natural woodland play areas, trails, seasonal events and open-air theatre. **Dogs**: welcome on leads in garden.

Access: [access symbols]
Manor [symbols] Malthouse [symbols]
Gardens [symbols]

Find out more: 01902 761400 or wightwickmanor@nationaltrust.org.uk Wightwick Bank, Wolverhampton, West Midlands WV6 8EE

Wightwick Manor		M	T	W	T	F	S	S
1 Jan–28 Mar*	10–4**	M	T	W	T	F	S	S
29 Mar–24 Oct*	10–5†	M	T	W	T	F	S	S
25 Oct–31 Dec*	10–4	M	T	W	T	F	S	S

*House: opens 11, entry by tour only 11 to 12; freeflow from 12. **January to March: fewer rooms open. Last entry to house one hour before closing. Shop and gallery: open 10:30. †Gardens and tea-room: open 9:30, 1 June to 31 August. Closed 25 and 26 December.

Wilderhope Manor

Longville, Much Wenlock, Shropshire TF13 6EG 1936

Charming Elizabethan manor house with commanding views across a secluded valley with many original features inside and lovely walks outside. **Note**: Youth Hostel, access may be restricted. Open 2 to 4 on Sunday, 5 January to 29 March and 4 October to 20 December; also Wednesday and Sunday, 1 April to 30 September.

Find out more: 01694 771363 (Hostel Warden YHA) or wilderhope@nationaltrust.org.uk

Additional countryside car parks in the West Midlands

Ignore satnav when close and follow signs

| Hawksmoor | ST10 3AW |
| Comer Wood (Dudmaston) | WV15 6QL |

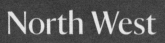

North West

Swimmers get set to brave the
waves at Formby, Liverpool

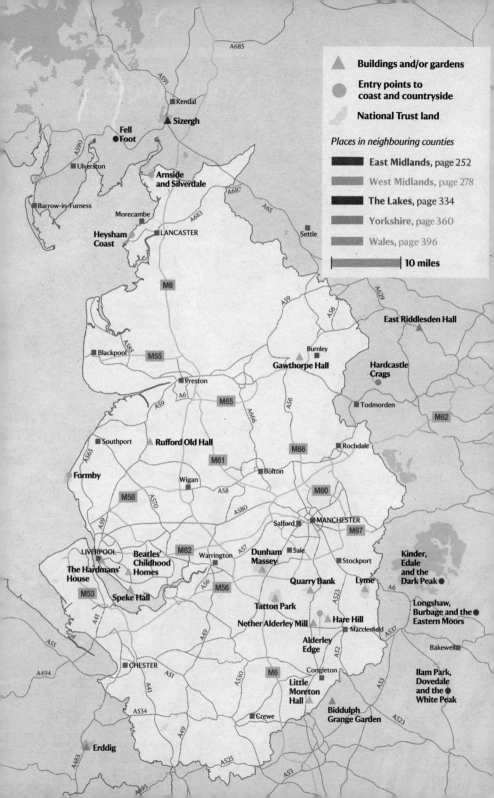

Buildings and/or gardens

Entry points to coast and countryside

National Trust land

Places in neighbouring counties

East Midlands, page 252

West Midlands, page 278

The Lakes, page 334

Yorkshire, page 360

Wales, page 396

10 miles

A685

A591

Kendal

▲ **Sizergh**

Fell Foot

Ulverston

Arnside and Silverdale

A687

A590

A683

A65

Barrow-in-Furness

Morecambe

Settle

Heysham Coast

LANCASTER

M6

A59

A56

A629

Blackpool

A585

M55

Burnley

East Riddlesden Hall

Gawthorpe Hall

Hardcastle Crags

Preston

A6

M65

A56

A666

Todmorden

M62

Rufford Old Hall

M61

A59

Southport

M66

Rochdale

Formby

A565

Wigan

Bolton

A58

A570

M58

A580

M60

Salford

MANCHESTER

M67

LIVERPOOL

Beatles' Childhood Homes

M62

Warrington

Dunham Massey

Sale

Kinder, Edale and the Dark Peak

The Hardmans' House

A57

Stockport

A6

M53

Speke Hall

M56

A56

Quarry Bank

Lyme

Longshaw, Burbage and the Eastern Moors

A523

Tatton Park

Hare Hill

Macclesfield

A537

Nether Alderley Mill

A49

Bakewell

A55

A41

CHESTER

A51

Alderley Edge

A52

A530

M6

Congleton

A494

Little Moreton Hall

A53

A537

Ilam Park, Dovedale and the White Peak

A534

Crewe

Biddulph Grange Garden

A523

Erddig

A483

A525

A53

A495

Alderley Edge and Cheshire Countryside

Nether Alderley, near Macclesfield, Cheshire

🏛️ ♿ 1946

Satnav: use SK10 4UB for Alderley Edge; ST7 3PA for Mow Cop; SY14 8LN for Bickerton.
Parking: at Alderley Edge, Mow Cop ST7 3PA and Bickerton SY14 8LN (plus roadside elsewhere).

The dramatic red sandstone escarpment of Alderley Edge has far-reaching views over the Cheshire Plain and towards the Peak District. There are plenty of paths to follow through open pasture and woodland. It's a Site of Special Scientific Interest because of its geology and history of copper mining dating back to the Bronze Age, and is also known for its wizard myth, which inspired the novel *The Weirdstone of Brisingamen*. There's more Cheshire countryside to explore: Bickerton, Bulkeley and Helsby Hills on the Sandstone Ridge, Thurstaston Common on the Wirral, and The Cloud and Mow Cop on the Staffordshire border. **Note**: toilets at Alderley Edge car park only.

Eat, shop, stay: at Alderley Edge you'll find refreshments at Wizard Tea-room and Wizard Inn (neither National Trust). Ice-cream van when the weather is fine (not National Trust). Picnic area close to car park.

Things to see and do: guided walks exploring industrial archaeology, geology and legends of Alderley Edge. Waymarked walking routes. Three orienteering courses. Ancient copper mine tours ran by Derbyshire Caving Club, twice a year. **Dogs**: welcome under close control; on leads near livestock and ground-nesting birds.

Access: 🅿️♿♿ Grounds ➡️

Find out more: 01625 584412 or alderleyedge@nationaltrust.org.uk

Alderley Edge	
Car park	
Open every day all year	8–5*

*1 April to 25 October, closes at 8.

Getting close to nature, above and below, at Alderley Edge in Cheshire

Arnside and Silverdale

near Arnside, Cumbria

🏛🏖🚶🐾 1929

The Kent Estuary at Arnside and Silverdale in Cumbria

Satnav: use LA5 0BP for Arnside Knott; LA5 0UG for Eaves Wood (Silverdale), both nearby. **Parking**: at Arnside Knott (signposted from Arnside Promenade) and Eaves Wood, Silverdale. Also in Silverdale village (not National Trust).

This wildlife-rich coastal landscape of grassland, woodland, meadows and rugged limestone pavement has miles of footpaths to explore, with views over Morecambe Bay. Arnside Knott and Eaves Wood are home to butterflies and wild flowers, while Jack Scout's cliffs are perfect for watching the sunset or spotting passing migrant birds.

Eat, shop, stay: variety of small shops, galleries and cafés in and around Arnside and Silverdale villages (none National Trust). Nearest National Trust café at Sizergh.

Things to see and do: viewpoint with toposcope (landmark orientation map) a short walk uphill from Arnside Knott car park. Stroll to Silverdale cove or follow Silverdale village heritage walk. **Dogs**: welcome under close control (on leads near livestock).

Find out more: 01524 701178 or arnsidesilverdale@nationaltrust.org.uk

The Beatles' Childhood Homes

Woolton and Allerton, Liverpool

🏠 2002

Parking: numerous car parks near collection point (not National Trust) for tours from city centre, or at Speke Hall for tours departing from there.

Explore Mendips and 20 Forthlin Road, the childhood homes of John Lennon and Paul McCartney. This tour is the only way to step inside the houses where The Beatles met, composed and rehearsed many of their earliest songs. You can walk through the back door into the kitchen and imagine John's Aunt Mimi cooking him his tea, or stand in the spot where Lennon and McCartney composed 'I Saw Her Standing There'. This is the opportunity to take a fascinating trip down memory lane in these two atmospheric houses, so typical of Liverpool life in the 1950s. **Note**: handbags, cameras and recording equipment must be left in secure facilities at both houses. Access by minibus tour only, from Liverpool city centre and Speke Hall (times vary, booking essential). Admission charges apply (including members).

Eat, shop, stay: you can buy guidebooks with your tour ticket. Refreshments are available at Jurys Inn, Liverpool (not National Trust) and at Speke Hall's Home Farm Restaurant.

Things to see and do: take a tour and step back in time to the 1950s and 60s to discover more about the birth of The Beatles.

Access: 🖼️🎫🏠♿🚻🅿️ Building ♿

Find out more: 0151 427 7231 (Speke Hall) or thebeatleshomes@nationaltrust.org.uk

Beatles' Childhood Homes		M	T	W	T	F	S	S
4 Mar–31 May	Tour*	·	·	W	T	F	S	S
1 Jun–1 Nov	Tour*	M	T	W	T	F	S	S
4 Nov–29 Nov	Tour*	·	·	W	T	F	S	S

*Admission by guided tour only (booking essential) – book online or by calling 0344 249 1895.

The Beatles' Childhood Homes, Liverpool, above and below

Dunham Massey

Altrincham, Greater Manchester WA14 4SJ

🏠🎫✥🐕🍽️ 1976

Parking: 200 yards.

Tucked away south of urban Manchester, Dunham Massey is a green haven; a place to meet, walk and escape. You can take a gentle stroll through the deer park and garden, buzzing with wildlife and home to ancient trees that put on a show every season. Once, the house and garden were only enjoyed by the family who lived here; now everyone is welcome. You can explore the garden and take in highlights such as one of the UK's largest winter gardens, bluebells and roses. Inside the house, changing spaces and displays celebrate the stories of the people connected to Dunham. The surrounding canals and footpaths make exploring the 1,200 hectares (3,000 acres) of rolling farmland easy.
Note: everyone requires a house and/or garden ticket, including members (available from reception on the day).

Eat, shop, stay: large shop selling food, locally sourced gifts and a wide range of plants. Stamford Café with indoor and outdoor seating, Stables Restaurant serving hot lunches and the Parlour offering drinks and snacks, including ice cream (hours vary).

The green haven of Dunham Massey, Greater Manchester

Places may occasionally close for events or bad weather, check at nationaltrust.org.uk

The winter garden at Dunham Massey, opposite, and discovering the house, above

Things to see and do: **Indoors** You can turn on the waterwheel in the old sawmill, see what life was like in the past in the servants' courtyard or get a taste of the vast collection in the house. **Outdoors** There's at least one free guided walk every day in the park or garden. Seasonal garden highlights include snowdrops, daffodils, bluebells, tulips, roses, hydrangeas and late-summer herbaceous borders. There are routes for walks, runs and cycling on the wider estate (cycling in the deer park for under-fives only). Seasonal events all year, including school holiday family activities, open-air cinema and theatre, and Christmas celebrations. **Dogs**: welcome on leads in deer park. Assistance dogs only in the house and garden.

Access: [icons]
House [icons] Garden and park [icons]

Find out more: 0161 942 3989 (Infoline).
0161 941 1025 or
dunhammassey@nationaltrust.org.uk

Dunham Massey		M	T	W	T	F	S	S
Gardens, café, restaurant, shop and stables								
1 Jan–14 Feb*	10:30–4**	M	T	W	T	F	S	S
15 Feb–1 Nov	10:30–5**	M	T	W	T	F	S	S
2 Nov–31 Dec*	10:30–4**	M	T	W	T	F	S	S
House and mill								
21 Mar–1 Nov†	11–5††	M	T	W	·	·	S	S
Park								
Open all year	8–6[1]	M	T	W	T	F	S	S

*Gardens, café, restaurant, shop and stables: closed 9 January, 10 November and 25 December.
**Gardens: close dusk if earlier; 3:30 on Christmas event nights (November/December); café, restaurant and shop: open 10; restaurant: closes one hour earlier; stables: open 11.
†House: 15 February to 20 March, access limited.
††House: closes dusk, if earlier; last entry one hour before closing; mill: open daily, 12 to 4; Thursday and Friday, ground floor only open. [1]Car park gates may close dusk if earlier.

Formby

near Formby, Liverpool

[icons] 1967

Satnav: use L37 1LJ for Victoria Road car park; L37 2EB for Lifeboat Road. **Parking**: on site (long traffic queues in summer).

As well as 3 miles of shifting sands and dynamic dunes, Formby offers scenic views over Liverpool Bay to the hills of North Wales. Along the shore, you might see footprint trails that are more than 5,000 years old reappearing as the sea erodes the ancient mudflats. In the sweeping pinewoods surrounding the beach, you can take a walk and spot red squirrels, or follow the Asparagus Trail to discover the local heritage of this vegetable. The beach at Lifeboat Road is supervised by lifeguards during summer weekends and holidays, making it the perfect setting for family days out. **Note**: toilets open when car parks are staffed.

Eat, shop, stay: a favourite place for picnics. Ice cream, soft drinks, coffee, light bites and confectionery available from mobile vans (not National Trust). Safe barbecue area at the Victoria Road family picnic site.

A rare red squirrel at Formby, Liverpool

Sandy family fun at Formby

Things to see and do: self-guided trails, including the Formby Asparagus Trail and the Ravenmeols Heritage Trail. Guided walks. Circular and longer walks linked to the Sefton Coastal Path. Orienteering and geocaching. **Dogs**: welcome on leads on Squirrel Walk and under close control elsewhere.

Access: [icons] Grounds [icons]

Find out more: 01704 878591 or formby@nationaltrust.org.uk

Formby		M	T	W	T	F	S	S
Car parks								
1 Jan–2 Feb	9–4	M	T	W	T	F	S	S
3 Feb–22 Mar	9–4:45	M	T	W	T	F	S	S
23 Mar–27 Sep	9–5:15	M	T	W	T	F	S	S
28 Sep–22 Nov	9–4:45	M	T	W	T	F	S	S
23 Nov–31 Dec	9–4	M	T	W	T	F	S	S

Closed 25 December.

Gawthorpe Hall

near Burnley, Lancashire

[icons] 1972

Satnav: use BB12 8SD then follow brown signs.
Parking: 150 yards, narrow access road.

This Elizabethan house, in the heart of urban Lancashire, has extravagant 19th-century interiors by Sir Charles Barry (known for his role in rebuilding the Houses of Parliament). The Hall displays textiles from the Gawthorpe Textile Collection, including needlework, lace and embroidery. You can enjoy the garden and woodland walks. **Note**: cared for in partnership with Lancashire County Council. Charges for special openings/events (including members).

Eat, shop, stay: tea-room serving sandwiches, cakes, scones and hot and cold drinks. Second-hand books.

Things to see and do: **Indoors** 17th-century panelling in drawing room. Guided tours, talks and exhibitions. Victorian Christmas. **Outdoors** Open-air theatre, events and family activities. **Dogs**: welcome under close control in grounds. Assistance dogs only in café.

Access: [icons]
Hall [icon] Café [icon] Grounds [icons]

Find out more: 01282 771004 or gawthorpehall@nationaltrust.org.uk
Burnley Road, Padiham, near Burnley, Lancashire BB12 8UA

Gawthorpe Hall		M	T	W	T	F	S	S
Hall and tea-room								
1 Apr–1 Nov	12–5*			W	T	F	S	S
Grounds								
Open all year	8–7	M	T	W	T	F	S	S

Hall and tea-room: open Bank Holidays. *Tea-room: opens 11, last orders 4:30. Opening times subject to change.

The Hardmans' House

59 Rodney Street, Liverpool, Merseyside L1 9ER

🏠 2003

Parking: none on site. Car parks at Anglican Cathedral and Slater Street, not National Trust (charge including members).

Discover Liverpool's best-kept secret and step inside a true time capsule – the home and studio of a 1950s society photographer. The handsome Georgian house, both glamorous workplace and modest, cluttered home for Edward Chambré Hardman and his talented wife Margaret, is packed with vintage treasures and fascinating photography. **Note**: guided tour only (booking advised). Entrance on Pilgrim Street at rear of property.

Eat, shop, stay: small shop selling unique photographic prints, postcards and guidebooks. The nearest café (not National Trust) is just a short walk away at the Anglican Cathedral.

Things to see and do: tours (book your place to avoid disappointment). Family trail. Virtual tour of the house. Special interest walking tours available.

Access: 🔲🔲🔲🔲🔲🔲🔲🔲 Building 🔲

Find out more: 0151 709 6261 or thehardmanshouse@nationaltrust.org.uk

The Hardmans' House		M	T	W	T	F	S	S
11 Mar–31 Oct	11–3:30	·	·	**W**	**T**	**F**	**S**	·

Admission by timed ticket only, booking advisable (places limited). Open Bank Holiday Mondays.

Hare Hill

Over Alderley, Macclesfield, Cheshire SK10 4PY

❀♿ 1978

Satnav: postcode takes you 109 yards west of car park. **Parking**: on site.

Hare Hill is a place to refresh the senses as well as the soul. Surrounded by farmland, this wooded garden is full of twists, turns and surprises, hidden paths and ponds. At its heart is the walled garden with its white flowering borders, which offers an oasis of tranquillity.

Eat, shop, stay: refreshments on weekends and Bank Holidays only (not National Trust). Picnics welcome in garden. Small shop in car park. Plants for sale. Information room with second-hand books (small donation).

Hare Hill, Cheshire: refreshment for the senses and soul

Appreciating the blooms at Hare Hill

Things to see and do: guides available on the history and planting of Hare Hill. Families can borrow a nature pack to explore the garden. **Dogs**: assistance dogs only in garden.

Access: ⬚⬚⬚⬚ Grounds ⬚

Find out more: 01625 829973 or harehill@nationaltrust.org.uk

Hare Hill		M	T	W	T	F	S	S
15 Feb–1 Nov	10:30–5	**M**	**T**	**W**	**T**	**F**	**S**	**S**

Heysham Coast

Heysham, near Morecambe, Lancashire 1996

A sandstone headland with a scenic walk through grassland and woodland, passing a ruined Saxon chapel and unusual rock-cut graves. **Note**: nearest facilities in village (not National Trust); park in the main village car park. For satnav use LA3 2RW.

Find out more: 01524 701178 or heysham@nationaltrust.org.uk

Little Moreton Hall

Congleton, Cheshire CW12 4SD

⬚⬚⬚⬚ 1938

Parking: 100 yards.

As you cross the moat into this Tudor fantasy you leave the chaos of modern life behind. Built to impress by craftsmen more than 500 years ago, the Hall has a unique quirky charm and homely feel. With its crooked walls and uneven floors, it seems so resilient yet still so fragile. Outside there's a manicured knot garden and borders with herbs and vegetables used by the Tudors. You can step back in time and reflect on the ups and downs of a simpler way of life at Little Moreton Hall, a remarkable survivor with an inspiring story to tell.

Eat, shop, stay: Little Tea-room (with outdoor seating) and Mrs Dale's Tea-room serving delicious homemade food made in the on-site bakery. Ice-cream kiosk (open on sunny days) and large shop in the car park selling gifts, plants and local products.

Things to see and do: Indoors Free guided tours and family trails. Tudor displays and activities most days. Costumes to try on. **Outdoors** Open-air theatre in summer and Tudor festivals throughout the year. **Dogs**: welcome on leads in car park and front lawn.

Access: 🅿️🐕♿🦽💺🖥️📷📹🚻♿📷
Hall ♿♿♿♿ **Reception** ♿♿
Grounds ♿♿♿♿➡️

Find out more: 01260 272018 or littlemoretonhall@nationaltrust.org.uk

Little Moreton Hall		M	T	W	T	F	S	S
Hall, garden, tea-room and shop								
12 Feb–1 Nov*	11–5**	·	·	W	T	F	S	S
4 Dec–20 Dec	11–4**	·	·	·	·	F	S	S
Shop								
7 Nov–29 Nov	12–4	·	·	·	·	·	S	S

Open Bank Holiday Mondays. *17 to 23 February, 6 to 19 April, 25 to 31 May, 20 July to 30 August, and 26 October to 1 November: open daily. **Upper floors may close early if light levels are poor.

Little Moreton Hall, Cheshire, below, is a Tudor fantasy, with unique, quirky charm. While Lyme, right, also in Cheshire, is the epitome of an English country house

Lyme

Disley, Stockport, Cheshire SK12 2NR

🏠➕♣️⚓🛏️ 1947

Parking: 200 yards.

If you imagine a classic English country house, you're probably picturing somewhere just like Lyme. The house sits in 570 hectares (1,400 acres) of moorland and deer park, with views across Manchester and the Cheshire Plain. Home to the Legh family for more than 550 years, the interiors tell the story of centuries of change up to its Regency heyday, when Thomas Legh created the house and garden as you see it today. You may recognise Lyme as 'Pemberley' from the BBC adaptation of *Pride and Prejudice*, starring Colin Firth. Lyme's ever-changing gardens, with the Reflection Lake, Orangery and Rose Garden, are an ideal place to unwind. The park is filled with paths, including links to the Gritstone Trail. **Note**: facility improvements may be disruptive (check before visiting).

Eat, shop, stay: choice of café and tea-rooms for snacks and lunch. The Salting Room Tea Parlour and Garden offers afternoon tea (booking essential). Timber Yard shop for gardening and outdoors products. Gift and bookshop. Holiday cottages with views across the park.

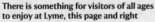
There is something for visitors of all ages to enjoy at Lyme, this page and right

Things to see and do: Indoors You can discover more about Thomas Legh, Lyme's very own Indiana Jones, see Lyme's Sarum Missal and find out why it is the most important printed book in the National Trust's collection. Why not relax in the library with a book, play the piano in the Entrance Hall or try your hand at billiards? **Outdoors** Regular running events and guided walks. Variety of levels of orienteering routes. Self-led woodland and moorland walks. Adventurous play in Crow Wood Playscape for five to 12 year olds.
Dogs: welcome under close control (on leads near livestock and vehicles); selected days in garden.

Access: 🅿️🗐🚐♿🅣🖐️📷🎧📹🔊🔆⊙🅐
House ♿🅐 Garden ♿🅐🅑🅓➡️🅐

Find out more: 01663 762023 or lyme@nationaltrust.org.uk

Lyme		M	T	W	T	F	S	S
House								
15 Feb–30 Mar	11–4*	M	T	·	·	F	S	S
31 Mar–31 May	11–5*	M	T	·	·	F	S	S
1 Jun–31 Aug	11–5*	M	T	·	T	F	S	S
1 Sep–1 Nov	11–5*	M	T	·	·	F	S	S
20 Nov–21 Dec**	11–3*	M	·	·	·	F	S	S
Garden, shop and tea-rooms								
1 Jan–14 Feb	11–3†	M	T	W	T	F	S	S
15 Feb–1 Nov	11–5†	M	T	W	T	F	S	S
2 Nov–31 Dec	11–3†	M	T	W	T	F	S	S
Estate								
1 Jan–29 Mar††	8–6¹	M	T	W	T	F	S	S
30 Mar–25 Oct	8–8¹	M	T	W	T	F	S	S
26 Oct–31 Dec††	8–6¹	M	T	W	T	F	S	S
Timber Yard shop and café²								
1 Jan–29 Mar	10–4	M	T	W	T	F	S	S
30 Mar–25 Oct	10–5	M	T	W	T	F	S	S
26 Oct–31 Dec	10–4	M	T	W	T	F	S	S

*House: last entry one hour before closing. **Parts of house open for Christmas events; also open 24 December. †Garden opens 10:30. †† Estate: 1 to 5 January and 23 to 31 December closes 5. ¹Gates locked at closing. ²Facilities improvements planned, check for details. Everything closed 25 December.

Nether Alderley Mill

Congleton Road, Nether Alderley, Macclesfield, Cheshire SK10 4TW

🏛 1950

Fully restored and operating Nether Alderley Mill, Cheshire

Parking: limited.

Hidden under the long sloping roof of this medieval building is a fully restored, working corn mill. You can take a guided tour to learn about the life of a miller, and spot centuries-old graffiti. Watch the waterwheels turn, powering the huge millstones that grind the flour. **Note**: view by guided tour only. Uneven floor, steep stairs and low ceilings. Sorry no toilets/catering.

Eat, shop, stay: you can buy the wholemeal stoneground flour produced in the mill using heritage machinery. Small range of souvenirs available. Nearest National Trust facilities at Alderley Edge (2 miles approximately).

Things to see and do: demonstrations show how the working heritage machinery turns grain into flour. Watch and listen to the machinery in action. Find out about the mill's restoration.

Access: 📶🚶📷🎥 Mill ♿🚻

Find out more: 01625 527468 or netheralderleymill@nationaltrust.org.uk

Nether Alderley Mill		M	T	W	T	F	S	S
2 Apr–4 Oct	12:30–4	·	·	·	**T**	·	**S**	**S**

Access by guided tour (book on arrival). Last tour 3:15.

Quarry Bank

Styal, Wilmslow, Cheshire SK9 4LA

🏠🏛️♿🐕🍽️ 1939

Parking: on site.

Standing in the gardens, you can almost feel the tranquillity of the river valley giving way to the clatter and bustle of a giant cotton mill as it led the way into the Industrial Revolution. The people here lived during a time of great change, from the mill-owning Greg family in Quarry Bank House, to the workers living in Styal village and the Apprentice House. Discover what life was like for the men, women and children toiling long hours in the heat of the mill, where you can still see working historic machinery in action. The very different lives led by the mill owners becomes apparent when you walk through their estate, picturesque gardens and elegant family home.

Living history at Quarry Bank in Cheshire

Historic looms at Quarry Bank, above, and exploring the Lower Garden, opposite

Eat, shop, stay: shops selling gifts, including cloth produced in the mill. Second-hand bookshop. Mill restaurant serving hot lunches, cakes and bakes. Garden café (open from May) for light lunches and snacks (outdoor seating). Stables Ice Cream Parlour. Picnic areas.

Things to see and do: **Indoors** You can explore Quarry Bank House, home of the mill owners, and join tours of the Apprentice House and workers' cottages – you'll see how their lives were worlds apart. In the mill, you can see (and hear) the machinery in action. Exhibitions and events. **Outdoors** Wander through the colourful gardens and explore the restored glasshouse, where you'll find exotic plants and fruits. You can walk through the woodland and follow the path of the winding River Bollin. Families will enjoy the natural play in Chapel Woods and playing Pooh sticks on the bridges. **Dogs**: welcome under close control on estate. On leads in garden, mill yard and meadow.

Access: 🅿️♿🚻♿🔊🐕♿👁️🦮
Mill 🦽♿♿🚻👥🚻♿ Gardens and estate 🦽♿➡️♿♿
Quarry Bank House/Apprentice House 🦽👥🚻♿

Find out more: 01625 527468 or quarrybank@nationaltrust.org.uk

Quarry Bank		M	T	W	T	F	S	S
1 Jan–5 Jan	10:30–4	·	·	W	T	F	S	S
11 Jan–14 Feb	10:30–4	·	·	W	T	F	S	S
15 Feb–1 Nov	10:30–5*	M	T	W	T	F	S	S
4 Nov–20 Dec	10:30–4	·	·	W	T	F	S	S
21 Dec–31 Dec	10:30–4	M	T	W	T	F	S	S

Everything closed 6 to 10 January for maintenance and 25 December. *30 May to 6 September: open 10 to 6 on Friday, Saturday and Sunday. Garden closes dusk if earlier. Estate open daily, 8 to 6.

Glorious blooms at Rufford Old Hall, Lancashire, above, and having fun dressing up, below

Rufford Old Hall

200 Liverpool Road, Rufford,
near Ormskirk, Lancashire L40 1SG

🏠 ✲ 🔔 1936

Parking: on site.

This black-and-white Tudor building, with its contrasting mellow red-brick Jacobean wing, hunkers in the low-lying mosslands of south-west Lancashire. More than 500 years old, this family home has many stories to tell about the intriguing people who used to live here, as well as a Great Hall that might make your jaw drop! Children can get closer to nature with bug-hunting and wild art kits, and you can unwind in the Victorian-style garden and grounds, with their colourful seasonal displays – from carpets of bluebells in spring, to golden leaves in autumn.

Eat, shop, stay: traditional Lancashire dishes served in the Victorian tea-room. Gifts and local treats available in the shop.

Things to see and do: **Indoors** Daily house talks and seasonal trails for children. Christmas events. **Outdoors** Guided garden tours. Events, including open-air theatre. Seasonal family trails and games. **Dogs**: welcome on leads in the courtyard and woodland.

Access: 🅿️♿🚻♿👓📷📱🔄🔥♿
House ♿♿♿♿♿ Grounds ♿♿♿➡️♿

Find out more: 01704 821254 or
ruffordoldhall@nationaltrust.org.uk

Rufford Old Hall		M	T	W	T	F	S	S
15 Feb–5 Apr	11–4	M	T	W	·	·	S	S
6 Apr–19 Apr	11–5	M	T	W	T	F	S	S
20 Apr–24 May*	11–5	M	T	W	·	·	S	S
25 May–1 Nov	11–5	M	T	W	T	F	S	S
7 Nov–29 Nov	11–4	·	·	·	·	·	S	S
3 Dec–20 Dec	11–4	·	·	·	·	T	F	S	S

*Also open Friday 8 May. Car park closes 30 minutes after closing. Tudor Great Hall occasionally closed to 1 for weddings (check before visiting).

Speke Hall

Speke, Liverpool L24 1XD

Parking: on site.

Almost 500 years ago, the Norris family replaced a medieval manor house on the banks of the River Mersey with the very latest in Tudor architecture. The iconic black-and-white Hall has seen centuries of turbulent history but was sympathetically restored in Victorian times as a cosy home. Surrounded by tranquil gardens and semi-ancient woodland, it's a slice of the past in the urban surroundings of Liverpool. Drive through the gates and leave the 21st century behind as you enter a peaceful world where you can be as restful or as active as you choose. The grounds are full of things to discover, from spring carpets of daffodils and bluebells to a Victorian-themed maze and natural woodland play trails.

Eat, shop, stay: Home Farm Restaurant serving regional and seasonal specialities. Stable Tea-room offering hot drinks and homemade cakes. Locally sourced gifts, as well as plants and books available in the shop. Second-hand bookshop in Kitchen Garden.

Things to see and do: Indoors Discover the Arts and Crafts restoration of the Hall and original William Morris wallpaper. Take a costumed guided tour. Try your hand at billiards. Solve a tricky family trail. **Outdoors** Wander through the formal gardens and discover the recently restored Secret Garden. Explore and spot wildlife, whatever the weather, with a coastal or woodland walk. Families can enjoy the formal play area, woodland play area and Childe of Hale play trail. Events all year, with family activities every school holiday and seasonal events, such as Tudor May Day, open-air theatre in summer, Christmas weekends and festive music evenings. **Dogs**: welcome on leads in the woodland and on signed estate walks.

Access: 🅿️♿🚾🚻🧑‍🦽🖐️🎧🏛️📷📖♿
Hall ♿🧑‍🦽♿ Grounds ♿➡️♿♿

Now peaceful, iconic black-and-white Speke Hall, Liverpool, has seen turbulent times over its 500-year history

Speke Hall's tranquil and inviting gardens, above, and bluebells in the semi-ancient woodland, left

Find out more: 0151 427 7231 or
spekehall@nationaltrust.org.uk

Speke Hall		M	T	W	T	F	S	S
House								
15 Feb–19 Jul	11–5*	·	·	W	T	F	S	S
21 Jul–30 Aug	11–5*	·	T	W	T	F	S	S
2 Sep–1 Nov	11–5*	·	·	W	T	F	S	S
27 Nov–13 Dec	11–4*	·	·	·	·	F	S	S
Gardens, grounds, restaurant and retail								
Open all year†	10:30–5**	M	T	W	T	F	S	S

*House: entry before 12:30 by guided tour only (tickets available from reception on day); 26 February to 8 March, entry by guided tour. **Shop: opens 11. †10 March, 10 November and 24 to 26 December: everything closed. Closing times may vary in winter (check on arrival).

Tatton Park

Knutsford, Cheshire

🏠🖼️❄️🦇🔔🍴 1960

Tatton Park, Cheshire: the impressive mansion

Satnav: use WA16 6SG. **Parking**: vehicle park entry charge £7 (including members).

Tatton Park is a grand country estate set in 400 hectares (1,000 acres) of historic deer park. The Egerton family acquired an impressive collection of paintings, books and rich furnishings, which can be seen in the 18th-century mansion – which also houses the servants' quarters. There is a medieval Old Hall and 20 hectares (50 acres) of award-winning gardens, including the 100-year-old Japanese Garden. The working farm and restored agricultural mill tell the story of Tatton's food production over the centuries, and you can see original machinery in action and meet rare breed animals and characters from the past. **Note**: financed and managed by Cheshire East Council. Building improvement work in the stableyard area. £7 vehicle park entry and charges for farm (50% discount), Old Hall, tours and special events, including Christmas and RHS Flower Show, apply to members.

Eat, shop, stay: self-service Stables Restaurant and award-winning Gardener's Cottage offering afternoon tea. Speciality shops include the Housekeeper's Store, selling local and estate-reared meat and produce. Gift, garden, farm and tuck shops. None of the shops or places to eat are National Trust.

Things to see and do: **Indoors** Changing mansion exhibitions. Old Hall tours and events on select days. Educational workshops and events. **Outdoors** Japanese Garden tours. Adventure playground. RHS Flower Show and other large events. **Dogs**: welcome on leads on farm and under close control in the parkland.

Access: 🅿️♿🚪🦽🔄🚻👶📷😊🅿️
Mansion 🔽♿🚪♿ Grounds ♿♿➡️🦽

Find out more: 01625 374400 or tatton@cheshireeast.gov.uk tattonpark.org.uk
Knutsford, Cheshire WA16 6QN

Tatton Park		M	T	W	T	F	S	S
Mansion*								
28 Mar–1 Nov	1–5	·	·	**W**	**T**	**F**	**S**	**S**
Farm**								
4 Jan–22 Mar	11–4	·	·	·	·	·	**S**	**S**
28 Mar–25 Oct	12–5	·	**T**	**W**	**T**	**F**	**S**	**S**
26 Oct–1 Nov	11–4	**M**	**T**	**W**	**T**	**F**	**S**	**S**
7 Nov–27 Dec	11–4	·	·	·	·	·	**S**	**S**
Gardens, parkland, shops and restaurants								
1 Jan–27 Mar	10–4†	·	**T**	**W**	**T**	**F**	**S**	**S**
28 Mar–1 Nov††	10–6†	**M**	**T**	**W**	**T**	**F**	**S**	**S**
3 Nov–31 Dec	10–4†	·	**T**	**W**	**T**	**F**	**S**	**S**

*Also open 1 to 5 January, Bank Holiday Mondays and for Christmas events; 30 September to 1 November, 12 to 4. **Also open 1 to 3 January, 17 to 21 February and Bank Holiday Mondays (closed during RHS Flower Show). Gardens: 26 October to 1 November close 4. †Parkland closes one hour later. Shops: 1 January to 27 March and 3 November to 31 December open 11; 28 March to 1 November 11 to 5. ††Restaurants: close 5. Old Hall special opening arrangements and charge. Mansion, farm, gardens and parkland: last entry one hour before closing. Everything closed 25 December.

The shimmering mirror-like mere at Tatton Park

Early morning light breaks through
the mist at Fell Foot, Cumbria

The Lakes

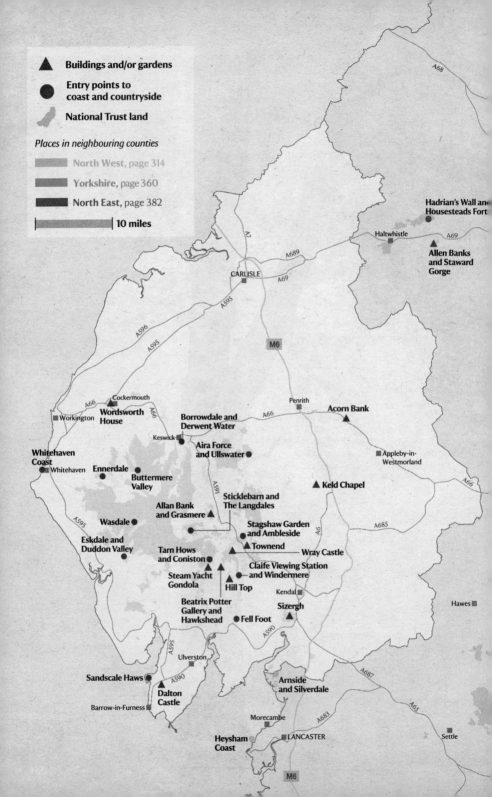

Buildings and/or gardens

Entry points to coast and countryside

National Trust land

Places in neighbouring counties

North West, page 314

Yorkshire, page 360

North East, page 382

10 miles

Hadrian's Wall and Housesteads Fort

Haltwhistle

A69

Allen Banks and Staward Gorge

A68

A689

CARLISLE

A69

M6

A595

A596

A595

A66

Cockermouth

Wordsworth House

A66

Penrith

A66

Acorn Bank

Workington

Borrowdale and Derwent Water

Keswick

Appleby-in-Westmorland

Whitehaven Coast

Aira Force and Ullswater

Whitehaven

Ennerdale

Buttermere Valley

Keld Chapel

A591

Sticklebarn and The Langdales

A66

Allan Bank and Grasmere

Stagshaw Garden and Ambleside

A6

A685

Wasdale

A595

Townend

Wray Castle

Eskdale and Duddon Valley

Tarn Hows and Coniston

Claife Viewing Station and Windermere

Steam Yacht Gondola

Hill Top

Kendal

Hawes

Beatrix Potter Gallery and Hawkshead

Fell Foot

Sizergh

A595

A590

Ulverston

Arnside and Silverdale

A687

Sandscale Haws

A590

A683

A65

Dalton Castle

Barrow-in-Furness

Morecambe

Settle

Heysham Coast

LANCASTER

M6

Acorn Bank

Temple Sowerby, near Penrith,
Cumbria CA10 1SP

🏠🖼️♿🚶🅿️ 1950

Parking: on site.

Close to Penrith and with views to the Lake District and Howgill Fells, Acorn Bank is a tranquil haven in the heart of the Eden Valley. Established by the Knights Templar around the 13th century; people have lived and worked here for more than 800 years. Today the walled gardens shelter a medicinal herb garden, herbaceous borders, lily-filled pond and traditional orchards carpeted with spring daffodils. Woodland walks reveal a half-hidden story of gypsum mining, working medieval watermill and a wildlife-rich estate. The 17th-century sandstone manor remains unfurnished and occasional guided tours shed light on its uses over the years. **Note**: some paths may be closed following wet weather.

Eat, shop, stay: tea-room with outdoor tables. Home-grown garden produce for sale. Shop selling local products, plants and flour (milled on site). Second-hand bookshop in house. Enjoy the estate after hours at Sandwath and Bankwood – spacious holiday apartments sleeping two to three.

Vivid tulips light up a border at Acorn Bank

Things to see and do: watermill working most weekends during summer. See newts in the pond in spring. Woodland trails. Children's wild play area and fairy houses hidden in the woodland to discover. Bird hide. **Dogs**: welcome in the woodland.

Access: 🅿️♿🛗🏠🚻♿ **Watermill** ♿🚶 **House** ♿🖼️♿ **Grounds** 🖼️➡️♿♿

Find out more: 017683 61893 or acornbank@nationaltrust.org.uk

Acorn Bank		M	T	W	T	F	S	S
15 Feb–1 Nov	10–5*	M	T	W	T	F	S	S
2 Nov–31 Dec**	10–3*	M	T	W	T	F	S	S

*Last admission one hour before closing.
House: partially open; guided tours available (places limited).
**Closed 25 and 26 December.

Lying at the heart of the Eden Valley, Acorn Bank, Cumbria, has a rich history dating back to the Knights Templar

Aira Force and Ullswater

near Watermillock, Penrith, Cumbria

♿ 1906

Satnav: use CA11 0JS for Aira Force; CA11 0NQ for Glencoyne Bay. **Parking**: at Aira Force, Aira Force High Cascades, Aira Force Park Brow and Glencoyne Bay.

An 18th-century pleasure ground, Aira Force was the backdrop for William Wordsworth's poem 'Somnambulist' – a Gothic tale of love and tragedy. There are so many woodland trails to discover in this landscape of contrasts. Quiet glades give way to dramatic waterfalls, with Aira Beck thundering down a 65-foot drop past ferns and rocks. If you walk to the summit of Gowbarrow, you will be rewarded with panoramic views over Ullswater. Starting your day in Glenridding, arriving at Aira Force by boat then strolling back along the lakeshore, allows you to take in the wonderful Ullswater Valley sights. **Note**: boat rides on Ullswater operated by Ullswater 'Steamers', not National Trust (charge including members).

Eat, shop, stay: tea-room serving light lunches, cakes, ice cream and hot and cold drinks. Shop selling gifts, ice cream, souvenirs and maps. Takeaway kiosk serving hot drinks and snacks. Picnics welcome.

Things to see and do: red squirrels, natural play area and tree trail. You can paddle at Aira Green and canoe at Glencoyne Bay. Arrive early for your best chance of seeing a red squirrel. **Dogs**: welcome on leads.

Access: ♿ ♿ ♿ ♿

Find out more: 017684 82067 or ullswater@nationaltrust.org.uk

Aira Force and Ullswater	
Tea-room and shop	
Open every day all year*	10–4:30

*Closed 23 to 26 December. Opening times may vary during low season.

Aira Force and Ullswater in Cumbria, above and below, is a place of contrasts, with waterfalls, woodlands and a lake

Allan Bank and Grasmere

near Ambleside, Cumbria

🏠 🏛 ✿ ♿ 1920

The lake view from Allan Bank and Grasmere, Cumbria

Satnav: use LA22 9TA for nearest car park.
Parking: nearest in village, not National Trust (charge including members).

Views of Grasmere lake and the surrounding fells can be enjoyed from the large bay windows and woodland grounds of this relaxed house. Once home to National Trust co-founder Canon Rawnsley, Allan Bank is now only partially decorated and is a great place to enjoy crafts, draw and paint. Red squirrels play in the grounds, there are picnic spots indoors and out, places for children to run free and you can even sit by the fire and read a book. Lakeshore strolls and adventurous fell-top rambles can be started from nearby Grasmere village. **Note**: limited accessible parking only on site. Follow directions on foot from The Inn at Grasmere.

Eat, shop, stay: tea and coffee (donations please). Picnics welcome indoors and out. Church Stile shop in Grasmere selling unusual gifts, local books and maps in Grade II-listed, 17th-century building.

Things to see and do: **Indoors** Draw, paint, play board games, read newspapers or borrow a book. Binoculars for spotting red squirrels and wildlife. **Outdoors** Deckchairs, woodland trail, wild play area, red squirrels, downloadable walks. **Dogs**: welcome on leads.

Access: 🅿 ♿ 🚻 🔣 🖼 House 🔣 🖼 🔣

Find out more: 015394 35143 or allanbank@nationaltrust.org.uk
near Ambleside, Cumbria LA22 9QB

Allan Bank and Grasmere		M	T	W	T	F	S	S
Allan Bank								
15 Feb–29 Mar	10:30–4	M	T	W	T	F	S	S
30 Mar–1 Nov	10:30–5	M	T	W	T	F	S	S
6 Nov–20 Dec	10:30–4	·	·	·	·	F	S	S

A young artist at Allan Bank

Beatrix Potter Gallery and Hawkshead

Main Street, Hawkshead, Cumbria LA22 0NS

🏠📷 1947

Things to see and do: **Indoors** Original Beatrix Potter artwork on display. **Outdoors** The Claife Community Bridleway links Hawkshead to Hill Top (2 miles). The Courthouse nearby has an interesting history (collect key from shop). **Dogs**: assistance dogs only.

Access: 🅿️♿♿ Gallery ♿🚻

Find out more: 015394 36355 (gallery). 015394 36471 (shop) or beatrixpottergallery@nationaltrust.org.uk

Beatrix Potter Gallery		M	T	W	T	F	S	S
Gallery								
15 Feb–1 Nov	10:30–4	M	T	W	T	F	S	S
Hawkshead shop								
15 Feb–1 Nov	10:30–5	M	T	W	T	F	S	S
2 Nov–31 Dec*	10:30–4	M	T	W	T	F	S	S

At busy periods, timed entry system in operation. Medieval Hawkshead Courthouse: open 28 March to 1 November (access by key from National Trust shop in Hawkshead). *Hawkshead shop closed 24 to 26 December.

Examining original artwork at the Beatrix Potter Gallery. Visitors of all ages love these miniature masterpieces

Beatrix Potter Gallery, Cumbria

Parking: 300 yards, not National Trust (charge including members).

This year's exhibition of Beatrix Potter's original artwork, illustrations and letters – 'Friendship by post – people who shaped Beatrix Potter's world' – explores how important correspondence was to Beatrix. The exhibition shows the sadness, humour, determination and energy of her genius. If you've ever been charmed by Beatrix's endearing characters, you can take a closer look at some of her miniature masterpieces in a rare opportunity to see the delicate watercolours that are shown only once a decade. Quaint Hawkshead village makes the perfect base for exploring the countryside that inspired Beatrix and many other famous poets, writers and artists. **Note**: nearest toilets 300 yards in main village car park (not National Trust).

Eat, shop, stay: gallery shop selling Beatrix Potter items (free entry). Hawkshead Corner shop stocks local products. Refreshments available at pubs and cafés in Hawkshead (not National Trust). Stay in nearby holiday cottages Summer House or Rose Castle, or camp at Low Wray.

Borrowdale and Derwent Water

near Keswick, Cumbria

🏠 🚻 🏛 ♿ 🛏 1902

Satnav: use CA12 5DJ for Keswick lakeside shop and CA12 5XN for Seatoller (at foot of Honister Pass). **Parking**: at Great Wood (CA12 5UP), Ashness Bridge (CA12 5UN), Surprise View (CA12 5UU), Watendlath (CA12 5UW), Kettlewell (CA12 5UN), Bowder Stone (CA12 5XA), Rosthwaite (CA12 5XB), Seatoller (CA12 5XN) and Honister Pass (CA12 5XN).

From the lakeshore at Crow Park, a few minutes' walk from the centre of the busy Lakeland town of Keswick, there are far-reaching views across Derwent Water and its islands to the high central fells, framed by Cat Bells and Walla Crag. Castle Crag sits between the lake and upper Borrowdale, where scenic drives, traditional hamlets and waymarked walks await. Nine car parks in the valley make it easy to access some of Lakeland's most photographed views and walks. During the summer Seatoller and Bowder Stone offer the best chance of a parking spot. October brings rich auburns and golden evening light to Ashness Bridge and Surprise View, and from Kettlewell the autumn colours are reflected in the lake. **Note**: charges apply to members on Force Crag Mine and Derwent Island House open days.

Eat, shop, stay: Keswick lakeside shop offers local knowledge to help you plan your visit, plus souvenirs, cold drinks and ice cream. There are tenant-run cafés at Watendlath and Rosthwaite. Watendlath Bothy (sleeps six) and Millbeck Towers (sleeps 12) provide perfect holiday bases.

View from the lakeshore at Derwent Water, Cumbria, above, and rock climbing at Borrowdale, below

Walkers enjoy a rest and the far-reaching view at Borrowdale and Derwent Water

Things to see and do: Seatoller car park is a good starting point for the Castle Crag circular walk or for heading into the high fells. Great Wood's waymarked walks take you along lakeshore paths, up into the protected Atlantic oakwoods, guide you on a gentle climb to Ashness Bridge or you can join the 10-mile round Derwent Water walk. If you're looking for something more unusual, our vehicle can take you to Force Crag Mine and rafted canoes are provided to get you to Derwent Island House – both places only open for five days each year, so booking is essential. **Dogs**: welcome under close control at lambing time.

Access: ♿ ♿ Derwent Island ♿
Force Crag Mine ♿ ♿ Derwent Water foreshore ➡

Find out more: 017687 74649 or borrowdale@nationaltrust.org.uk

Borrowdale and Derwent Water		M	T	W	T	F	S	S
Shop and visitor centre								
4 Jan–9 Feb	10–4	.	.	.	.	.	S	S
10 Feb–1 Nov	10–5	M	T	W	T	F	S	S
2 Nov–6 Dec	10–4	M	.	.	.	F	S	S
12 Dec–27 Dec	10–4	.	.	.	.	.	S	S

Shop and visitor centre: open weekends, 2 January to 14 February 2021. For open days at Derwent Island House and Force Crag Mine, check 'What's on' page online.

Buttermere Valley

near Cockermouth, Cumbria

🍴🏛️♿♿ 1935

Dramatic Buttermere Valley in Cumbria

Satnav: use CA13 9UZ for Buttermere; CA13 0RT for Crummock Water; CA13 0RU for Loweswater. **Parking**: at Honister Pass (CA12 5XN), just outside Buttermere village (CA13 9UZ), Lanthwaite Green (CA13 9UY), Crummock Water (CA13 0RT) and Maggie's Bridge (CA13 0RU) at Loweswater.

This dramatic valley encompasses the lakes of Buttermere, Crummock Water and Loweswater, all offering easy low-level lakeshore walks and access onto the high fells. Buttermere's 4½-mile round-the-lake path takes in shingle beaches, cascading waterfalls and a hand-cut Victorian tunnel, perfect for family adventures. Top tip: arrive early to get parking. **Note**: toilets at Buttermere village only (charge, not National Trust).

Eat, shop, stay: pubs and cafés in Buttermere and Loweswater hamlets (none National Trust). Picnics welcome. Stay at Watergate Farm or choose simplicity at Holme Wood Bothy, a camping barn on Loweswater's shore.

Things to see and do: easy scenic waymarked walks open April to June, when a stretch of Buttermere's lakeshore path is closed to protect nesting sandpipers (alternative round-the-lake route available). **Dogs**: welcome under close control at lambing time.

Access: Lakeshore path 🔁

Find out more: 017687 74649 or buttermere@nationaltrust.org.uk

Claife Viewing Station and Windermere West Shore

near Far Sawrey, Cumbria LA22 0LW

🏛️♿👕♿ 1962

Satnav: use LA22 0LP for Ash Landing; LA22 0LR for Harrowslack; LA22 0JH for Red Nab (all nearby). **Parking**: at Ash Landing and Harrowslack for Claife Viewing Station and Windermere west shore. Red Nab is further north along the lakeshore, close to Wray Castle.

Perched on the tranquil west shore of Windermere, minutes from the Bowness ferry, Claife Viewing Station was built in the 1790s for the first tourists to the Lake District. Today, you can enjoy the same panoramic views of the lake from the platform, framed by coloured glass. At the café you can sit by a cosy fire or under the fairy lights that welcome you into the courtyard. There are 4 miles of lakeside paths leading towards Wray Castle for cycling or walking, or you could explore the landscape around Hill Top and Hawkshead that so inspired Beatrix Potter. **Note**: toilets at nearby Ferry House. Passenger boats operated by Windermere Lake Cruises; council-run car ferry.

Claife Viewing Station and Windermere West Shore, Cumbria: the Viewing Station was built in the 1790s

Exploring the shore of Windermere

Eat, shop, stay: café in the courtyard beneath the viewing station serving light lunches, drinks and cakes (not National Trust). Picnics welcome on lakeshore or in picnic area. Stay at High or Low Strawberry Garden cottages, with England's largest lake on your doorstep.

Things to see and do: the platform offers a unique viewpoint over Windermere – bring your camera or sketchbook and be inspired. Walk or cycle along the lakeshore path or paddle in the water. **Dogs**: welcome under close control.

Access: [Pd] [⚲] Viewing Station [♿] Café [♿] [🚻]

Find out more: 015394 41456 or claife@nationaltrust.org.uk

Dalton Castle

Market Place, Dalton-in-Furness, Cumbria LA15 8AX [1965]

Standing proud in Dalton town centre, this impressive 14th-century tower was once the manorial courthouse of Furness Abbey. **Note**: opened on behalf of the National Trust by the Friends of Dalton Castle. Parking in Dalton town centre (not National Trust). Open Saturday, 28 March to 26 September, 2 to 5.

Find out more: 015395 69816 or daltoncastle@nationaltrust.org.uk

Ennerdale

Bowness Knott, Croasdale, Ennerdale Bridge, Cumbria

[🏕][🏛][⚲] [1927]

Satnav: use CA23 3BA for Ennerdale Bridge; CA23 3AU for Bowness Knott; CA23 3AS for Bleach Green. **Parking**: at Bowness Knott and Bleach Green (not National Trust).

Peaceful, yet dramatic, Ennerdale is home to one of the UK's largest wildland partnerships – Wild Ennerdale. A horseshoe of rugged fells surrounds the wooded valley where Galloway cattle roam free and the untamed River Liza flows. The views widen across Ennerdale Water, which is circled by lakeshore paths and beaches. **Note**: nearest toilets at Ennerdale Bridge (not National Trust).

Eat, shop, stay: bunkbarns, hostels and B&Bs throughout the valley. Pubs in nearby Ennerdale Bridge, as well as The Gather café and shop (none National Trust).

Ennerdale, Cumbria, offers miles of traffic-free tracks

Things to see and do: accessible Ennerdale Views trail starting from Bleach Green. Miles of traffic-free walking and cycling from Bowness Knott, including the 2-mile waymarked Smithy Beck Trail. **Dogs**: welcome under close control near livestock.

Access: Ennerdale Centre [♿]
Bleach Green lakeshore [➡]

Find out more: 017687 74649 or ennerdale@nationaltrust.org.uk

Eskdale and Duddon Valley

Eskdale, near Ravenglass; Duddon Valley, near Broughton in Furness, Cumbria

🏛️♿🚻🅿️🏕️ 1926

Parking: in lay-bys, along roadsides and at small car parks in some villages (not National Trust).

Eskdale is a valley of contrasts. Upper Eskdale leads to the high mountains, including Scafell and Bowfell; the valley floor has meandering riverside and woodland paths, including the Eskdale Trail, for walkers and cyclists. Across high mountain passes lies the Duddon Valley, with meadows, woodlands, mountains, hill farms and rivers.

Eat, shop, stay: stay at National Trust Eskdale Campsite or cottages (Bird How or Thrang). Pubs at Eskdale Green, Boot, Seathwaite; shops at Eskdale Green, Boot, Ulpha; café Dalegarth station (none National Trust).

Things to see and do: walks to Harter Fell and Seathwaite Tarn and from 'La'al Ratty' railway. Duddon Valley woodland and riverside paths. Hardknott Roman Fort (English Heritage).
Dogs: welcome under close control (please follow local and seasonal guidance). On leads around livestock.

Find out more: 019467 26064 or eskdaleandduddon@nationaltrust.org.uk

Eskdale and Duddon Valley	M	T	W	T	F	S	S
Eskdale Campsite*							
29 Feb–31 Dec		M	T	W	T	F	S	S

*Also open 1 January 2021. For detailed opening times and bookings please visit ntlakescampsites.org.uk or call 015394 32733.

Duddon Valley in Cumbria: a place of contrast

Fell Foot

Newby Bridge, Windermere, Cumbria

🏠👥🍴 1948

Satnav: use LA12 8NN.
Parking: two large car parks on site.

Less than a 20-minute drive from the M6 at the most southern end of Windermere, Fell Foot is one of the few places where you can access England's largest lake. This family-friendly park is perfect for paddling, boat hire or swimming, whether you're experienced or a beginner, and state-of-the-art changing facilities at the Active Base offer a comfortable place to dry off after a day on the water. If you'd rather stay on land, relax on the lawn for a summer picnic with impressive mountain views, or stroll along the paths to the flower meadows and Pinetum – the park's collection of specimen trees. Three recently restored Gothic revival boathouses uncover the park's rich history.
Note: improvements under way; building work possible. Additional charges (including members) for launch facilities, rowing boats, paddleboards and kayaks (mid-April to October). Also for Active Base (pass needed – available from shop).

Fell Foot, Cumbria, this page and opposite, offers so many activities, from family picnics, to kayaking and exploring

Eat, shop, stay: Boathouse Café serving drinks, soup, hot meals and cakes. Wood-fired pizza in summer. Boathouse shop selling toys, gifts, maps and picnic rugs. Active Base shop stocking local products and outdoor gear for people and dogs. Picnics welcome.

Things to see and do: seasonal rowing boat, paddleboard and kayak hire (weather permitting) on weekends and school holidays. Fell Foot's Active Base makes it easy to spend a day on the lake with changing rooms and launch facilities. Toddler playground, wild play area and lakeside 'beach' for paddling. Newly restored Grade II-listed Victorian boathouses open. Regular activities, including weekly parkrun, fitness classes, yoga and open-water swimming classes. Easy meadow walks with wild flowers, butterflies and birds. Get the ferry from Fell Foot across to Lakeside, where you can join a Windermere Lake Cruise or hop on a steam train (neither National Trust).
Dogs: welcome on leads.

Access: 🅿♿♿♿♿🎵
Boathouses 🚶 Active Base 🚶

Find out more: 015395 31273 or fellfoot@nationaltrust.org.uk

Fell Foot		M	T	W	T	F	S	S
Park, Active Base and car park								
1 Jan–20 Mar	9–5	M	T	W	T	F	S	S
21 Mar–10 Jul	8–6	M	T	W	T	F	S	S
11 Jul–6 Sep	8–7	M	T	W	T	F	S	S
7 Sep–1 Nov	8–6	M	T	W	T	F	S	S
2 Nov–31 Dec**	9–5	M	T	W	T	F	S	S
Boathouse Café*								
1 Jan–20 Mar	10–4	M	T	W	T	F	S	S
21 Mar–10 Jul	10–5	M	T	W	T	F	S	S
11 Jul–6 Sep	10–6:30	M	T	W	T	F	S	S
7 Sep–1 Nov	10–5	M	T	W	T	F	S	S
2 Nov–31 Dec**	10–4	M	T	W	T	F	S	S
Boathouse shop								
21 Mar–30 Sep	10–5	M	T	W	T	F	S	S

*Café: open 9 on Saturday. **Everything closed 25 December.

Hill Top

Near Sawrey, Hawkshead, Ambleside,
Cumbria LA22 0LF

🏠 ✿ 👁 1944

The inviting entrance hall at Hill Top

Parking: limited and for visitors to
Hill Top only.

Beatrix Potter's beloved farmhouse Hill Top
was her sanctuary and a source of inspiration
for her much-loved children's tales. Near
Sawrey village and Beatrix's garden path
are home to landmarks and scenes from
her illustrations. Filled with her personal
possessions, including Lakeland furniture and
trophies for her prize-winning Herdwick sheep,
the house is a true reminder of Beatrix's legacy.
It remains much as she left it when it came
into the Trust's care in 1944. The surrounding
landscape is great for exploring – it inspired
Beatrix to gift 14 farms and 1,618 hectares
(4,000 acres) to the National Trust.
Note: timed-ticket entry for the house.
Tickets not needed for the shop or garden.
Parking limited.

Eat, shop, stay: shop selling Beatrix Potter
collectables, including items exclusive to Hill
Top, drinks and ice creams. Refreshments
available at Sawrey House Hotel or Tower Bank
Arms (not National Trust). Stay at High or
Low Strawberry Garden cottages on
Windermere's west shore.

Things to see and do: the Claife Community
Bridleway links Sawrey to Hawkshead and the
Beatrix Potter Gallery (2 miles). Spot frogs
among the lily pads planted by Beatrix at Moss
Eccles Tarn (1 mile). **Dogs**: welcome on leads in
garden. Assistance dogs only in the house.

Hill Top, Beatrix Potter's much-loved farmhouse in Cumbria, inspired many of her children's stories

Why not share your pictures with us? #nationaltrust

Find out more: 015394 36269. 015394 36801 (shop) or hilltop@nationaltrust.org.uk

Hill Top		M	T	W	T	F	S	S
House, shop and garden*								
15 Feb–21 May**	10–4:30	M	T	W	T	·	S	S
23 May–30 Aug	10–5:30	M	T	W	T	F	S	S
31 Aug–1 Nov**	10–4:30	M	T	W	T	·	S	S
Shop and garden								
7 Nov–20 Dec	10:30–4	·	·	·	·	·	S	S

*House: entry by timed ticket (places limited), free entry to garden and shop. **Shop and garden: also open Fridays; house opens some Fridays during school holidays (check before visiting). 15 February to 1 November exclusive tours, 1 and 2, on Friday when house is closed for conservation work.

Keld Chapel

Keld Lane, Shap, Cumbria CA10 3NW 1918

Tucked away in east Cumbria, this rustic 16th-century stone Chapel was once the chantry for Shap Abbey. **Note**: sorry no facilities. Open every day all year, dawn to dusk (for key, please see notice on Chapel door).

Find out more: 017683 61893 or keldchapel@nationaltrust.org.uk

Sandscale Haws National Nature Reserve

near Barrow-in-Furness, Cumbria 1984

This beach has wild, grass-covered dunes and Lakeland mountain views; it's the perfect habitat for rare wildlife, including natterjack toads. **Note**: for satnav use LA14 4QJ. Welcome hut serving light refreshments. Red Hut open daily, 2 March to 1 November, and weekends, 2 November to 31 December, 10 to 4.

Find out more: 01229 462855 or sandscalehaws@nationaltrust.org.uk

Sizergh

Sizergh, near Kendal, Cumbria LA8 8DZ

🏠🍴🏛️♿🛏️ 1950

Imposing medieval Sizergh in Cumbria

Satnav: use LA8 8DZ – takes you to the Strickland Arms, then follow National Trust signs. **Parking**: 250 yards (cars and bikes only).

Standing proud at the gateway to the National Park, this imposing medieval manor is home to the Strickland family and a great place to stop on your way in or out of the Lake District. Built more than 650 years ago and filled with thousands of items collected by 26 generations of the family, the jewel in Sizergh's crown is the elaborate wooden panelling in the Inlaid Chamber, one of the best examples of Elizabethan craftsmanship in the world. The 647-hectare (1,600-acre) estate contains wetlands, woodlands and orchards and is home to fritillary butterflies, deer and elusive hawfinches. There's somewhere to relax in the garden whatever the season, with an apple orchard, herbaceous border, fruit wall and rock garden. **Note**: house may be closed occasionally for private events. Separate admission charges may apply for some tours.

Eat, shop, stay: contemporary licensed café serving drinks, hot meals, snacks and cakes. Shop selling local products, home accessories, gifts and toys. Plant donation stalls. Strickland Arms pub (tenant-run). You can stay on the Sizergh estate at Holeslack Farmhouse or Courtyard Cottage.

Entry is still possible at most places up to 30 minutes before closing

Things to see and do: Indoors New exhibition exploring Sizergh's history from the viewpoint of the present Strickland family. Varied contents, including portraits of exiled Stuart monarchs, Jacobite relics and family collection of Catholic items. Guided tours, including new rooftop tour. **Outdoors** Working organic kitchen garden with bees and hens. Mirror lake, wildflower banks and four National Collections of Hardy Ferns. More than 65 types of apple in the orchard, including rare local varieties. Estate footpaths leading to Helsington Church, Sizergh Fell and through Brigsteer Wood to wetland area and bird hide at Park End Moss. Orienteering. Children's wild play trail. **Dogs**: welcome in the café, shop and wider estate (on leads near livestock).

Access: 🅿♿🏛🔊♿🅿♿📷🎵
Building ♿🚻♿ **Garden** 🏛➡♿♿

Find out more: 015395 60951 or sizergh@nationaltrust.org.uk

Sizergh		M	T	W	T	F	S	S
House								
21 Mar–1 Nov	12–3:30	·	T	W	T	F	S	S
Garden, café and shop								
1 Jan–5 Jan*	10–4	·	·	W	T	F	S	S
18 Jan–20 Mar*	10–4	M	T	W	T	F	S	S
21 Mar–1 Nov	10–5	M	T	W	T	F	S	S
2 Nov–31 Dec*	10–4	M	T	W	T	F	S	S
Estate								
Open all year	Dawn–dusk	M	T	W	T	F	S	S

*Garden: areas subject to closure. Car park: open all year 9 to 6. Everything closed 25 December.

The grand Banqueting Hall at Sizergh, opposite, and children looking at hens in the orchard, below

Stagshaw Garden and Ambleside

near Windermere, Cumbria

🏛🏠♿♿ 1927

Satnav: use LA22 0HE for Stagshaw Garden and Skelghyll Woods; LA22 9AN for Bridge House. **Parking**: small car park at Stagshaw Garden. Several car parks in Ambleside, not National Trust (charge including members).

Perched above Ambleside, this quiet, informal woodland garden (above) is hidden from the hustle and bustle of the town below. Rambling paths and unusual combinations of shrubs, trees and plants give an enchanted feel. In spring it becomes a kaleidoscope of colour with daffodils, bluebells, azaleas and rhododendrons in full bloom. **Note**: Ambleside Roman Fort (see below) owned by English Heritage, run by the National Trust.

Eat, shop, stay: places to eat and drink in Ambleside (none National Trust). Nearest National Trust pub at Sticklebarn, Langdale. National Trust shop in Grasmere, 4 miles.

Things to see and do: Bridge House, Ambleside's smallest building, built on a bridge. Tall Tree Trail at Skelghyll Woods, home to Cumbria's tallest trees. Ambleside Roman Fort remains (free). **Dogs**: welcome on leads.

Access: Bridge House ♿ Stagshaw Garden ♿♿

Find out more: 015394 46402 or stagshawgarden@nationaltrust.org.uk

Stagshaw Garden and Ambleside	
Stagshaw Garden	
Open every day all year	Dawn–dusk

Stagshaw Garden is at its best April to July.

Steam Yacht Gondola

Coniston Pier, Lake Road, Coniston,
Cumbria LA21 8AN

♿🔔☂ 1980

Parking: at Coniston Pier, 50 yards, not
National Trust (charge including members).

A steam-powered yacht on Coniston Water,
Gondola was rebuilt by the National Trust
based on the original 1859 version. With
inspiration taken from a traditional Venetian
'Burchiello' boat, Steam Yacht Gondola
features the carved figurehead of Sid the
Golden Sea Serpent at the bow of her
streamlined hull and an elegant cabin with
two indoor saloons. The Coniston Fells provide
an impressive backdrop to your cruise, with
opportunities to alight at jetties around the
lake. As you pass famous landmarks, the crew
provide a commentary on Gondola's history
on the lake and association with the famous
Swallows and Amazons. **Note**: cruises depart
from Coniston Pier (subject to weather
conditions). Sorry no toilet on scheduled
sailings. Steam Yacht Gondola (a member of
National Historic Ships Fleet) is very costly to
run. Charges for members with 10 per cent
discount on scheduled round-trip cruises.

Steam Yacht Gondola, Coniston, Cumbria

Enjoying sitting at the bow of elegant
Steam Yacht Gondola on a trip on Coniston Water

Eat, shop, stay: small shop on board selling
souvenirs. Gift experiences available online.
Bluebird Café at Coniston Pier and coffee
house/restaurant at Brantwood (neither
National Trust). Rose Castle Cottage above
Tarn Hows is a perfect base for ramblers,
or camp at Hoathwaite.

Things to see and do: See the steam engine
in action through an open window.'Engineer
for the day' gift experience. Grand Victorian
Circular Tour package for small groups. Private
charters available. Guided and downloadable
walks. **Dogs**: welcome in outside areas.

Access: 🅿♿♿👓♿ Gangway ♿♿

Find out more: 015394 32733 or
sygondola@nationaltrust.org.uk

Steam Yacht Gondola		M	T	W	T	F	S	S
South Lake Cruise								
28 Mar–1 Nov	10:45–11:45*	M	T	W	T	F	S	S
North Lake Cruise								
28 Mar–1 Nov	12–12:45*	M	T	W	T	F	S	S
28 Mar–1 Nov	1:30–2:15*	M	T	W	T	F	S	S
Full Lake Cruise								
28 Mar–1 Nov	2:30–4:15*	M	T	W	T	F	S	S

*Times show duration of cruise. All sailings depart from
Coniston Pier. You can 'hop off/hop on' at other piers:
Monk Coniston and Parkamoor (National Trust),
Lake Bank and Brantwood (not National Trust).
Cruises subject to weather conditions.

Sticklebarn and The Langdales

near Ambleside, Cumbria

🎫 🏛 ♿ 🛏 👶 🚹 🍽 1925

Satnav: use LA22 9JU for Sticklebarn; LA22 9PG for Blea Tarn; LA22 9HP for Elterwater; LA22 9HJ for High Close Estate. **Parking**: at Stickle Ghyll, Old Dungeon Ghyll, Blea Tarn, Elterwater village and High Close Estate.

A striking U-shaped valley, Langdale was described by the leading English art critic John Ruskin, as 'the loveliest rock scenery, chased with silver waterfalls that I have ever set foot or heart upon'. This outdoor playground offers miles of walking, cycling and climbing routes, from a high-level scramble on the Langdale Pikes to a low-level stroll around Blea Tarn. Below the peaks sits Sticklebarn, a National Trust-run pub serving food and drink that celebrates Cumbria's food heritage and local produce. An outdoor terrace and open fires offer the perfect place to share stories of adventures on the fells over a pint of Cumbrian ale.

The Langdales, Cumbria: mist floats across atmospheric Blea Tarn as the sun rises

Eat, shop, stay: Sticklebarn serves planet-friendly food and drinks, including Cumbrian real ales (outdoor seating on terrace). Sleep under the stars at Langdale campsite or stay at Silverthwaite cottage (sleeps eight) in Langdale Valley.

Things to see and do: **Indoors** Sticklebarn is a great place to relax whatever the Lakeland weather throws at you. There are open log fires and board games, regular film screenings and live music sessions. **Outdoors** Within minutes of the car park you can be walking and climbing in the fells or following the off-road cycle trail from Sticklebarn to Skelwith Bridge. Close by there's a riverside ramble from Elterwater or High Close Estate and Arboretum offers 4.5 hectares (11 acres) of tranquillity and more than 100 years of fascinating history, with trees from around the globe.
Dogs: welcome on leads.

Access: 🅿️♿🏫♿ Sticklebarn ♿♿

Find out more: 015394 37356 (Sticklebarn) or sticklebarn@nationaltrust.org.uk

Sticklebarn: walkers take a well-earned break, above, and an accessible path at Elterwater, below

Sticklebarn and The Langdales		M	T	W	T	F	S	S
Sticklebarn*								
24 Jan–29 Mar	11–9**	M	T	W	T	F	S	S
30 Mar–1 Nov	11–10:30**	M	T	W	T	F	S	S
2 Nov–31 Dec†	11–9**	M	T	W	T	F	S	S
Great Langdale Campsite††								
Open all year		M	T	W	T	F	S	S

*Sticklebarn: open 1 January, 11 to 10:30.
**Bar: open to 11, Friday and Saturday. †Closed 24 and 25 December; 31 December open 11 to 1 in the morning.
††For detailed opening times and bookings please visit ntlakescampsites.org.uk or call 015394 32733.

Tarn Hows and Coniston

near Coniston, Cumbria

🔲🔲🔲 1930

Satnav: does not work, follow signs from B5285, Coniston or Hawkshead Hill. **Parking**: on site at Tarn Hows, also at Glen Mary nearby. Parking available in Coniston (not National Trust).

An accessible walk for all the family whatever the weather, Tarn Hows showcases ever-changing scenery and views of the high fells. The circular 1¾-mile path through a 19th-century man-made landscape makes it a favourite with walkers of all abilities. Arrive early or late for a meditative moment with mountain views. **Note**: toilets in main car park. Mobility scooters free to hire (donations welcome). Livestock grazing.

Eat, shop, stay: ice-cream van (most summer days). Picnics welcome. Pubs and cafés in nearby Coniston and Hawkshead (none National Trust). Find a quiet countryside retreat at Rose Castle holiday cottage.

Things to see and do: take a leisurely Steam Yacht Gondola cruise across Coniston Water, then walk through Monk Coniston Hall's grounds to Tarn Hows. **Dogs**: welcome on leads.

Access: 🔲🔲🔲 Grounds 🔲🔲🔲

Find out more: 015394 41456 or tarnhows@nationaltrust.org.uk

Tarn Hows and Coniston	M	T	W	T	F	S	S
Hoathwaite Campsite*							
3 Apr–13 Sep	M	T	W	T	F	S	S

*For detailed opening times and bookings please visit ntlakescampsites.org.uk or call 015394 32733.

Townend

Troutbeck, Windermere, Cumbria LA23 1LB

🔲🔲 1948

Parking: 300 yards.

A cosy farmhouse near Windermere brimming with character. Home to the Browne family for 400 years, Townend is full of intricately carved furniture and rare books, including 44 that are the only remaining copies in the world. Warm yourself by the open fire and spend time in the cottage garden. **Note**: unfortunately we cannot take card payments.

Eat, shop, stay: picnics welcome. Small shop in the house. Tea-room in Troutbeck village (not National Trust).

Things to see and do: **Indoors** Guided tours at 11 and 12 (places limited). 'A Taste of Townend', living-history cooking demonstrations on Thursdays. **Outdoors** Children's garden trail. Traditional games. **Dogs**: welcome in the garden only.

Access: 🔲🔲🔲🔲🔲 Building and grounds 🔲

Find out more: 015394 32628 or townend@nationaltrust.org.uk

Townend		M	T	W	T	F	S	S
14 Mar–1 Nov	1–5*			W	T	F	S	S

*Guided tours at 11 and 12 (places limited). Open Bank Holiday Mondays. May close early due to poor light.

Cosy Townend in Cumbria brims with character

Wasdale

near Gosforth, Cumbria

✚ 🍴 🏛 🎒 ♿ 👜 📷 ⛺ 1920

Satnav: use CA20 1EX. **Parking**: at Lake Head CA20 1EX; Overbeck CA20 1EX (limited space); Nether Wasdale CA20 1ET (limited space).

Wasdale sits below some of England's highest mountains. From the tops of Illgill Head and Whin Rigg the screes sweep down creating ever-changing reflections in Wastwater below. Great Gable stands at the head of the valley with Scafell Pike nearby. This is a remote mountain landscape for hill-walking, climbing and exploring. Towards the southern end of the lake and Nether Wasdale, winding paths weave through woodland and along the water's edge, revealing a gentler aspect to the valley. Planning ahead will give you the best experience: remember to check the weather forecast, prepare well and enjoy your day. **Note**: temporary toilet facilities – new visitor facilities opening in spring.

Wasdale, Cumbria: walkers at the summit of Scafell Pike

Enjoy a night under the stars at Wasdale Campsite

Eat, shop, stay: stay in in our cosy cottage, a tent, tipi, pod or bring your campervan to Wasdale Campsite. Perfect for digital-detox holidays. Campsite shop. Pub and shop at Wasdale Head; pubs in Nether Wasdale and Santon Bridge (none National Trust).

Things to see and do: walking and climbing in England's highest mountains. Lakeshore, riverside and woodland rambles. Wild swimming and paddling in Wastwater and rivers. Herdwick sheep graze in fields and on fellsides. **Dogs**: welcome under close control; on leads around livestock (please follow local and seasonal guidance).

Find out more: 019467 26064 or wasdale@nationaltrust.org.uk

Wasdale		
Wasdale Campsite*		
Open every day all year		

*For detailed opening times and bookings please visit ntlakescampsites.org.uk or call 015394 32733.

Whitehaven Coast

Whitehaven, Cumbria 2008

Coast with a proud mining past. Enjoy bracing clifftop walks to St Bees Head from the sandstone Georgian harbour. **Note**: sorry no toilets. For satnav use CA28 9BG for clifftop car park and CA28 7LY for Whitehaven Harbour.

Find out more: 017687 74649 or whitehavencoast@nationaltrust.org.uk

Wordsworth House and Garden

Main Street, Cockermouth, Cumbria CA13 9RX

🏠 ✿ 🔔 ⊤ 1938

Eat, shop, stay: browse through Wordsworth books and souvenirs, plants, gifts, accessories and indulgent treats in the shop. Free tea or coffee and homemade scones in the upstairs discovery room make the perfect end to a visit. Picnics welcome. Second-hand books for sale.

Things to see and do: 'William's Lakeland legacy' and 'Wordsworth House in the 20th century' displays. Children's trail, replica costumes, toys and games. Holiday art and craft activities. Family-friendly garden tours. Heritage chickens. Evening talks.
Dogs: assistance dogs only.

Access: 🐾 ⚡ ♿ 🅿 📷 📺 🚻 ♿ 🅰
Building ♿ 🔼 ♿ Grounds ♿ ♿

Find out more: 01900 820884 (Infoline).
01900 824805 or
wordsworthhouse@nationaltrust.org.uk

Wordsworth House		M	T	W	T	F	S	S
15 Feb–8 Nov	11–5*	M	T	W	T		S	S

*House: last entry one hour before closing (timed tickets may operate on busy days). Open 8 May and selected Fridays in holidays (please call for details).

Dressing-up fun at Wordsworth House and Garden, Cumbria, left, and towering hollyhocks, below

Parking: in town-centre car parks, none National Trust (charge including members). Please note long-stay car park signposted as coach park, 300 yards, Wakefield Road.

Wandering among the heritage fruit trees, flowers and vegetables of William Wordsworth's garden as the River Derwent gurgles by, it's easy to picture the wild child born here 250 years ago and imagine how his childhood home inspired a love of nature and lifetime of creativity. Indoors, hands-on rooms, animations, and audio and guided tours offer a window into the Georgian world. Costumed servants cook in the kitchen, gossip and tell tales on selected days. A special anniversary exhibition of personal belongings and new insights reveals the happiness and heartache that shaped one of the world's favourite poets.

Wray Castle

Low Wray, Ambleside, Cumbria LA22 0JA

🏠 ♿ 🚻 ⛺ | 1929 |

Parking: restricted car parking. Please come by boat, bike or boot to avoid disappointment.

In the 1840s a surgeon and an heiress from Liverpool began building a castle with panoramic Lake District views that would only ever have to defend itself from the Cumbrian weather. With all the furniture and artwork long gone and the last family moving out in the 1920s, the castle has had mixed use and first opened to visitors in 2011. With church-like interiors, the castle is a work in progress, as we're continually learning about its past. You can discover more about the castle's colourful history by joining one of the daily talks or tours. Families can explore the activity rooms, where there's plenty of space for creative play inspired by the story of Wray Castle. **Note**: steep walk from jetty if arriving by boat. Limited car parking.

Arriving by boat at Wray Castle in Cumbria, right, and a glimpse of the panoramic views beyond the castle, below

Find out more: 015394 33250 or
wraycastle@nationaltrust.org.uk

Wray Castle		M	T	W	T	F	S	S
Castle								
15 Feb–27 Mar	10–4	M	T	W	T	F	S	S
28 Mar–1 Nov	10–5	M	T	W	T	F	S	S
7 Nov–20 Dec	10–4	·	·	·	·	·	S	S
Grounds								
Open all year	Dawn–dusk	M	T	W	T	F	S	S
Low Wray Campsite*								
27 Mar–1 Nov		M	T	W	T	F	S	S

*For detailed opening times and bookings please visit
ntlakescampsites.org.uk or call 015394 32733.

Additional countryside car parks in The Lakes

Borrowdale and Derwent Water

Great Wood	CA12 5UP
Kettlewell	CA12 5UN
Ashness Bridge	CA12 5UN
Surprise View	CA12 5UU
Watendlath	CA12 5UW
Bowder Stone	CA12 5XA
Rosthwaite	CA12 5XB
Seatoller	CA12 5XN

Buttermere Valley

Buttermere	CA13 9UZ
Crummock Water	CA13 0RT
Honister Pass	CA12 5XN
Lanthwaite Green	CA13 9UY
Maggie's Bridge	CA13 0RU

Ullswater

Glencoyne Bay	CA11 0NQ
High Cascades	CA11 0JY
Park Brow	CA11 0JY

Wasdale

Lake Head	CA20 1EX
Overbeck	CA20 1EX
Nether Wasdale	CA20 1ET

The Langdales

Blea Tarn	LA22 9PG
Old Dungeon Ghyll	LA22 9JY
Stickle Ghyll	LA22 9JU
Elterwater	LA22 9HP
High Close	LA22 9HJ

Coniston

Glen Mary	LA21 8DP

Windermere West Shore

Red Nab	LA22 0JH
Harrowslack	LA22 0LR
Ash Landing	LA22 0LP

Eat, shop, stay: Kitchen Court café serving drinks, sandwiches, soup and cakes (open most of year). Indoor picnic room. Shop selling family games, gifts and souvenirs. Stay at The Summer House holiday cottage or camp at Low Wray. Picnics welcome.

Things to see and do: **Indoors** Talks, tours and activities shed light on the castle's enigmatic past, architecture and the surrounding landscape. Explore the family-friendly rooms upstairs, including the Peter Rabbit Adventure, dressing up and castle-building. **Outdoors** Take a boat from Ambleside or Brockhole to the castle's jetty (sailings by Windermere Lake Cruises). Grounds, parkland and woods to explore, including play trail with treehouse and rope swings. Find the shingle beach, climb up Latterbarrow hill or take the lakeshore path to Claife Viewing Station (4 miles). **Dogs**: welcome on leads everywhere, excluding castle.

Access: 🅿️ 🚻 ♿ ♿ ♿ 🚗 ♿ Castle ♿ ♿

Yorkshire

Family time well spent in the midst of the blooms at
Wentworth Castle Gardens, South Yorkshire

Barnard Castle

MIDDLESBROUGH

Ormesby Hall

Darlington

Stokesley

Roseberry Topping

Whitby

Richmond

Mount Grace Priory

Northallerton

Bridestones, Crosscliff and Blakey Topping

Yorkshire Coast

Braithwaite Hall

A1(M)

Rievaulx Terrace

Scarborough

Thirsk

Pickering

A170

Filey

Nunnington Hall

A168

A19

Yorkshire Dales

Ripon

A64

Bridlington

Fountains Abbey

Settle

Brimham Rocks

Harrogate

Beningbrough Hall

A166

Treasurer's House

Skipton

Goddards House

YORK

Beverley

Wetherby

Middlethorpe Hall

Kingston upon Hull

East Riddlesden Hall

Keighley

A64

Selby

M62

Burnley

Hardcastle Crags

Bradford

Leeds

A63

M621

Halifax

M62

Pontefract

Rochdale

Huddersfield

Wakefield

Nostell

M18

Marsden Moor

M1

M180

BARNSLEY

Doncaster

M62

Wentworth Castle Gardens

A635

A159

A1(M)

M60

Wentworth Woodhouse

M18

A631

Kinder, Edale and the Dark Peak

SHEFFIELD

Lyme

Longshaw, Burbage and the Eastern Moors

Worksop

A158

Clumber Park

M6

Hardwick

A61

A46

A617

M1

A52

A1

Legend

▲ **Buildings and/or gardens**

● **Entry points to coast and countryside**

🗺 **National Trust land**

Ⓗ **Historic House Hotel**

Places in neighbouring counties

East Midlands, page 252

North West, page 314

⊢——⊣ **10 miles**

Beningbrough Hall, Gallery and Gardens, North Yorkshire, above and below: so much to discover, both inside and out

Beningbrough Hall, Gallery and Gardens

Beningbrough, York,
North Yorkshire YO30 1DD

🏛️ ❄️ ♿ 🛏️ 1958

Parking: on site.

Surrounded by parkland, with riverside and woodland walks on all sides, the view of the Hall as you turn onto the long drive evokes images of an intriguing past. From the wealthy teenager who inherited it, to the Hall's use as an RAF billet, Beningbrough has been shaped for more than 300 years by the people who lived here. The architecture, intricate panelling and furnished ground-floor rooms tell the story of a grand country house, and the spacious and light-filled Saloon Galleries display exhibitions of contemporary and historic art.

The gardens are experiencing a renaissance. New planting schemes and garden rooms, designed by award-winning designer Andy Sturgeon, enhance the herbaceous borders, walled and American gardens.

Eat, shop, stay: the Walled Garden Restaurant serves hot lunches, sandwiches and snacks. You can choose from plants and extensive home and garden ranges in the shop. A holiday apartment above the Victorian laundry provides exclusive out-of-hours access to the gardens.

For information about getting to National Trust places, please see page 8

Beningbrough Hall		M	T	W	T	F	S	S
4 Jan–16 Feb*	11–3:30	·	·	·	·	·	S	S
18 Feb–23 Feb*	11–3:30	·	T	W	T	F	S	S
29 Feb–1 Mar*	11–3:30	·	·	·	·	·	S	S
3 Mar–31 May	10:30–5**	·	T	W	T	F	S	S
1 Jun–31 Aug	10:30–5**	M	T	W	T	F	S	S
1 Sep–1 Nov	10:30–5**	·	T	W	T	F	S	S
7 Nov–27 Dec†	11–3:30††	·	·	·	·	·	S	S

Open Bank Holidays, except 25 December. *Hall and Saloon
Galleries: closed. **Hall and Saloon Galleries: open 11:30 to 4.
Shop: opens 12. †Hall: closed. ††Saloon Galleries: open 11:30.
Saloon Galleries closed selected days (conservation work).

Braithwaite Hall

East Witton, Leyburn, North Yorkshire
DL8 4SY 1941

Grand 17th-century tenanted farmhouse in the
heart of Coverdale, close to the River Cover
and surrounded by farmland and woodland.
Note: sorry, no toilet. Parts of the Hall are open
in June, July and August (by arrangement in
advance with the tenant).

Find out more: 01969 640287 or
braithwaitehall@nationaltrust.org.uk

Bridestones, Crosscliff and Blakey Topping

near Pickering, North Yorkshire 1944

On the North York Moors, the Bridestones are
geological wonders – rock formations with
moorland views, woodland walks and grassy
valleys. **Note**: nearest toilets at Staindale Lake
car park. For satnav use YO18 7LR. Nearest
car parks at Bridestones and Staindale Lake.
Road access is via Dalby Forest Drive starting
2½ miles north of Thornton le Dale: toll
charges payable (including members) to
Forestry England. Dalby Forest Drive toll
road open every day all year, 8 to 8.

Find out more: 01723 870423 or
bridestones@nationaltrust.org.uk

**Warm afternoon sun lights up the west front of
Beningbrough Hall, opposite; the glasshouse, above**

Things to see and do: **Indoors** Spark your
curiosity in history and art by joining one of
the pop-up activities on the top floor – from
demonstrations to talks and hands-on creative
workshops – designed for different ages
and interests. Glimpse servant life in the
Victorian laundry. **Outdoors** You can see the
Mediterranean garden being created, as the
team plants the next area of the design. All year
the gardens and parkland are alight with colour
– from snowdrops, crocuses and daffodils to
dahlias, pumpkins and apples. Families can let
off steam in the wilderness play area. There's
a diverse programme of family and adult
activities all year. **Dogs**: welcome on short
leads in the garden and parkland only.

Access: 🅿♿🏠🍴🛍📷♿🐾⓪ Stable block ♿♿
Hall ♿♿🔼🚻♿ Gardens ♿▶♿♿

Find out more: 01904 472027 or
beningbrough@nationaltrust.org.uk

Brimham Rocks

Summerbridge, Harrogate,
North Yorkshire HG3 4DW

⚏ 1970

Parking: on site.

Brimham Rocks, which offer panoramic
views across Nidderdale and wider Yorkshire
countryside, are an incredible collection of
eye-catching rock formations. Sculpted by
320 million years of ice, wind and continental
movement, these rocks have been moulded
into magical shapes and have names such as
the Dancing Bear and Druid's Writing Desk.
It's a natural playground for those seeking
adventure, but also offers tranquillity when
exploring the surrounding moorland – with
its rare wildlife habitat and internationally
important plants. Brimham is a great place
for walkers, climbers, nature-spotters and
artists, as well as families looking for the
freedom to explore. **Note**: nearest toilets
600 yards from car park.

**Brimham Rocks in North Yorkshire: the eye-catching
shapes were sculpted by millions of years of wind and ice**

Eat, shop, stay: kiosk serving hot and
cold drinks and snacks, including cake,
sandwiches and sausage rolls. Picnic benches
are available, with additional indoor seating
at the visitor centre. Shop selling souvenirs,
gifts and local products.

Things to see and do: activities include
guided walks, orienteering, geocaching,
yoga, photography workshops, family nature
activities and climbing taster days. In the visitor
centre, hear about Brimham's geology and
social history and conservation work.
Dogs: welcome on leads.

Access: 🅿🅿🚻🚼♿📷♨ Visitor centre/shop 🐾
Car park welcome building ♿ Countryside ➡♿

Find out more: 01423 780688 or
brimhamrocks@nationaltrust.org.uk

Brimham Rocks		M	T	W	T	F	S	S
Countryside								
Open all year	Dawn–dusk*	M	T	W	T	F	S	S
Visitor centre, shop and kiosk								
1 Jan–5 Jan	11–4			W	T	F	S	S
11 Jan–9 Feb**	11–3						S	S
15 Feb–3 Apr	11–4	M	T	W	T	F	S	S
4 Apr–1 Nov	10–4:30	M	T	W	T	F	S	S
7 Nov–20 Dec	11–4						S	S
21 Dec–31 Dec†	11–4	M	T	W	T	F	S	S

*Main gate: closes 9, or dusk if earlier. **Visitor centre and shop:
closed 11 January to 9 February. †Visitor centre, shop and
kiosk: closed 24 and 25 December. Open 1 to 3 January 2021.

Places may occasionally close for events or bad weather, check at nationaltrust.org.uk

East Riddlesden Hall

Bradford Road, Riddlesden, Keighley,
West Yorkshire BD20 5EL

🏠🏵🐾📷🍸 1934

Parking: 250 yards (limited space
during peak times).

This hidden gem was saved from demolition
in 1934 and today offers a friendly Yorkshire
welcome to all who pass through its
400-year-old doors. The house and its history
continues to surprise us, as we unravel the
stories of ambition, success and failure of all
those who lived and worked here. The intimate
garden offers a relaxing space all year. From
fresh shoots in spring, to cottage garden
flowers in summer and trees laden with fruit
in autumn. The natural play area, with mud-pie
kitchen and den-building corner, will spark
the imagination of the whole family.

Eat, shop, stay: shop and tea-room in the
historic bothy selling plants, local and seasonal
products, as well as homemade scones.
Accessible tables on the ground floor and we're
proud that East Riddlesden Hall has won an
award for being dementia friendly.

Things to see and do: **Indoors** Historic house
with blackwork embroidery and plaster
ceilings. Barn with oak beams displaying
400-year-old markings of proud craftsmen.
Outdoors Intimate gardens, natural play areas,
duck pond and bird hide. **Dogs**: welcome on
lower field. Assistance dogs only in house,
garden, shop and tea-room.

Access: 🅿♿🐕🔔📻🏠📷👓🖼
House, shop and tea-room ♿♿♿ **Garden** ♿♿♿

Find out more: 01535 607075 or
eastriddlesden@nationaltrust.org.uk

East Riddlesden Hall		M	T	W	T	F	S	S
15 Feb–1 Mar	10:30–4:30	**M**	**T**	**W**	**T**	·	**S**	**S**
7 Mar–22 Mar	10:30–4:30	·	·	·	·	·	**S**	**S**
23 Mar–1 Nov*	10:30–4:30	**M**	**T**	**W**	**T**	·	**S**	**S**
7 Nov–13 Dec**	10:30–3:30	·	·	·	·	·	**S**	**S**

*Open Good Friday. Tea-room: last entry 15 minutes
before closing. Hall: November and December, entry
by guided tour (limited access), check before visit.
**No guided tours 5 and 6 December.

Unravel stories of ambition, success and failure at East Riddlesden Hall in West Yorkshire, above and below

Fountains Abbey and Studley Royal Water Garden

near Ripon, North Yorkshire HG4 3DY

🏠✝🏛🏚♿❀🧺🛏🔔🍽 1983

Parking: on site at visitor centre
(six electric vehicle charging points),
West Gate car park and Studley Lakeside.

Deep within the Skell Valley lies Fountains Abbey and Studley Royal, a World Heritage Site waiting to be explored. Humans have tamed and teased the valley's wild waters over hundreds of years, creating an expansive landscape with sweeping Georgian water garden and imposing Abbey ruins. Cistercian monks chose this place to establish Fountains Abbey in 1132, and the walls echo with centuries-old stories. A riverside path leads to Studley Royal, a playful water garden designed by visionaries John and William Aislabie in the 18th century. You'll find art in the garden this summer, as contemporary art programme, 'Folly!', returns. Go beyond the lake to Studley Royal deer park, with ancient tree avenues and red, fallow and sika deer.
Note: Studley tea-room may be closed for refurbishment this year.

Eat, shop, stay: restaurant serving daily specials and Sunday lunch. Lighter bites at Mill Café and Studley tea-room with lake views/terrace. Picnics welcome. Shop with gardening section. Stay at one of 14 holiday cottages, including cosy waterside lodge and apartments inside Fountains Hall.

Exploring Fountains Abbey and Studley Royal Water Garden, North Yorkshire, this page and opposite

Things to see and do: **Indoors** You can watch the water flow at Fountains Mill and uncover the Abbey's extensive history in Porter's Lodge. Try medieval crafts in Swanley Grange and learn about the Settlers Society at Fountains Hall, before visiting St Mary's Church, a Victorian Gothic masterpiece, in the deer park. **Outdoors** Children's play area with zip wire. The orchard and herb garden are great for exploring. There are miles of walks in the deer park and water garden, dotted with follies. Visit the vegetable garden at Swanley Grange. Free guided tours and shuttle bus across the estate. **Dogs**: welcome on leads (water bowls and dog-friendly eating areas outside restaurant and tea-room).

Access: 🅿♿🚻♿🍽♿📷👓🅰
Fountains Abbey ♿♿♿ Fountains Hall ♿
Water Garden ♿▶♿♿

Find out more: 01765 608888 or
fountainsabbey@nationaltrust.org.uk

Fountains Abbey		M	T	W	T	F	S	S
Abbey and Water Garden, visitor centre restaurant, shop								
1 Jan–30 Jan	10–5*	M	T	W	T	.	S	S
1 Feb–27 Mar	10–5*	M	T	W	T	F	S	S
28 Mar–25 Oct	10–6*	M	T	W	T	F	S	S
26 Oct–31 Dec**	10–5*	M	T	W	T	.	S	S
Deer park								
Open all year	6–6	M	T	W	T	F	S	S

Last admission one hour before closing.
*Visitor centre restaurant and shop close one hour earlier.
**Closed 24 and 25 December. Fountains Hall, mill, tea-rooms, Studley Royal shop and St Mary's Church: check opening times before visiting.

Parking is free for members, but don't forget to scan your card in the car park when you visit

Goddards House and Garden

27 Tadcaster Road, Dringhouses, York, North Yorkshire

🏠 ❄ 🍸 1984

Satnav: enter 27 Tadcaster Road, Dringhouses, York, not postcode.
Parking: accessible parking or drop-off only. Park on Knavesmire Road (off A1036) by York racecourse, 1 mile, or use city car parks, none National Trust (charge including members), 1 to 2 miles – frequent buses.

Discover the Terry family's story and confectionery history (think Chocolate Orange) in their former home. Imagine living at a gentler pace as you explore this warm Arts and Crafts building. You're invited to make yourself at home in the drawing room with a sherry or indulge your nostalgic side remembering your favourite Terry's sweets in the 'factory rooms'. Outside, the Terry factory clock tower can be spotted from the paddock orchard overlooking the racecourse. You can take your time and meander through the garden 'rooms', fragrant borders and hidden corners or simply soak up the sunshine on the terrace.

Eat, shop, stay: lunch is served in the Terry's dining room. You can relax with coffee or afternoon tea in the drawing room, or tuck into a slice of Chocolate Orange cake on the terrace, enjoying views of the Arts and Crafts garden.

Things to see and do: **Indoors** Chocolate box displays conjure up memories of old favourites. Make your own chocolate box to take home. **Outdoors** Beautifully restored Arts and Crafts garden. Outdoor games and family trails. **Dogs**: welcome on leads in the garden.

Access: 🅿 🚻 ♿ 🪑 📷 🎧 ♿
House 🅿 ♿ 👨‍👩‍👧 Garden ♿ ➡

Find out more: 01904 771930 or goddards@nationaltrust.org.uk

Goddards House		M	T	W	T	F	S	S
27 Feb–29 Mar	10:30–5				**T**	**F**	**S**	**S**
1 Apr–1 Nov*	10:30–5			**W**	**T**	**F**	**S**	**S**
18 Nov–20 Dec	10:30–4			**W**	**T**	**F**	**S**	**S**

*Open Bank Holidays.

Goddards House and Garden in North Yorkshire: warm and welcoming Arts and Crafts house, above and below

Hardcastle Crags

near Hebden Bridge, West Yorkshire

🏞️ 🚣 🛏️ ⚓ ☂ 1950

Satnav: for Midgehole car park use HX7 7AA;
Clough Hole car park HX7 7AZ.
Parking: at Midgehole car park, 1 mile
to Gibson Mill, or Clough Hole car park,
¾ mile (steep walk).

This picturesque valley has more than 25 miles
of footpaths and 160 hectares (400 acres)
of woodland to explore. You'll see tumbling
streams, waterfalls, deep ravines and
natural flood management interventions.
It's home to the northern hairy wood ant
and internationally rare waxcap grasslands.
Seasonal highlights include sweet-smelling
bluebells in late spring, carpets of golden leaves
in autumn and rare, delicate frost flowers in
winter. You can walk along the riverside to
Gibson Mill, a former cotton mill and
Edwardian entertainment emporium, where
you'll find the café and can discover how the
valley has changed over the past 200 years.
Note: steep paths, rough terrain. Toilets and
café at Gibson Mill, 1 mile from car parks.

Eat, shop, stay: café serving drinks, light
lunches and cakes, with log burner in cooler
weather. Outdoor ice-cream parlour during
summer months. Shop selling walking trails,
books, gifts and sweets. Stay longer at one of
the holiday cottages.

Things to see and do: **Indoors** Find out about
the mill's history and the local area. See 'off the
grid' technology and occasional exhibitions.
Outdoors Walking trails, guided walks,
picnics, wildlife and family activities.
Dogs: welcome under close control,
including in café. On leads near livestock.

Access: 🅿️🅿️🦽🔺🏬🚶 Mill ♿🚻

Find out more: 01422 844518 (weekdays).
01422 846236 (weekends) or
hardcastlecrags@nationaltrust.org.uk

Hardcastle Crags, West Yorkshire, offers more than
25 miles of footpaths through woodland and ravines

Hardcastle Crags		M	T	W	T	F	S	S
Gibson Mill and Weaving Shed Café								
1 Jan–5 Jan	11–3	·	·	W	T	F	S	S
11 Jan–16 Feb	11–3	·	·	·	·	·	S	S
17 Feb–23 Feb	11–3	M	T	W	T	F	S	S
29 Feb–15 Mar	11–3	·	·	·	·	·	S	S
16 Mar–1 Nov*	11–4	M	T	W	T	F	S	S
7 Nov–20 Dec	11–3	·	·	·	·	·	S	S
21 Dec–31 Dec	11–3	M	T	W	T	·	S	S

*Mill closes occasionally for private events
(check before visiting).

Marsden Moor

near Huddersfield, West Yorkshire

🏛♿🐕 1955

Satnav: use HD7 6DH for the Information Room, guided walks, plant sales and Marsden village. HD3 3FT for Buckstones and HD9 4HW for Wessenden Head. **Parking**: Marsden village (not National Trust), Buckstones and Wessenden Head.

This Site of Special Scientific Interest, with far-reaching views across the South Pennines and Peak District, has more than 2,000 hectares (5,500 acres) of countryside to explore. There's plenty of wildlife to spot, and regular guided walks will take you along miles of footpaths to favourite viewpoints. **Note**: sorry no toilets.

Eat, shop, stay: cafés/pubs in Marsden village (not National Trust). Plant sales Friday and Sunday in spring and summer. Handmade recycled wooden planters and wildlife homes available. Christmas tree sales on December weekends.

Things to see and do: downloadable walks. Events and guided walks all year. Due to ground-nesting birds please keep to footpaths. **Dogs**: welcome on leads (livestock roaming and ground-nesting birds).

Access: Information Room ♿

Find out more: 01484 847016 or marsdenmoor@nationaltrust.org.uk

Marsden Moor	
Information Room	
Open every day all year*	8:30–4:30**

*Closed 25 December. **Open 9 to 5 on Saturday and Sunday.

Middlethorpe Hall Hotel, Restaurant and Spa

Bishopthorpe Road, York, North Yorkshire YO23 2GB

🏛❄♿🛏♿🍴 2008

Middlethorpe Hall is a country house just outside York, built of mellow red brick during the reign of William III in 1699 and set in 8 hectares (20 acres) of gardens. Furnished with antiques and paintings, Middlethorpe still has the look and feel of a well-kept manor house. The comfortable bedrooms are complemented by elegant public rooms, including the drawing room and wood-panelled dining room, where imaginative meals are served. The gardens include a rose garden, a walled garden and a meadow leading to a tree-ringed lake. In the spa, which has a small gym, indoor swimming pool and sauna, the trained therapists use Aromatherapy Associates products. **Note**: access for guests staying at the hotel, using the spa or enjoying luncheon, afternoon tea and dinner. Children over the age of six welcome.

Find out more: 01904 641241 or info@middlethorpe.com middlethorpe.com

Mount Grace Priory, House and Gardens

Staddle Bridge, Northallerton, North Yorkshire DL6 3JG 1953

Explore the well-preserved ruins of a medieval priory, set in woodland with gardens and an Arts and Crafts manor house. **Note**: managed by English Heritage; National Trust members free, except on event days. Open daily 1 April to 1 November. Limited opening other times. Check with English Heritage for details.

Find out more: 01609 883494 or mountgracepriory@nationaltrust.org.uk

Nostell

Doncaster Road, Nostell, near Wakefield,
West Yorkshire WF4 1QE

🏠✝✿🐿🔔🍴 1954

Parking: 650 yards.

Built to impress in the 18th century, Nostell is
one of the great treasure houses in the north
of England. Generations of the Winn family
employed the best architects, craftsmen and
artists to create a showcase for fashionable
design. Discover interiors by influential
architect Robert Adam, a world-class collection
of furniture, textiles and wallpaper supplied by
Thomas Chippendale, priceless paintings, a
Georgian doll's house and a rare John Harrison
clock. Home to wildlife including swans,
kingfishers and bats, the surrounding
121-hectare (300-acre) estate includes
parkland, lakes, a working kitchen garden
and the tranquil Menagerie Garden.
With displays of snowdrops, daffodils
and bluebells, woodland cycle trails and
all-weather paths, you can find new things
to see and do in every season.

Eat, shop, stay: Courtyard Café serving
hot food and refreshments. Shop selling
gifts, souvenirs and plants. Second-hand
bookshop and kiosk offering snacks and
drinks open at peak times. Picnics welcome
in the park and gardens.

Things to see and do: **Indoors** You can find
out more about Nostell's collections through
temporary exhibitions and events or learn a
new skill in artist-led sessions for adults.
Families can follow the house trail and make
masterpieces in the Workshop every school
holiday. **Outdoors** Explore the parkland paths
by bike, foot, scooter or wheelchair, or practise
your twists and turns on the cycle-only trails.

Imposing Nostell in West Yorkshire, above and below, is one of the north of England's great treasure houses

Cycle trails through Nostell's parkland allow the whole family to go wild on two wheels

Children can go wild with led activities every school holiday and enjoy nature-spotting, geocaching, den-building and the woodland play area all year. **Dogs**: assistance dogs only in gardens/house. Under close control, on leads when requested, in park.

Access: ♿🅿️♿♿♿♿♿♿
House ♿♿♿ Grounds ♿♿➡️♿♿

Find out more: 01924 863892 or nostell@nationaltrust.org.uk

Nostell		M	T	W	T	F	S	S
House								
7 Mar–1 Nov*	11–4**	·	·	W	T	F	S	S
5 Dec–20 Dec	11–3**	·	·	·	·	·	S	S
Gardens, shop and café								
1 Jan–6 Mar	10–4	M	T	W	T	F	S	S
7 Mar–1 Nov	10–5	M	T	W	T	F	S	S
2 Nov–31 Dec	10–4	M	T	W	T	F	S	S
Parkland								
Open all year	7–7†	M	T	W	T	F	S	S

*Open Bank Holidays. **House: check additional opening arrangements before visiting. †Parkland: last entry 6. Closed 25 December.

Nunnington Hall

Nunnington, near York,
North Yorkshire YO62 5UY

🏠 ❄ 1953

Parking: on site.

At this welcoming house and garden, in its beautiful setting on the River Rye, you can discover stories about the Fife family in the 1920s, as well as the rise and fall of Lord Preston during the 17th century. The organic garden is ideal for relaxing and you can picnic in wildflower meadows and fruit orchards. This year the 'Essex House Tapestries: The Life of Julie Cope' by Grayson Perry, are hanging in place of the 17th-century tapestries, which are away for conservation. There is also the Carlisle Collection of miniature rooms, renowned for its high-quality craftsmanship, to enjoy.

Eat, shop, stay: licensed waitress-service tea-room inside house, serving homemade lunches and cakes. Outdoor garden kiosk (peak times) with seating next to the River Rye. Shop (third floor) selling gifts. Second-hand bookshop.

Nunnington Hall, North Yorkshire, below, sits surrounded by a beautiful organic garden, above

Things to see and do: **Indoors** Carlisle Collection of miniature rooms. Guided tours (selected days). Touring art exhibitions and events throughout the year.
Outdoors Garden games and natural play area.
Dogs: welcome on leads in the garden.

Access: 🅿️♿🚻 Building 🔔♿♿ Grounds ♿♿

Find out more: 01439 748283 or nunningtonhall@nationaltrust.org.uk

Nunnington Hall		M	T	W	T	F	S	S
8 Feb–8 Mar	10:30–4	·	T	W	T	F	S	S
10 Mar–31 May	10:30–5	·	T	W	T	F	S	S
1 Jun–6 Sep	10:30–5	M	T	W	T	F	S	S
8 Sep–1 Nov	10:30–5	·	T	W	T	F	S	S
20 Nov–20 Dec	10:30–4	·	·	·	·	F	S	S

Last entry 45 minutes before closing. Open Bank Holiday Mondays and Mondays in school holidays.

Ormesby Hall

Ladgate Lane, Ormesby, near Middlesbrough, Redcar & Cleveland TS3 0SR

🏠 ♣ ♨ 🔔 ▼ 1962

Parking: 200 yards.

A working estate on ancient farmland, this green space, with the Pennyman family home at its heart, is the last surviving historic estate in Middlesbrough. The Pennymans loved their garden and pleasure grounds, which now have newly opened vistas, a revived, colourful spring garden and a restored Victorian fernery. The 400-year-old estate has had many owners, from the scandalous Sir James Pennyman, the 6th Baronet, to the generous Ruth and Jim. This year hear stories of family illnesses and discover how James Stovin Pennyman helped the wellbeing of the local community by developing a cottage hospital and school.

Eat, shop, stay: Pennyman pantry tea-room serving a range of hot and cold drinks, soup, sandwiches, hot lunches, cakes and scones. Shop selling National Trust products, children's toys and plants. Second-hand bookshop. Picnics welcome in the garden.

Things to see and do: Indoors Baking days in the Victorian kitchen, model railway layouts and behind-the-scenes tours. **Outdoors** Natural play area, barefoot walk, seasonal flowers, garden games, estate walks and garden history. **Dogs**: welcome on leads in garden, courtyards and wider estate.

Access: 🅿️ 🚹 ♿ 🍴 🏠 📷
House ♿ 🏠 Grounds 🏠 ➡️

Find out more: 01642 324188 or ormesbyhall@nationaltrust.org.uk

Ormesby Hall		M	T	W	T	F	S	S
8 Feb–19 Apr*	10:30–5	M	T	W	T		S	S
20 Apr–18 Oct*	10:30–5	M	T	W	T			S
19 Oct–8 Nov	10:30–5	M	T	W	T		S	S
21 Nov–21 Dec	10:30–4	M					S	S

Last entry one hour before closing. *Closed 29 February, 3 May and 20 September.

Classic Georgian Ormesby Hall, Redcar & Cleveland, above and below, has a history of scandal and philanthropy

Rievaulx Terrace

Rievaulx, Helmsley, North Yorkshire YO62 5LJ

🏠❄️♿ 1972

Parking: 100 yards.

Rievaulx Terrace, North Yorkshire: designed to impress

Designed to impress, Rievaulx Terrace was created by the Duncombe family in the 18th century and feels just as grand and tranquil today. Enjoy a peaceful woodland walk out onto the terrace with views of Rievaulx Abbey and look inside the Ionic Temple to see the beautifully painted ceiling. **Note**: no access from Rievaulx Terrace to Rievaulx Abbey (managed by English Heritage).

Eat, shop, stay: pre-packed snacks, ice cream, hot and cold drinks available. Picnics welcome. Shop selling gifts and souvenirs.

Things to see and do: furnished Ionic Temple opens at intervals throughout the day. Woodland natural play area for children and outdoor games.
Dogs: welcome on leads in garden.

Access: 🅿️♿🚻♿♿
Visitor centre 🏠 Temples 🏠 Grounds 🏠➡️♿

Find out more: 01439 798340 (summer). 01439 748283 (winter) or rievaulxterrace@nationaltrust.org.uk

Rievaulx Terrace		M	T	W	T	F	S	S
8 Feb–1 Mar	10–4	·	·	·	·	·	S	S
2 Mar–27 Sep	10–5	M	T	W	T	F	S	S
28 Sep–1 Nov	10–4	M	T	W	T	F	S	S

Last entry one hour before closing.

Roseberry Topping

near Newton-under-Roseberry, North Yorkshire 1985

Affectionately known as 'Yorkshire's Matterhorn', Roseberry Topping has woodland walks and wildlife on its slopes, and views from its summit. **Note**: nearest parking at Newton-under-Roseberry, not National Trust (charge including members). Nearest toilets also in this car park. For satnav use TS9 6QR.

Find out more: 01723 870423 or roseberrytopping@nationaltrust.org.uk

Treasurer's House, York

Minster Yard, York, North Yorkshire YO1 7JL

🏠❄️🍴☕ 1930

Parking: nearest at Lord Mayor's Walk (not National Trust). Park and ride from city outskirts recommended.

Tucked behind York Minster, Treasurer's House is not as it first appears. In 1897 it was bought by Frank Green, the grandson of a wealthy industrialist, and by 1900 he had transformed it at great speed into an elaborately decorated town house, ready for the visit of Edward VII.

Fascinating Treasurer's House, York

The award-winning garden at Treasurer's House, York, offers an oasis of calm in the midst of this busy city

Hear about Frank Green's life and find out how he saved Treasurer's House and changed it from a ramshackle collection of buildings into the grand show home we see today. The award-winning garden is an oasis of calm, offering unrivalled views of York Minster, making it an ideal place to relax. **Note**: charges for Roman Ghost Cellar and Rooftop Servants' Quarters tours (including members).

Eat, shop, stay: Below Stairs Café serves morning coffee, lunch and cakes. Around the corner, the National Trust's large shop sells a wide selection of gifts. Stay a little longer in either of our city-centre holiday apartments.

Things to see and do: family trails. Hard-hat tours into the cellar (over fives), the site of York's most famous ghost story, and town-house tours (both on selected days). The house is decorated for Christmas. **Dogs**: welcome on leads in the garden.

Access: 🅿️🎨📷🖼️♿ House ♿♿♿ Garden ♿

Find out more: 01904 624247 or treasurershouse@nationaltrust.org.uk

Treasurer's House, York		M	T	W	T	F	S	S
1 Apr–8 Nov*	11–4:30	M	T	W	T	F	S	S
14 Nov–20 Dec	11–4:30	M	T	W	T	F	S	S

*On selected days access is by guided tour only.

Wentworth Castle Gardens

Park Drive, Stainborough, Barnsley,
South Yorkshire S75 3EN

🏵️🏆 2018

Parking: on site.

Working together with Barnsley Council and
Northern College, this estate, rooted in rivalry,
provides a space to bring people together.
Royal diplomat Thomas Wentworth was
outraged when a cousin inherited his family
home in 1695 and was determined to outdo
him, creating what was once known as
'the finest garden in England'. Today it is
South Yorkshire's only Grade I-registered
landscape, with acres of parkland and gardens
to explore. There are surprises along every
avenue, including a castle that is not what it
seems. **Note**: house closed to visitors as
it houses Northern College, which offers
residential adult education courses.

Eat, shop, stay: café serving light meals,
cakes and refreshments. Shop selling gifts
and souvenirs. Kiosk offering snacks and
drinks open at peak times. Picnics welcome
in the parkland and gardens.

Things to see and do: garden houses three
national plant collections: rhododendron,
magnolia and camellia species, with Victorian
conservatory, flower garden and fernery. 200
hectares (500 acres) of parkland. Adventure
play area and orienteering. **Dogs**: welcome on
leads in the gardens and parkland.

Access: 🅿️🐕🦽🍼📷🖼️ Long Barn 🏛️🚻♿🔄

Find out more: 01226 776040 or
wentworthcastlegardens@nationaltrust.org.uk

Wentworth Castle Gardens		M	T	W	T	F	S	S
Whole property								
1 Jan–1 Mar	10–3:30	M	T	W	T	F	S	S
2 Mar–1 Nov	10–5	M	T	W	T	F	S	S
2 Nov–31 Dec*	10–3:30	M	T	W	T	F	S	S

*Closed 25 December.

Wentworth Castle Gardens, South Yorkshire: the Rotunda, above, and the intriguing sham ruined castle, below

Wentworth Woodhouse

Cortworth Lane, Wentworth, Rotherham, South Yorkshire S62 7TQ 2017

Large 18th-century country house, saved for the nation by Wentworth Woodhouse Preservation Trust, which is working to restore it. **Note**: house operated by Wentworth Woodhouse Preservation Trust, which is undertaking an ambitious restoration project. For satnav use S62 7TQ. National Trust members receive 50 per cent discount on all tours. House and garden open for guided tours, Wednesday to Sunday, 10 to 4. Tea-room and shop open Tuesday to Sunday, 10 to 4.

Find out more: 01226 351161 or info@wentworthwoodhouse.org.uk

The Yorkshire Coast, left and above

Yorkshire Coast

near Ravenscar, North Yorkshire

🏚🏊🚲🐾🛏🏘 1976

Satnav: for Ravenscar use YO13 0NE.
Parking: on roadside at Ravenscar.
Pay and display at Saltburn, Runswick Bay and Robin Hood's Bay, not National Trust (charge including members).

The coastline from Saltburn to Filey has a rich heritage. Explore via clifftop walks or cycling routes, and discover sandy bays that are perfect for rock-pooling and fossil-hunting. Ravenscar Visitor Centre offers inspiring ideas for your visit, and there's a coastal exhibition at the Old Coastguard Station, Robin Hood's Bay.

Eat, shop, stay: Old Coastguard Station shop sells gifts, books, maps and toys. Ravenscar Visitor Centre offers limited selection of drinks and snacks. Holiday cottages at Ravenscar and Robin Hood's Bay (sea views).

Things to see and do: **Indoors** Exhibitions at the Old Coastguard Station, the 'Town that Never Was' story at Ravenscar Visitor Centre. **Outdoors** Family events, watersports, wildlife activities, guided walks. **Dogs**: welcome on leads around livestock, at most events and in Ravenscar Visitor Centre.

Access: 🅿️🅿️🅿️🅿️ Old Coastguard Station 🦽

Find out more: 01723 870423 or yorkshirecoast@nationaltrust.org.uk

Yorkshire Coast		M	T	W	T	F	S	S
Old Coastguard Station and Ravenscar Visitor Centre								
1 Jan–5 Jan	10–4	·	·	W	T	F	S	S
11 Jan–26 Jan	10–4	·	·	·	·	·	S	S
1 Feb–29 Nov	10–5	M	T	W	T	F	S	S
5 Dec–20 Dec	10–4	·	·	·	·	·	S	S
28 Dec–31 Dec	10–4	M	T	W	T	·	·	·

Yorkshire Dales

North Yorkshire

🅿️♿️🐕🚻 1946

Satnav: use BD23 5JA for Upper Wharfedale; BD24 9PT for Malham Tarn; DL10 4TJ for Hudswell Woods.
Parking: for Upper Wharfedale use car parks in Kettlewell and Buckden, not National Trust (charge including members). For Malham Tarn parking is either off-road at Waterhouses or at Watersinks car park. For Hudswell Woods use Round Howe car park, not National Trust (charge including members).

The Yorkshire Dales is a great place to relax and explore the great outdoors. Take in the limestone landscape with its dry-stone walls and barns, fields of sheep and cows, and wildflower meadows and pastures. You can walk along the boardwalk at the National Nature Reserve at Malham Tarn and explore the river and woodland valleys of Upper Wharfedale on foot or by bike. Further north, Hudswell Woods has over 5 miles of footpaths through ancient woodlands and there are peaceful spots along the River Swale to enjoy a picnic or perhaps skim a stone. **Note**: nearest toilets located at National Park Centre car parks or council car park (Hudswell Woods).

Eat, shop, stay: tea-rooms, shops, pubs and facilities in Buckden and Malham village (none National Trust). You can stay at The Old Smithy or Town Head Barn in Buckden, Darnbrook Cottage, or our new camping bothies (Ragged Robin and Meadowsweet) near Malham Tarn.

Things to see and do: accessible boardwalk and Tramper for hire at Malham Tarn. Walking routes, cycling trails and events. Exhibitions at the Orchid House, Malham Tarn and Town Head Barn in Malham village. **Dogs**: welcome (excluding Malham Tarn boardwalk) under close control and on leads near livestock.

Access: Town Head Barn 🏠 Grounds ▣ ♿

Find out more: 01729 830416 or yorkshiredales@nationaltrust.org.uk

There are so many different types of landscapes to explore in the Yorkshire Dales, above and below

'Dunstanburgh Castle sits alone on a rocky outcrop on the Northumberland coast, and it's easy to imagine the activities of medieval England unfolding around it. The fresh sea air and the unspoilt panoramic views make this such a special place to visit.'

David Southern lives near Dunstanburgh Castle and loves to walk the coastal path and photograph the castle throughout the seasons

North East

Atmospheric skies above Dunstanburgh Castle, Northumberland, after a day of rain. Competition entry from David Southern

383

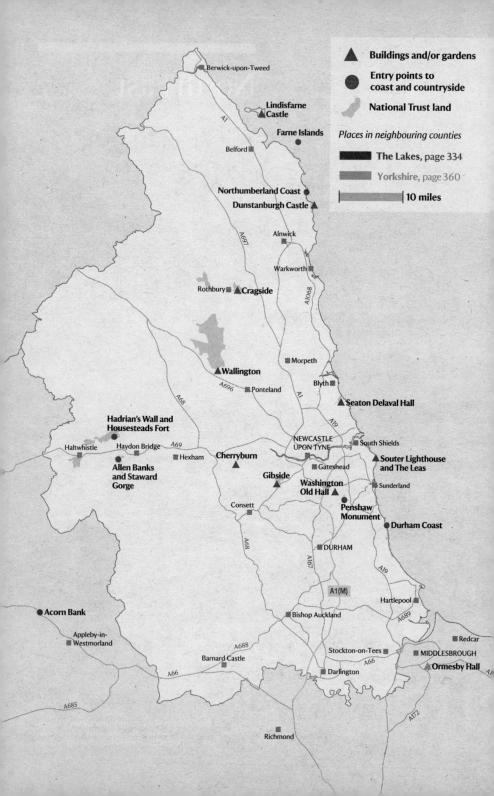

Berwick-upon-Tweed

▲ Lindisfarne Castle

● Farne Islands

■ Belford

● Northumberland Coast
Dunstanburgh Castle ▲

■ Alnwick

■ Warkworth

Rothbury ■ ▲ Cragside

■ Morpeth

Blyth ■

▲ Wallington

A696 ■ Ponteland

▲ Seaton Delaval Hall

Hadrian's Wall and
Housesteads Fort

Haydon Bridge

Haltwhistle

■ Hexham

▲ Cherryburn

NEWCASTLE
UPON TYNE

South Shields

Allen Banks
and Staward
Gorge

Gibside ▲

● Gateshead

▲ Souter Lighthouse
and The Leas

Washington
Old Hall ▲

■ Sunderland

Consett

● Penshaw
Monument

● Durham Coast

■ DURHAM

A1(M)

Hartlepool ■

● Acorn Bank

Appleby-in-
Westmorland

■ Bishop Auckland

A688

A66

Barnard Castle

A66

Stockton-on-Tees ■

■ Redcar

■ MIDDLESBROUGH

▲ Ormesby Hall

Darlington

A172

A685

Richmond

Legend

▲ Buildings and/or gardens

● Entry points to
coast and countryside

National Trust land

Places in neighbouring counties

■ The Lakes, page 334

■ Yorkshire, page 360

|— 10 miles

Allen Banks and Staward Gorge

near Ridley Hall, Bardon Mill, Hexham, Northumberland NE47 7BP

🏛️ ♿ 1942

Allen Banks and Staward Gorge in Northumberland

Satnav: postcode directs to Ridley Hall – turn left at Ridley Hall gates for Allen Banks car park. **Parking**: at Allen Banks.

With its deep gorge created by the River Allen, these ancient woods are the ideal backdrop for an outdoor adventure and the perfect place for nature lovers of all ages. The semi-natural woodland is the largest in Northumberland, with miles of waymarked walks, sun-dappled paths and treetop views. **Note**: site suffered severe storm damage in 2015 – please check for open sections before visiting.

Eat, shop, stay: picnics welcome in the woodland. Picnic benches by the car park. Sorry no refreshments on site; hot and cold drinks, sandwiches and snacks available at nearby Housesteads Fort.

Things to see and do: woodland walks and wildlife to spot, including red squirrels, deer and over 70 species of bird. Medieval pele-tower, man-made ornamental tarn and restored summerhouse. **Dogs**: welcome under close control.

Access: 🅿️ 👁️ 🚶

Find out more: 01434 321888 or allenbanks@nationaltrust.org.uk

Cherryburn

Station Bank, Mickley, Stocksfield, Northumberland NE43 7DD

🏛️ ♿ ❄️ 1991

Satnav: some misdirect, follow brown signs. **Parking**: on site.

Set in a tranquil garden with views across the Tyne Valley, this unassuming Northumbrian farmstead was the birthplace of celebrated artist and naturalist Thomas Bewick. Cherryburn is still surrounded by the natural world that inspired his work. Explore the museum with Bewick's pioneering wood engravings and meet the farm animals.

Eat, shop, stay: books and a selection of Bewick prints from original blocks to buy. Cosy café selling hot and cold drinks, snacks, scones and ice cream. Picnics welcome in the garden.

Things to see and do: **Indoors** Printing demonstrations, temporary art installations and museum. **Outdoors** Cottage garden. Family trail and activities; mini wild-play area. Paddock walk and farmyard with animals (seasonal). **Dogs**: welcome on short leads in garden and grounds (animals in farmyard).

Access: 🅿️📷🏠🚻🎨🚶 Birthplace 🚶♿ Café and museum ♿♿🚻 Grounds 🚶♿♿➡️

Find out more: 01661 843276 or cherryburn@nationaltrust.org.uk

Cherryburn		M	T	W	T	F	S	S
15 Feb–5 Apr	11–4	M	T	W	T	F	S	S
6 Apr–27 Sep	11–5	M	T	W	T	F	S	S
28 Sep–1 Nov	11–4	M	T	W	T	F	S	S

Cherryburn in Northumberland: the printing workshop

Cragside

Rothbury, Morpeth, Northumberland NE65 7PX

🏛️ ✿ 🐾 🛏️ | 1977 |

Satnav: may try and bring you through exit. Please follow brown signs to main entrance. **Parking**: nine car parks on estate.

Trip the light fantastic to the home where modern living began. Cragside was the first house in the world to be lit by hydroelectricity, making it a wonder of the Victorian age. What started as a modest country retreat for engineer and inventor William Armstrong and his wife Margaret became the most technologically advanced house of its time with every home comfort imaginable, as well as being an Arts and Crafts masterpiece. Outside, Lord and Lady Armstrong were equally ambitious with the garden and grounds, engineering the landscape and experimenting with plants on a massive scale. Rocky crags, tumbling water, open lakes, towering North American conifers and great drifts of rhododendrons create changing scenery. **Note**: challenging terrain and distances outside, stout footwear essential.

Four views of Cragside in Northumberland: a place where Victorian inventiveness abounds

Eat, shop, stay: tea-room serving hot meals, sandwiches, handmade treats and cream teas. Seasonal catering outlets at the house and play area. Shop selling souvenirs, gifts, local crafts and plants. Holiday cottages in the formal garden, plus bunkhouse sleeping up to 16 people.

Things to see and do: **Indoors** Armstrong's Victorian home packed full of ingenious gadgets and a large collection of British art and furniture. Victorian baking demonstrations, behind-the-scenes events and family activities all year. **Outdoors** Rugged landscape with colourful rhododendron displays, trickling burns and rock garden. Engineering highlights, including an Archimedes' Screw, Iron Bridge and Power House. New this year, Debdon Gorge walk. Six-mile carriage drive through woodland and numerous footpaths, with walks for all abilities. Intimate formal garden with seasonal planting and views across Northumberland. Family highlights include a labyrinth and adventure play area. Free shuttle bus between main features. **Dogs**: welcome outdoors on leads.

Access: 🅿️ 🚫 🏢 🚌 🥾 🐕 🎒 🏛️ 🎦 ♿ 👓 📷

House 🏠♿ **Visitor centre** 🏢♿♿ **Estate** 🏞️➡️

Find out more: 01669 620333 or
cragside@nationaltrust.org.uk

Cragside		M	T	W	T	F	S	S
Gardens and woodland								
1 Jan–14 Feb	11–3*	M	T	W	T	F	S	S
15 Feb–1 Nov	10–5*	M	T	W	T	F	S	S
2 Nov–31 Dec†	11–3*	M	T	W	T	F	S	S
House								
4 Jan–9 Feb	11–3**						S	S
15 Feb–1 Nov	11–5**	M	T	W	T	F	S	S
7 Nov–29 Nov	11–3**						S	S
30 Nov–31 Dec†	11–3**	M	T	W	T	F	S	S

*Last admission at gate one hour before closing. Carriage Drive closes at 5:30, or sunset if earlier. **House: also open 1 January, 11 to 3; last entry one hour before closing. †Everything closed 24 and 25 December.

Dunstanburgh Castle

Craster, Alnwick, Northumberland
NE66 3TT 1961

This imposing castle ruin occupies a dramatic position on the Northumberland coastline, a mile from Craster, towering over Embleton Bay. **Note**: managed by English Heritage. National Trust members admitted free. Sorry no toilets – closest at Craster car park. Parking at Craster pay-and-display car park, not National Trust (charge including members). Call English Heritage on 01665 576231 or visit english-heritage.org.uk for opening times. Closed 1 January and 24 to 26 December.

Find out more: 01665 576231 or
dunstanburghcastle@nationaltrust.org.uk

Durham Coast

between Seaham and Horden, County Durham

🧍🚶♿ 1987

Satnav: use SR7 7PS for Nose's Point car park (not National Trust) near Seaham.
Parking: Nose's Point near Seaham, Easington Colliery and Horden (none National Trust).

Rocky headlands, sheltered bays, rare magnesian limestone grasslands and wildlife-rich wooded valleys characterise this coastline, part of Durham's Heritage Coast. The 'black beaches' of the coal-mining days have been cleaned up; clifftop paths look over a revitalised coastal landscape you can now explore. **Note**: nearest toilets at Seaham.

Eat, shop, stay: café in the Dene at Castle Eden Dene National Nature Reserve, Peterlee (partnership with Natural England).

Things to see and do: events exploring and celebrating the heritage, landscape and wildlife of the coast. The Durham Coast Half Marathon has become a popular annual sporting event.
Dogs: welcome (including most events). On leads near livestock.

Find out more: 01723 870423 or durhamcoast@nationaltrust.org.uk

Farne Islands

Northumberland

➕♿🚶 1925

Satnav: use NE68 7RQ. **Parking**: in Seahouses, not National Trust (charge including members).

Immerse yourself in nature. An exhilarating boat trip takes you into the world of 23 seabird species during nesting season and offers unrivalled close-ups of thousands of puffins, Arctic terns and guillemots (May to July). Each autumn, more than 2,000 grey seal pups are born on the islands.

Note: Inner Farne island: basic toilets; easy-access boardwalk. Staple Island: sorry no toilets; challenging, slippery terrain. Access by boat from Seahouses (not National Trust), charge applies (including members). Please show membership cards at harbour trailer (no facility to check membership validity).

Eat, shop, stay: shop in Seahouses selling local produce and puffin products. Small shop in Inner Farne Visitor Centre selling souvenirs. Five cottages at nearby Low Newton and Holy Island.

Grey seals on the Farne Islands in Northumberland

Things to see and do: wildlife-spotting paradise. Bring a hat – terns dive-bomb! On Inner Farne: St Cuthbert's Chapel, Victorian lighthouse and small visitor centre. Lindisfarne Castle and Northumberland coast nearby.
Dogs: sorry, not allowed (including assistance dogs) due to extremely sensitive nature of resident wildlife.

Access: Inner Farne 🖼 Staple Island ♿

Find out more: 01665 721099 (Seahouses shop). 01289 389244 (Lindisfarne Castle) or farneislands@nationaltrust.org.uk

Farne Islands		M	T	W	T	F	S	S
Inner Farne Island								
1 Apr–30 Apr	10–5	M	T	W	T	F	S	S
1 May–31 Jul	1:15–5:30	M	T	W	T	F	S	S
1 Aug–31 Oct	10–5	M	T	W	T	F	S	S
Staple Island								
1 May–31 Jul	10–1:30	M	T	W	T	F	S	S
Shop								
3 Jan–29 Feb	11–4			W	T	F	S	S
1 Mar–30 Jun	10–5	M	T	W	T	F	S	S
1 Jul–31 Aug	10–5:30	M	T	W	T	F	S	S
1 Sep–31 Oct	10–5	M	T	W	T	F	S	S
1 Nov–31 Dec*	10–4	M	T	W	T	F	S	S

Landings on Inner Farne and Staple Island only.
Landings on both islands subject to rangers' discretion for visitor safety and bird welfare. *Seahouses shop: closed 25 and 26 December.

Gibside

near Rowlands Gill, Gateshead,
Tyne & Wear NE16 6BG

⊞🍴✿🛏♿🏕🍽 1974

Parking: 382 yards from café and shop
(uphill walkway).

A rare example of an 18th-century landscape
garden, Gibside was created with spectacular
views in mind. The vision of coal magnate
George Bowes and once a pleasure ground for
the Georgian elite, this 243-hectare (600-acre)
estate can now be enjoyed by everyone.
A tree-lined avenue, Palladian chapel and
orangery sit among pockets of peaceful
woodland. The grand ruin of Gibside Hall offers
a glimpse into the dramatic story of heiress
Mary Eleanor Bowes. Adventure play areas and
spotting wildlife, including otters and red kites,
will keep families busy. Explore for longer on
Friday and Saturday evenings during summer.
Note: as part of a new project, there may be
improvements taking place across the estate.

Eat, shop, stay: café serving food, drinks and
seasonal scones and shop in the marketplace.
Renwick's second-hand bookshop and
dog-friendly Carriage House Coffee Shop in
stables courtyard. Group accommodation at
Stables Bunkhouse and glamping at yurt
village. Refreshment kiosk at play area
(weekends/holidays).

Things to see and do: **Indoors** Columned
chapel with unique three-tier pulpit. Discover
Gibside's history and wildlife at the stables.
Outdoors Miles of footpaths. Wildlife-spotting.
Weekly runs, guided walks, tours and events.
Play areas. **Dogs**: welcome on leads. Assistance
dogs only in Strawberry Castle play area.

Access: 🅿♿🚶♿🐾📷♿👁♿ Stables ♿
Chapel 📷♿♿ Garden 📷♿♿➡🐾♿

Find out more: 01207 541820 or
gibside@nationaltrust.org.uk

Gibside		M	T	W	T	F	S	S
Garden, woodlands and café								
1 Jan–1 Mar	10–4*	M	T	W	T	F	S	S
2 Mar–11 Oct**	10–6*	M	T	W	T	F	S	S
12 Oct–31 Dec†	10–4*	M	T	W	T	F	S	S
Chapel								
4 Jan–1 Mar	10–4						S	S
2 Mar–11 Oct	10–5	M	T	W	T	F	S	S
17 Oct–27 Dec†	10–4						S	S

*Garden, woodlands and café: open 9:30 at weekends.
**Café closes at 5. †Everything closed 24 and 25 December.

Two views of Gibside, Tyne & Wear: once a pleasure ground for the Georgian elite, now a place for all to enjoy

Hadrian's Wall and Housesteads Fort

near Bardon Mill, Hexham,
Northumberland NE47 6NN

 1930

![photograph of Hadrian's Wall]

Satnav: can misdirect, follow brown signs.
Parking: at Housesteads, Steel Rigg, Cawfields,
not National Trust (charge including members).

A UNESCO World Heritage Site, Hadrian's Wall
is the Roman Empire's best preserved outpost
in northern Europe. Sitting high within the
dramatic landscape, this epic structure joins
geology and human engineering. Follow
ancient footsteps, exploring alongside the wall,
and at the fort learn more about the soldiers'
lives. **Note**: fort is National Trust-owned,
English Heritage-managed and is a half-mile
uphill walk from visitor centre. Car park is run
by Northumberland National Park Authority,
parking charges apply (including members).

Eat, shop, stay: visitor centre offering
sandwiches, snacks, ice cream and drinks.
Shop selling books, cards, gifts, souvenirs
and plants. Picnics welcome. Three holiday
cottages, ideal for walkers and stargazers.

Things to see and do: fort, and museum (not
National Trust) – dressing up and video. Walk
to Milecastle 37 and Sycamore Gap. Play area.
Events, including rock climbing and stargazing.
Dogs: welcome on leads.

Access: 🅿️♿♿♿♿♿♿♿
Visitor centre 🅰️ Museum ♿

Find out more: 01434 344525 or
housesteads@nationaltrust.org.uk

Hadrian's Wall and Housesteads Fort
Housesteads Fort: open daily, except some days at Christmas;
opening hours vary by season (please check before visiting).

Lindisfarne Castle

Holy Island, Berwick-upon-Tweed,
Northumberland TD15 2SH

🅿️♿♿♿♿ 1944

Parking: at main island car park, 1 mile, not
National Trust (charge including members).
Intermittent locally operated shuttle bus
service (not National Trust).

Experience the magical feeling of travelling
across the causeway to Lindisfarne Castle.
Perched high on a crag and commanding
far-reaching views, this iconic castle presides
over Holy Island. One of the UK's most
recognisable backdrops, it was converted from
a fort into a holiday home for the owner of
Country Life magazine by architect Sir Edwin
Lutyens in 1903. This year, this atmospheric
and romantic castle, without the majority of its
furniture, is hosting a contemporary exhibition.
Beyond the castle, you can explore the
award-winning, summer-flowering Gertrude
Jekyll walled garden and Victorian lime kilns
and visit the National Trust shop.
Note: unfurnished rooms. Limited toilet
facilities. Island accessed by tidal causeway –
check safe crossing times.

Eat, shop, stay: shop in the village with a large range of homeware and gardenware. There are two holiday cottages on the island: Lutyens-designed St Oswald's with castle views (dog-friendly) and Glen House in the village. Refreshments in the village (not National Trust).

Things to see and do: **Indoors** Lutyens's architecture to explore. **Outdoors** Panoramic views from Upper Battery. Castle Point walk. Sheltered walled garden filled with vegetables, herbs and colourful flowers. Farne Islands (boats from Seahouses) nearby.
Dogs: welcome on leads in the grounds. Assistance dogs only in castle.

Access: 🅿♿ Castle ♿⛰ Lime kilns ♿

Find out more: 01289 389244 or lindisfarne@nationaltrust.org.uk

Lindisfarne Castle		M	T	W	T		F	S	S
Castle									
13 Feb–1 Nov	10–4*	**M**	**T**	**W**	**T**		**F**	**S**	**S**
Garden									
Open all year		**M**	**T**	**W**	**T**		**F**	**S**	**S**

*Opening times change daily due to tides (always check before visiting).

Sitting high on a rocky crag, Lindisfarne Castle in Northumberland is straight out of a fairy tale

Northumberland Coast

Northumberland

🚻♿🏛🐕🛏 1935

Exploring rock pools on the Northumberland Coast

Satnav: for Low Newton use NE66 3EH; Druridge Bay NE61 5EG; St Aidan's Dunes NE68 7SH. **Parking**: limited at Druridge Bay. Also at Holy Island, Seahouses, Beadnell, Newton-by-the-Sea and Craster, none National Trust (charge including members).

From Lindisfarne to Druridge Bay, you'll find wide open skies and miles of sandy beaches, teeming with wildlife. Coastal walks take you past dramatic castle ruins, unspoilt dunes and excellent rock pools. Spot seals, dolphins, wading shorebirds along the coast, and see the nesting terns at Long Nanny shorebird site. **Note**: public car parks only (charge including members).

Eat, shop, stay: shops on Holy Island and in Seahouses; cafés, pubs and shops in nearby towns and villages (none National Trust). Holiday cottages on Holy Island, Low Newton and Newton-by-the-Sea.

Things to see and do: little tern breeding colony at Long Nanny (June to August). Events, '50 things' activities, wildlife-spotting. Newton Pool bird hides. Farne Islands and Lindisfarne Castle nearby. **Dogs**: welcome, some local restrictions may apply. On leads around/at Long Nanny shorebird site.

Find out more: 01665 576874 or northumberlandcoast@nationaltrust.org.uk

Penshaw Monument

near Penshaw, Tyne & Wear DH4 7NJ [1939]

This Wearside landmark can be seen from miles around. A sign of home for many, with woodland walks and views. **Note:** sorry no toilets. Walking routes nearby. Tours to the top of the monument on Saturdays, Sundays and Bank Holidays, 4 April to 27 September.

Find out more: 0191 416 6879 or penshaw.monument@nationaltrust.org.uk

Seaton Delaval Hall

The Avenue, Seaton Sluice, Northumberland NE26 4QR

🏠 ✿ ♿ [2009]

Parking: 500 yards.

Seaton Delaval Hall in Northumberland, above and left: come and see conservation work as it happens

Designed by Sir John Vanbrugh (Castle Howard, Blenheim Palace) and home to the flamboyant Delaval family, the Hall bears the scars of fierce fires which almost condemned it to ruin 200 years ago. In an age known for extremes of behaviour, the 'gay Delavals' were the most notorious of all Georgian partygoers and pranksters, whose dramatic personalities are matched by Vanbrugh's bold architecture. This year we continue to turn the place upside down in true Delaval style, with a major project. It's not an ordinary visit; we're staying open so you can see the conservation work as it happens. **Note:** major restoration project under way, please check latest information on opening arrangements before you visit.

Eat, shop, stay: Brewhouse café opening this year serving light meals. East Wing café serving drinks, snacks and sweet treats – in fine weather the summerhouse serves drinks and ice cream. Shop in visitor welcome selling souvenirs, gifts and plants.

Things to see and do: Indoors Vanbrugh's architecture, including central hall, with fire-damaged interior and original statues. Ongoing conservation and projects. **Outdoors** Formal garden and walks. Stables. New play area in north-west woodland. **Dogs:** welcome on leads outdoors.

Access: 🅿️ 📷 💺 📖 🎵
Hall 🔲 Stables 🔲 Grounds ➡️

Find out more: 0191 237 9100 or seatondelavalhall@nationaltrust.org.uk

Seaton Delaval Hall		M	T	W	T	F	S	S
2 Jan–16 Feb	10–3*				T	F	S	S
20 Feb–1 Nov**	10–5*				T	F	S	S
5 Nov–31 Dec†	10–3*				T	F	S	S

*Last admission 45 minutes before closing. **Open Bank Holiday Mondays. †Closed 24 to 27 December. Major restoration project under way (please check before visiting).

Parking is free for members, but don't forget to scan your card in the car park when you visit

Souter Lighthouse and The Leas

Coast Road, Whitburn, Sunderland,
Tyne & Wear SR6 7NH

[icons] 1990

Parking: on site.

Breathe in the bracing North Sea air and climb all 76 steps to the top of the first lighthouse in the world designed and built to be lit by electricity. To the north stretches The Leas, with its wildflower meadows dotted with orchids. To the south is Whitburn Coastal Park, cared for by our rangers and great for wildlife – its nature reserve provides nesting sites, water and rest for migrating birds. The Engine Room and Keeper's Cottage give a flavour of life in a working lighthouse, while displays and exhibitions tell local stories. **Note**: Whitburn Coastal Park owned by South Tyneside Council, leased and managed by the National Trust.

Eat, shop, stay: Lighthouse Café serving light lunches, soup, cakes and refreshments. Local dishes Panackelty and Singin' Hinnies are a must-try. Shop stocking coastal gifts and Souter souvenirs. Picnic area. Extend your visit and stay in the picturesque, clifftop Lighthouse Keeper's cottages.

Souter Lighthouse and The Leas, Tyne & Wear: looking out from the lantern, top, and selfie time, below

Things to see and do: events and activities, including exhibitions, holiday crafts, seashore safaris, bug-hunting, nature walks, birdwatching, sports days, coasteering and car-boot sales. Self-led family activity packs available. Play area. Foghorn demonstrations. Wildlife garden.
Dogs: welcome on leads outdoors.

Access: [icons]
Building [icons] Grounds [icons]

Find out more: 0191 529 3161 or souter@nationaltrust.org.uk

Souter Lighthouse and The Leas		M	T	W	T	F	S	S
Lighthouse								
1 Feb–29 Nov	11–5	M	T	W	T	F	S	S
Café								
1 Jan–31 Jan	10–4	M	T	W	T	F	S	S
1 Feb–31 Oct	10–5*	M	T	W	T	F	S	S
1 Nov–31 Dec**	10–4	M	T	W	T	F	S	S
Shop								
4 Jan–26 Jan	11–4	·	·	·	·	·	S	S
1 Feb–31 Oct	11–5	M	T	W	T	F	S	S
1 Nov–29 Nov	11–4	M	T	W	T	F	S	S
5 Dec–20 Dec	11–4	·	·	·	·	·	S	S

*Café: closes 6, July and August.
**Café: closed 21 to 27 December.

Wallington

Cambo, near Morpeth,
Northumberland NE61 4AR

🏠🔳🔆🔆🛏 1941

Parking: on site.

Sitting in a rural corner of Northumberland
yet only 20 miles north-west of
Newcastle-upon-Tyne, Wallington is a large
estate where a historic country house sits amid
rolling hills, swathes of woodland and enchanting
walled gardens. Take time to discover the
variety of spaces, both indoors and out, and
keep your eyes peeled for the native wildlife –
from red squirrels and nuthatches, to
white-clawed crayfish and otters. For an active
adventure, take to the Dragon Cycle Trail on
two wheels and be inspired by far-reaching
views across the Northumbrian countryside.
Once home to the unconventional and socialist
Trevelyan family, the informal house is full of
treasured collections, while the three outdoor
play parks capture the spirit of the adventurous
Trevelyan children. **Note**: cycle hire charges
apply (including members).

Eat, shop, stay: Clocktower Café serving
hot and cold refreshments. Seasonal kiosks
in the walled garden, courtyard and west
woods. Shops and plant centre offering gifts
and souvenirs. Holiday at the Bunkhouse
or Bolt Cottage.

Wallington, Northumberland: glorious blooms in the conservatory, above, and exploring the grounds, below and right

Things to see and do: **Indoors** Wallington's welcoming house team are eager to share their knowledge of the fine collection of paintings, ceramics, books and rich history of the donor family. Family activities at weekends and holidays in the indoor playspace. For special memories, visit at Christmas. **Outdoors** Wonderful walled garden and Edwardian conservatory. 100,000 purple crocuses carpet the grounds in March. You can hire a bike or bring your own to explore the Dragon Cycle Trail. Stroll along the River Wansbeck on the almost 2-mile circular walk, where only the sound of trickling water and birdsong disturb the peace. **Dogs**: welcome on leads outdoors and on all walks.

Access: 🅿🐕👓♿🚪📷🖥🚶 House 🚶♿⬆♿
Garden and grounds 🚶♿♿➡🚲♿

Find out more: 01670 773600 or wallington@nationaltrust.org.uk

Wallington		M	T	W	T	F	S	S
Walled garden, woodland and estate								
Open all year	10–dusk*	M	T	W	T	F	S	S
House								
15 Feb–1 Nov	12–5	M	T	W	T	F	S	S
28 Nov–20 Dec	10–7:30**	·	·	·	·	F	S	S
21 Dec–23 Dec	10–4	M	T	W	·	·	·	·
Shops and café								
1 Jan–14 Feb	10:30–4:30	M	T	W	T	F	S	S
15 Feb–1 Nov	10:30–5:30	M	T	W	T	F	S	S
2 Nov–31 Dec††	10:30–4:30†	M	T	W	T	F	S	S

*Walled garden: closes 7 in summer; 4 in winter.
**House: opens 4:30 on Fridays and closes 4 on Sundays.
†Shops and café: 28 November to 23 December, close at 7:30 on Fridays and Saturdays. Café: last orders 30 minutes before closing. ††Closed 24 to 26 December.

Washington Old Hall

The Avenue, Washington Village, Washington, Tyne & Wear NE38 7LE

🏠❄🍴 1956

Parking: on site (additional unrestricted parking on The Avenue).

The original Washington and medieval home of George Washington's ancestors. This small manor house has a diverse past: from its links to the first US President, to a 17th-century home and even a crowded tenement. Discover tranquil gardens and explore the 'nuttery' – a haven for nature and wildlife.

Eat, shop, stay: café serving soup, cakes, homemade scones, hot and cold drinks. Small seating areas indoors and outside. Small shop selling books, children's toys, confectionery, jams, local beers and ciders.

Things to see and do: **Indoors** 17th-century hall, tenement and Washington room. Events in the holidays and Christmas. **Outdoors** Gardens, terrace, bird hide, mini play area, Fourth of July ceremony. **Dogs**: welcome on leads (garden only). Assistance dogs only in café.

Access: 🅿♿👓🚶♿:·📷
Building 🚶♿ Grounds 🚶♿➡

Find out more: 0191 416 6879 or washingtonoldhall@nationaltrust.org.uk

Washington Old Hall		M	T	W	T	F	S	S
Hall and gardens								
15 Feb–31 Mar	10–4	M	T	W	T	F	S	S
1 Apr–26 Oct	10–5	M	T	W	T	F	S	S
27 Oct–27 Nov	10–4	M	T	W	T	F	S	S
28 Nov–24 Dec	12–6*	M	T	W	T	F	S	S
Café								
15 Feb–30 Nov	10–4	M	T	W	T	F	S	S
1 Dec–24 Dec	12–6*	M	T	W	T	F	S	S

*24 December: everything closes at 3.

'I don't come to the Snowdonia area often, but when I do I get a sense of freedom and accomplishment, especially when the routes and weather come together like this.'

Toby Cross recalls scaling the exhilarating heights of Carnedd Dafydd in Wales

Cymru Wales

A humbling mountain view from Carnedd Dafydd
within Carneddau and Glyderau, Gwynedd.
Competition entry from Toby Cross

Cemlyn

Holyhead

LLANGEFNI

A55

Plas Newydd

CAERNARFON

Porthdinllaen

Porthor

Porth Meudwy

Porth
y Swnt

Plas yn
Rhiw

Llanbedrog
Beach

Abersoch

Criccieth

Porthmadog

Llandudno

Conwy

Bangor

Penrhyn
Castle

Bodysgallen Hall

Rhyl

LIVERPOOL

Beatles'
Childhood
Homes

Speke
Hall

M56

Conwy Suspension Bridge

Aberconwy House

Bodnant Garden

Ogwen Cottage

Segontium

Hafod y Llan

Craflwyn and
Beddgelert

Tŷ Isaf

Carneddau and Glyderau

Tŷ Mawr Wybrnant

A5

CHESTER

A494

A483

A534

Wrexham

Erddig

A525

A41

A5

Oswestry

A483

Chirk Castle

A495

A5

A53

Shrewsbury

Dolmelynllyn
Estate

Dinas Oleu

DOLGELLAU

A470

A487

A494

A458

A489

A470

Machynlleth

WELSHPOOL

A458

Powis Castle

Attingham
Park

A49

A487

A470

Newtown

A483

ABERYSTWYTH

A44

A483

LLANDRINDOD
WELLS

A44

Croft Castle

Berrington
Hall

A44

Llanerchaeron

Builth Wells

A438

The Weir
Garden

A417

Mwnt

Penbryn

Cardigan

Cilgerran Castle

A487

Dolaucothi
Estate

Dolaucothi Mines

A483

HEREFORD

Cwmdu

A40

BRECON

A465

A49

St David's
Visitor
Centre

A40

Southwood
Estate

Martin's
Haven

Marloes
Sands
and Mere

Freshwater
West and
Gupton
Farm

Colby
Woodland
Garden

A4076

A487

Pembroke

Stackpole

Stackpole
Centre

Tudor Merchant's
House

CARMARTHEN

A477

A40

Paxton's
Tower

Dinefwr

A40

A48

A483

Llanelli

Rhosili

SWANSEA

A4070

Pennard,
Pwll Du and
Bishopston
Valley

Aberdulais

Neath

Port Talbot

M4

Bridgend

CARDIFF

Brecon
Beacons

A40

Merthyr Tydfil

A470

A40

A479

Sugar Loaf
and Usk
Valley

Skenfrith
Castle

The Kymin

A4042

A449

Chepstow

Tredegar
House

NEWPORT

M48

Dyffryn Gardens

M5

A48

A38

A37

A4

Buildings and/or gardens

Places in neighbouring counties

Entry points to
coast and countryside

West Midlands, page 278

National Trust land

North West, page 314

10 miles

H Historic House Hotel

Aberconwy House

Castle Street, Conwy LL32 8AY

🏠 1934

Parking: none on site.

This is the only medieval merchant's house in Conwy to have survived the turbulent history of the walled town over seven centuries. Furnished rooms and helpful volunteers bring different periods in its history to life. **Note**: nearest toilets 50 yards. Steps to all parts of property.

Eat, shop, stay: the shop is located on the ground floor. Low and ancient beams provide wonderful character for Conwy's oldest shop. Our range includes National Trust brands and locally sourced products.

Things to see and do: Easter events.
Dogs: assistance dogs only.

Access: 🅿 Building 🄻

Find out more: 01492 592246 or aberconwyhouse@nationaltrust.org.uk

Aberconwy House		M	T	W	T	F	S	S
House								
12 Mar–1 Nov	10–5	M	T	W	T	F	S	S
7 Nov–20 Dec	11–4	·	·	·	·	·	S	S
Shop								
2 Jan–29 Feb	11–5	·	T	W	T	F	S	S
1 Mar–31 Dec*	10–5	M	T	W	T	F	S	S

*Closed 25, 26 December and 1 January 2021.

Aberdulais

near Neath, Neath Port Talbot

🏠🏚🧺🍽 1980

Satnav: postcode misdirects, follow brown signs. **Parking**: 50 yards.

Explore one of the earliest industrial sites in Britain. Long before the Industrial Revolution, water from the River Dulais and the dramatic waterfall were powering industries at Aberdulais. Archaeologists have helped uncover the secrets hidden among the remains of the last pioneering industry: the Victorian tinplate works. Its story is shared in our exhibition and family Tracker Packs. Today water power is harnessed by an underground turbine and the largest generating waterwheel in Europe. **Note**: waterwheel and turbine subject to water levels and conservation work.

Eat, shop, stay: light lunches and refreshments available to enjoy anywhere on site with the new eco-friendly Food 2 Go offer. Gift shop and second-hand bookshop.

Things to see and do: activities all year, including seasonal events such as Easter and Victorian Christmas. **Dogs**: welcome on leads throughout site (including inside buildings).

Access: 🅿🅿🅿🅿🅿🅿 Grounds 🄻🄻🄻➡🄻
Stable and Tin Exhibition 🄻🄻🄻
Turbine House 🄻🄻🄻🄻🄻

Find out more: 01639 636674 or aberdulais@nationaltrust.org.uk
Aberdulais, near Neath, SA10 8EU

Aberdulais		M	T	W	T	F	S	S
4 Jan–16 Feb	10–4	·	·	·	·	·	S	S
17 Feb–17 Jul	10–4	M	T	W	T	F	S	S
18 Jul–31 Aug	10–5	M	T	W	T	F	S	S
1 Sep–30 Oct	10–4	M	T	W	T	F	S	S
31 Oct–20 Dec	10–4	·	·	·	·	·	S	S

Bodnant Garden

Tal-y-Cafn, near Colwyn Bay, Conwy LL28 5RE

🏠 ✿ 🔔 1949

Parking: 150 yards. Electric vehicle charging point opposite café.

This Grade I-listed garden in Snowdonia's foothills, with historic plant collections and breathtaking mountain views, was established in 1874 by Victorian entrepreneur Henry Pochin. Five generations of the family have gone on to transform the 32-hectare (80-acre) Conwy Valley hillside with rare trees and shrubs from around the world. Since 1949 the garden has been nurtured in collaboration with the National Trust. You can enjoy Italianate terraces with formal flowerbeds, pools and parterres, informal shrub borders, woods, meadows and riverside dells with waterfalls and towering conifers. Every season brings new delights – magnolias and rhododendrons in spring, roses and water lilies in summer, followed by rich leaf colour in autumn and a stunning Winter Garden. **Note**: work to upgrade facilities will be going on all year.

Bodnant Garden, Conwy: a guided tour, below, and the Pin Mill and Canal Terrace, right

Walks suitable for all at Bodnant Garden

Eat, shop, stay: enjoy a meal in The Pavilion or light bites at The Magnolia Tea-room and Dell Kiosk. Outdoor seating in The Dell and picnic areas around the garden. Gift shop, neighbouring garden centre and craft units (not National Trust).

Things to see and do: events all year, including regular gardener-guided walks, bird tours and history talks. The Poem mausoleum is open every last Tuesday of the month (March to end of October). Don't miss the Laburnum Arch flowering in May and June. Pin Mill open days (please check website), musical Sundays on the Canal Terrace and outdoor dining events in summer. Daily outdoor family trails and activities outdoors during school holidays. Seasonal craft events in the Old Mill. Children's play area. In winter enjoy the brazier at the Old Mill. **Dogs**: welcome daily October to end March; 5 to 8, April to end September (short leads).

Access: 🅿 🐕 ⛪ ♿ 🚻 🎨 🚶 **Grounds** 🏡 ➡ ♿

Find out more: 01492 650460 or bodnantgarden@nationaltrust.org.uk

Bodnant Garden		M	T	W	T	F	S	S
1 Jan–29 Feb	10–4	M	T	W	T	F	S	S
1 Mar–30 Apr*	10–5	M	T	W	T	F	S	S
1 May–30 Jun*	9–5	M	T	W	T	F	S	S
1 Jul–31 Oct*	10–5	M	T	W	T	F	S	S
1 Nov–31 Dec**	10–4	M	T	W	T	F	S	S

Tea-room: open daily from 10. *Garden: open to 8 on Wednesdays, April to end September.
**Garden and tea-room: closed 24 to 26 December.

Bodysgallen Hall Hotel, Restaurant and Spa

The Royal Welsh Way, Llandudno,
Conwy LL30 1RS

🏠❄♨🛏🔔🍽 2008

This Grade I-listed 17th-century house, set
within 89 hectares (220 acres) of parkland,
has the most spectacular views towards Conwy
Castle and Snowdonia. The romantic gardens,
which have won awards for their restoration,
include a rare parterre filled with sweet-smelling
herbs, as well as several follies, a cascade,
walled garden and formal rose gardens.
Beyond, the parkland offers miles of stunning
walks and views to the coastline. **Note**: access
is for paying guests of the hotel, including for
luncheon, afternoon tea and dinner, and the
spa. Children over the age of six welcome.

Find out more: 01492 584466 or
info@bodysgallen.com bodysgallen.com

Brecon Beacons

Powys

🏛♨ 1947

Brecon Beacons, Powys: the footpath between
Corn Du and Pen y Fan, above, and taking a break, left

Satnav: use LD3 8NL.
Parking: main car park at Pont ar Daf, off A470;
alternatives not all National Trust.

The Brecon Beacons have captivated visitors
for hundreds of years with their soaring peaks,
including southern Britain's highest mountain
Pen y Fan. From the popular mountaintops to
the tranquil valleys, lush farmland to ancient
woodland, they are perfect for hill-walking and
exploring. Not forgetting South Wales's highest
waterfall, Henrhyd Falls, which plunges 90 feet
into the wooded Graig Llech Gorge, a haven
for rare mosses and ferns. In contrast, you
can discover the vast remote moorlands of
Abergwesyn Commons in the heart of
Wales or ramble over the Begwns with
panoramic views of the Brecon Beacons.
Note: disruption possible at Pont ar Daf
due to redevelopment of car park.

Things to see and do: Indoors Dan y Gyrn
bunkhouse in the Tarell Valley near Pen y Fan.
Outdoors Why not visit nearby Aberdulais
to explore the tin works and waterfall?
Dogs: welcome on leads.

Find out more: 01874 625515 or
brecon@nationaltrust.org.uk

Carneddau and Glyderau

Nant Ffrancon, Bethesda, Gwynedd

🏕️♿ 1951

Satnav: use LL57 3LZ.
Parking: at Ogwen Lake (not National Trust).

This 8,498-hectare (21,000-acre) mountainous area includes Cwm Idwal National Nature Reserve, renowned for its geology and Arctic-Alpine plants, such as the rare Snowdon lily. There are nine tenanted upland farms here and nine peaks over 3,000 feet, including the famous Tryfan, where Edmund Hilary trained for his ascent of Everest. The area is home to a variety of wildlife, including otters, feral ponies and rare birds, such as ring ouzel and twite. The 60 miles of footpaths attract more than 500,000 walkers each year, while the bleak, photogenic landscapes have proved popular with artists. **Note**: mountainous and difficult terrain – please come well equipped and check the weather. Charges apply in the National Park car parks.

Home to a variety of wildlife, such as feral ponies, above, Carneddau and Glyderau in Gwynedd, offers 60 miles of footpaths across spectacular terrain, below

Eat, shop, stay: food kiosk on site (not National Trust). Warden centre run in partnership with Snowdonia National Park and Natural Resources Wales. There are two holiday cottages in Dyffryn Mymbyr and one near Llyn Ogwen.

Things to see and do: you can walk to Cwm Idwal and enjoy dramatic mountain views, following in the footsteps of Charles Darwin (who 'discovered' glaciation here).
Dogs: welcome on leads.

Find out more: 01248 605739 or carneddau@nationaltrust.org.uk

Cemlyn

Anglesey

＋🏠🏛🎣⚓🚴🐾🛶 1971

Satnav: use LL67 0DY.
Parking: at Bryn Aber car park, Cemlyn.

Part of Anglesey's Area of Outstanding Natural Beauty, the north-west coast has a ruggedly beautiful coastline of rocks, small bays and headlands and is a delight for walkers. Cemlyn is a North Wales Wildlife Trust Nature Reserve and a Site of Special Scientific Interest.

Renowned for its breeding colony of Sandwich, common and Arctic terns, Cemlyn Bay is a hive of seabird activity in spring and summer. Headland paths offer dramatic land and seascapes during autumn and winter. The brackish lagoon is separated from the sea by a remarkable shingle ridge. **Note**: nearest toilets in Cemaes Bay, 3 miles (not National Trust).

Things to see and do: numerous footpaths and downloadable walks to help you explore. Events, including pram walks and walking festival. Summer fair at Swtan, a restored whitewashed cottage nearby (LL65 4EU). **Dogs**: welcome on leads.

Find out more: 01248 714795 or cemlyn@nationaltrust.org.uk

Ruggedly beautiful Cemlyn on the north coast of Anglesey, is a hive of seabird activity in spring and summer

Chirk Castle

Chirk, Wrexham LL14 5AF

🏠🏰🛍️✛♿👥🛏️🍴🍴 1981

Parking: at Home Farm by ticket office, approximately 220 yards via steep hill to castle. Two electric vehicle charging points at Home Farm.

Completed by Marcher Lord Roger Mortimer in 1310, Chirk is the last Welsh castle from the reign of Edward I still inhabited today. You can explore medieval towers and dungeons, visit the 17th- and 18th-century rooms of the Myddelton family home, including the historic laundry, and discover the story of influential 20th-century tenant and polymath Lord Howard de Walden. The prized gardens contain clipped yews, herbaceous borders and rock gardens. A terrace gives stunning views over the Cheshire and Shropshire plains, while the large estate, divided by King Offa's Dyke, provides habitat for rare invertebrates, wild flowers and veteran trees.

Eat, shop, stay: café serving hot and cold food, drinks and cakes. Seasonal kiosk at Home Farm selling hot and cold drinks and snacks. Gift shops in Home Farm and courtyard, with plant sales and second-hand books. Three holiday cottages on the estate.

Things to see and do: Indoors Medieval fortress and dungeon, Myddelton family home, Servants' Hall and Victorian laundry to explore.

Outdoors Discover the formal gardens, Pleasure Ground Wood and a 194-hectare (480-acre) estate. **Dogs**: welcome on leads. Assistance dogs only in formal gardens and Pleasure Ground Wood.

Access: 🅿️♿♿♿♿♿♿🖼️♿♿
Castle ♿♿ Adam's Tower ♿👥
Gardens ♿♿♿♿

Find out more: 01691 777701 or chirkcastle@nationaltrust.org.uk

Chirk Castle		M	T	W	T	F	S	S
Castle								
2 Jan–5 Jan	11–4	·	·	·	T	F	S	S
7 Mar–1 Nov*	12–4**	M	T	W	T	F	S	S
7 Nov–29 Nov	Tour†	·	·	·	·	·	S	S
5 Dec–31 Dec††	11–4	M	T	W	T	F	S	S
Garden, Adam's Tower, shop and café								
2 Jan–1 Nov	10–4**	M	T	W	T	F	S	S
7 Nov–29 Nov	10–4	·	·	·	·	·	S	S
5 Dec–31 Dec††	10–4	M	T	W	T	F	S	S

*Guided tours at 11:15 (places limited).
**April to September: closes 5. †11 to 4: access by guided tour only, timed tickets available on day (places limited).
††Closed 25 December and 1 January 2021.

Chirk Castle in Wrexham: lawn tennis, left, and the main entrance on the north front, below

Cilgerran Castle

near Cardigan, Pembrokeshire SA43 2SF 1938

13th-century castle overlooking the Teifi Gorge – the perfect location to repel attackers. Walk the walls and admire the stunning views. **Note**: under the guardianship of Cadw – Welsh Government's historic environment service. Dogs welcome on leads. Open daily, 2 January to 31 March, 10 to 4; 1 April to 1 November, 10 to 5; 2 November to 31 December, 10 to 4 (closed 24 to 26 December).

Find out more: 01239 621339 or cilgerrancastle@nationaltrust.org.uk

Colby Woodland Garden in Pembrokeshire: a young naturalist, left, and the walled garden, above

Colby Woodland Garden

near Amroth, Pembrokeshire SA67 8PP

[icons] 1980

Parking: 50 yards.

A short walk from the beach, this hidden wooded valley, with its secret garden and industrial past, is a place for play. There are fallen trees to climb, rope swings and playful surprises everywhere. Spring brings bluebells, camellias, rhododendrons and azaleas, while the walled garden gives year-round colour, peace and seclusion. There are woodland walks, meandering streams and ponds with stepping stones and log bridges in the wildflower meadow, and the whole valley teems with wildlife. **Note**: sorry, house not open.

Eat, shop, stay: browse our gift shop, plant sales and second-hand bookshop. Pack a picnic or enjoy a bite to eat at the Bothy Tea-room (not National Trust). Three holiday cottages nearby.

Things to see and do: follow walking trails, enjoy natural play with rope swings, pond-dipping and children's '50 things to do before you're 11¾' adventures. Seasonal events, including walks, talks and family activities. **Dogs**: welcome on leads in woodland garden and meadow.

Access: [icons]
Grounds [icons]

Find out more: 01834 811885 or colby@nationaltrust.org.uk

Colby Woodland Garden		M	T	W	T	F	S	S
Woodland and walled gardens*								
6 Jan–14 Feb	10–3	M	T	W	T	F	S	S
15 Feb–1 Nov	10–5	M	T	W	T	F	S	S
2 Nov–18 Dec	10–3	M	T	W	T	F	S	S
Shop								
15 Feb–1 Nov	10–5	M	T	W	T	F	S	S
Tea-room								
4 Apr–1 Nov	10–4:30	M	T	W	T	F	S	S

*Car park and Bothy exhibition open as woodland and walled gardens.

Conwy Suspension Bridge

Conwy LL32 8LD

🏠 🚾 1965

Parking: none on site.

Designed in the 1820s by Thomas Telford, this graceful bridge with its beautifully restored tiny toll-keeper's house has stunning views over the Conwy Estuary. Kept open by a husband and wife at a time when trade and travel brought Conwy to life, it never closed, whatever the weather. **Note**: sorry no toilet.

Eat, shop, stay: why not bring a picnic to enjoy on the grassed area?

Things to see and do: superb views of the river and castle. **Dogs**: allowed on the bridge and grassed areas only.

Conwy Suspension Bridge, Conwy: grace and strength

Access: Building 🏠 Grounds 🅿️

Find out more: 01492 573282 or conwybridge@nationaltrust.org.uk

Conwy Suspension Bridge
Suspension bridge open 12 March to 1 November. For Toll House opening times call Aberconwy House (01492 592246).

Craflwyn and Beddgelert

near Beddgelert, Gwynedd

🏛️ 🚻 1994

Craflwyn and Beddgelert, Gwynedd: history and legend

Satnav: use LL55 4NG. **Parking**: in Craflwyn.

The 81-hectare (200-acre) Craflwyn Estate is set in the heart of beautiful Snowdonia, within a landscape steeped in history and legend. There's a network of paths and woodland walks to explore and tumbling waterfalls to discover. At Craflwyn you can learn about the Princes of Gwynedd, before venturing up to nearby Dinas Emrys, legendary birthplace of the red dragon of Wales. Within a couple of miles of Craflwyn, there are great walks for all abilities – from a village stroll at pretty Beddgelert to the rugged Fisherman's Path down the spectacular Aberglaslyn Pass. **Note**: Craflwyn Hall is run and managed by HF Holidays (surrounding land open to the public).

Eat, shop, stay: picnics welcome at Craflwyn. Local crafts on offer in Tŷ Isaf shop in Beddgelert. The village also has a selection of restaurants, cafés, taverns and hotels (not National Trust). Holiday cottage, chalet and campsite at Hafod y Llan.

Things to see and do: you can learn about Prince Llywelyn's legendary faithful hound by visiting Gelert's Grave. Children's adventure packs, maps and guides available from Tŷ Isaf shop in the centre of the village. **Dogs**: welcome on a lead (near livestock).

Find out more: 01766 510120 or craflwyn@nationaltrust.org.uk

Craflwyn and Beddgelert, above and below, lies in the heart of beautiful Snowdonia

Cwmdu

Llandeilo, Carmarthenshire 1991

Georgian terrace with pub, post office, chapel and vestry. Representing a rural Welsh village of the past. **Note**: pub and shop run by community. For satnav use SA19 7DY. Inn open Wednesday to Saturday, 2 January to 30 December, 7 to 11. Shop and post office open Tuesday to Saturday, 2 January to 28 December, 9:30 to 1:30 (close 12:30 on Saturdays). Restaurant open selected Saturdays.

Find out more: 01558 685088 or cwmdu@nationaltrust.org.uk

Dinas Oleu

near Barmouth, Gwynedd 1895

Mrs Fanny Talbot gave the Trust this gorse-clad hill 125 years ago – our first donation. Come and help us celebrate. **Note**: some steep rocky terrain and steps to reach the top. Nearest parking in town, not National Trust (charge including members).

Find out more: 01341 440238 or dinasoleu@nationaltrust.org.uk

Dinefwr

near Carmarthen, Carmarthenshire

🏠🖼️✝️🏛️🎣❄️🚲🐕🛏️♿🍷 1990

Satnav: enter Dinefwr, not postcode.
Parking: 50 yards. Electric vehicle charging point at Home Farm on 'The Granary'.

A special place in the heart of Carmarthenshire, Dinefwr's historic parkland is protected as a UK National Nature Reserve. From flower-rich hay meadows to dense ancient woodland … it's all here for you to discover. The winding driveway offers views of our rare-breed White Park cattle, grazing the land as they have done for 1,000 years. Newton House retains its 1660 façade as well as the 17th-century Gothic elements. Inside you can hear historical and mythical stories, while outside you can relax in the garden, spot roaming deer, then walk in the footsteps of ancient Welsh princes to the castle. **Note**: Dinefwr Castle is owned by the Wildlife Trust and is under the guardianship of Cadw.

Eat, shop, stay: The Billiard Room Café (fully licensed). Inner courtyard shop and plant sales. Second-hand bookshop. Black Raven Gallery. Holiday cottages and bunkhouse.

Things to see and do: **Indoors** Relaxed hands-on visit. **Outdoors** Seasonal tours of parkland National Nature Reserve and to spot White Park cattle. School holiday and family activities. **Dogs**: welcome on leads in pop-up café and outer park only (cattle/sheep grazing).

Access: 🅿️🚗♿🚻🍴🚼🔊 Castle ♿🏛️
Newton House ♿🏛️🛗🚻♿ Parkland 🏞️🏞️➡️

Find out more: 01558 824512 or dinefwr@nationaltrust.org.uk
Llandeilo, near Carmarthen, Carmarthenshire SA19 6RT

Dinefwr		M	T	W	T	F	S	S
1 Jan–28 Mar*	11–3	M	T	W	T	F	S	S
29 Mar–1 Nov	10–5	M	T	W	T	F	S	S
2 Nov–31 Dec**	11–3	M	T	W	T	F	S	S

*Newton House: closed 6 to 17 January for housekeeping and conservation (grounds remain open 10 to 3). Grounds: open 10 to 4 November to March, and 10 to 5 April to October.
**Everything closed 24 and 25 December.

Dinefwr in Carmarthenshire: the view from Newton House across the garden

Dolaucothi Estate Woodland

near Pumsaint, Llanwrda,
Carmarthenshire 1944

Hours of woodland walks and multi-user
trail with route information signage at the
Gold Mines and Pumsaint village car parks.
Note: for satnav use SA19 8US.

Find out more: 01558 650809 or
dolaucothi@nationaltrust.org.uk

Dolaucothi Gold Mines

Pumsaint, Llanwrda,
Carmarthenshire SA19 8US

🦽🏠🛆⛺ 1941

Parking: on site; overflow car park
opposite main entrance.

Panning for gold at Dolaucothi Gold Mines in
Carmarthenshire, below, and touring the mines, right

Not your average National Trust visit, this
hidden gem reveals the story of the quest for
gold more than 2,000 years ago. Try your luck
by panning for gold, and anything you find you
keep. Or you can venture on an overground
tour of the Roman archaeology, go
underground to experience the harsh
conditions of Victorian times and listen to
what 1930s miners had to say in their very
own words about their final efforts to search
for gold. Why not join us for the ultimate
adventure and discover centuries of stories
in just one day? **Note**: steep slopes, stout
footwear essential. Minimum height 1 metre.
No carried children underground.

Eat, shop, stay: our Mine Yard Café serves light
lunches, soup, cakes and refreshments. Splash
out on real Welsh gold jewellery from our gift
shop. Sleep under dark skies, enjoy peace and
tranquillity at our caravan site.

Things to see and do: guided tours throughout the day, level tour available. Self-guided audio of the Roman workings. Gold panning. 1930s machinery display sheds. 15½ miles of footpaths across the Dolaucothi Estate. **Dogs**: welcome on leads, although not on all guided tours.

Access: ⓟⓓⓖⓙⓑⓐⓙ
Café ⓐ Machinery sheds ⓐ Mine yard ⓐ ➡

Find out more: 01558 650809 (mines). 01558 650365 (caravan site) or dolaucothi@nationaltrust.org.uk

Dolaucothi Mines		M	T	W	T	F	S	S
1 Apr–19 Jul	11–4:30	M	T	W	T	F	S	S
20 Jul–31 Aug	10:30–5:30	M	T	W	T	F	S	S
1 Sep–1 Nov	11–4:30	M	T	W	T	F	S	S

Last tour leaves 90 minutes before closing. Caravan and motorhome park: open daily, April to October.

Dolmelynllyn Estate

Ganllwyd, Near Dolgellau, Gwynedd

⛵ ⬆ ♿ 1936

Spectacular Dolmelynllyn Estate in Gwynedd

Satnav: use LL40 2TF. **Parking**: on site.

A 696-hectare (1,719-acre) estate, including woodland, two tenanted farms and Grade II-listed Dolmelynllyn Hall, with ornamental lake and parkland. There's a network of paths to explore with highlights which include the impressive Rhaeadr Ddu waterfall, ruins of Cefn Coch gold mines and wildlife-rich oak woodlands. **Note**: Dolmelynllyn Hall is a privately run hotel, not a pay-to-enter property.

Eat, shop, stay: four holiday cottages nearby. Two National Trust-owned but tenanted hotels on the estate offering refreshments and light meals. Picnic site.

Things to see and do: Dinas Oleu, at Barmouth, the first parcel of land donated to the National Trust, and remote Cregennan Lakes are both just 12 miles away. **Dogs**: welcome on leads.

Find out more: 01341 440238 or dolmelynllyn@nationaltrust.org.uk

Dyffryn Gardens

St Nicholas, Vale of Glamorgan CF5 6SU

🏠 ✿ 2013

Parking: on site. Electric vehicle charging point in main car park beside play area.

A garden for all seasons, Dyffryn is undergoing an ambitious project to return it to its full Edwardian splendour. There is so much to discover. Winding paths lead to exquisitely designed garden rooms, grand lawns and an impressive arboretum. The walled gardens yield a bounty of fresh produce and the enormous glasshouse contains a striking collection of rare cacti and orchids. Designed by eminent landscape architect Thomas Mawson, the gardens are the early 20th-century vision of plantsman Reginald Cory. At the heart of the grounds stands Grade II*-listed Dyffryn House. This eclectic, partially furnished Victorian mansion is just the place to take in the views and see the restoration in action. Dyffryn Gardens truly inspire and enthral.

Eat, shop, stay: Gardens Café by the Nant Bran stream at reception and The Gallery café within the gardens, connected to Dyffryn House. A large portion of produce comes directly from the kitchen gardens. Shop selling plants and gifts. Second-hand bookshop inside house.

Things to see and do: network of garden rooms and champion trees in the arboretum to discover. There are family events and a wild play area inside the arboretum, with another play area next to café. Tredegar House is nearby. **Dogs**: welcome on short leads in gardens.

Access: ⬚⬚⬚⬚
House ⬚⬚ Grounds ⬚⬚⬚⬚⬚

Find out more: 02920 593328 or dyffryn@nationaltrust.org.uk

Dyffryn Gardens		M	T	W	T	F	S	S
Gardens, shop and café								
1 Jan–13 Feb	10–4	M	T	W	T	F	S	S
14 Feb–19 Mar	10–5	M	T	W	T	F	S	S
20 Mar–27 Sep	10–6	M	T	W	T	F	S	S
28 Sep–1 Nov	10–5	M	T	W	T	F	S	S
2 Nov–31 Dec*	10–4	M	T	W	T	F	S	S
House								
1 Jan–13 Feb	12–3:30	M	T	W	T	F	S	S
14 Feb–1 Nov	12–4	M	T	W	T	F	S	S
2 Nov–31 Dec*	12–3:30	M	T	W	T	F	S	S

Gardens: last entry one hour before closing. Gardens Café: opens 10; last orders 30 minutes before closing. Hot food orders 12 to 3:30. *Closed 25 and 26 December.

Dyffryn Gardens, Vale of Glamorgan, this page and opposite

Erddig

near Wrexham, Wrexham

🏠 ✝ 🏛 ✿ ♿ 1973

Satnav: do not use, follow brown signs.
Parking: on site, 200 yards from ticket office.
Electric vehicle charging point in car park.

A haven of natural beauty and modern sanctuary for wellbeing, Erddig's 485-hectare (1,200-acre) pleasure park, designed by William Emes, welcomes walkers (and their four-legged friends), beginner runners, Nordic walkers and those seeking a natural boost in the great outdoors. At its heart, above the River Clywedog, is Erddig Hall – an unexpected survivor, rescued from dereliction in the 1970s. Discover the story of a family's unique relationship with its servants – a large collection of servants' portraits and carefully preserved rooms capture their lives across the generations, where saw and spade are as treasured as silver and silk. Outdoors, relax in a restored 18th-century walled garden with tranquil water features, trained fruit trees and apple orchards growing over 180 varieties.

Eat, shop, stay: you can enjoy lunch in the Hayloft restaurant, light bites in the tea parlour and tea garden, or fresh coffee in Wolf's Den on busy days. Don't forget to visit our gift shop and second-hand bookshop before leaving.

Things to see and do: **Indoors** Discover how generations of the Yorke family took an almost curatorial attitude to their possessions, bequeathing one of the largest, most diverse and fragile collections in the National Trust.

Erddig in Wrexham tells the story of the unique relationship between the gentry and servants who lived in this house

Outdoors Year-long programme, including spring displays, atmospheric open-air theatre evenings, Christmas and Easter trails, garden tours and guided estate walks. Regular sporting activities on the estate include Nordic walking, beginner running groups and parkruns. Children can let off steam in the Wolf's Den natural play area and fly on the rope swing, climb the obstacles or enjoy building dens. **Dogs**: welcome in country park, Midden Yard and tea garden only.

Access: 🅿️🚌🐕‍🦺♿🔊📷📹🚻🧸♿
Building 🏛️🧎 Grounds 🧎🧎♿

Find out more: 01978 355314 or erddig@nationaltrust.org.uk
Erddig, near Wrexham, Wrexham LL13 0YT

Learning about the garden at Erddig

Erddig		M	T	W	T	F	S	S
House								
1 Jan–5 Jan*	11:30–2:30	·	·	W	T	F	S	S
15 Feb–27 Mar*	11:30–2:30	M	T	W	T	F	S	S
28 Mar–1 Nov	12:30–3:30	M	T	W	T	F	S	S
2 Nov–31 Dec*	11:30–2:30	M	T	W	T	F	S	S
Garden, restaurant and shop								
1 Jan–27 Mar	11–4	M	T	W	T	F	S	S
28 Mar–1 Nov	10–5	M	T	W	T	F	S	S
2 Nov–31 Dec	11–4	M	T	W	T	F	S	S
Natural play area								
15 Feb–27 Mar	11–4	M	T	W	T	F	S	S
28 Mar–1 Nov	10–5	M	T	W	T	F	S	S

*Ground-floor servants' quarters only. Regular tours weekdays, self-guided during school holidays and weekends. Closed 25 December. Timed tickets for the house operate on Bank Holidays and during busy periods.

Freshwater West and Gupton Farm

near Castlemartin, Pembrokeshire

🚗 🚻 ♿ 🏕 🛏 ⛺ 1976

Green Field ⛺

Satnav: for Gupton Farm use SA71 5HW.
Parking: on site.

Freshwater West lies on a wild stretch of coast that's great for water sports and sandy adventures. Beyond the beach, you can discover Gupton Farm, our campsite, surf lodge accommodation and visitor hub. The perfect rustic escape for adventurous souls and nature lovers; go wildlife-watching, follow walking trails, make the most of the coast and sleep easy under the stars.

Eat, shop, stay: surf lodge accommodation and campsite at Gupton Farm. Shop selling gifts, camping essentials and beach goods. Picnics welcome. Seasonal catering available at Freshwater West (not National Trust).

Things to see and do: learn about this special place at our visitor information hub. Follow walking trails, watch wildlife and try water sports with the on-site Surf and SUP school (not National Trust).
Dogs: welcome under close control.

Access: 🚾 ♿ 🛗

Find out more: 01646 661640 or freshwater@nationaltrust.org.uk

Freshwater West and Gupton Farm	M	T	W	T	F	S	S
Campsite							
3 Apr–28 Sep	M	T	W	T	F	S	S

Interpretation room and surf lodge (National Trust holiday accommodation) open every day all year.

Freshwater West and Gupton Farm in Pembrokeshire: the campsite, above and below, on this wild, sandy coast

Hafod y Llan

near Beddgelert, Gwynedd

Satnav: use LL55 4NQ.
Parking: on farm for campsite guests only.
Electric vehicle charging point at campsite
for guests. For the Watkin Path, use
pay-and-display car park (not National Trust)
at Bethannia, opposite farm entrance.

Set in the beautiful Nantgwynant Valley,
Hafod y Llan is the largest farm run by the
National Trust. Extending from the valley floor
to the summit of Snowdon, part of the farm is
designated a National Nature Reserve as well a
a Site of Special Scientific Interest. Visitors are
free to wander the many paths which cross this
unique landscape. **Note**: this is a working farm,
so access to the farmyard is on foot only.

Eat, shop, stay: holiday cottage, two chalets
and campsite on the farm. Refreshments
available at nearby Caffi Gwynant
(not National Trust).

Things to see and do: a network of paths
crosses Hafod y Llan, including a low-level
adventure trail. At the farm entrance the
Watkin Path leads to the summit of Snowdon.
Dogs: welcome on leads.

Find out more: 01766 890473 or
hafodyllan@nationaltrust.org.uk

Hafod y Llan in Gwynedd, above and below, is the largest farm run by the National Trust

The Kymin

Monmouth, Monmouthshire NP25 3SF

⌂⬛▲☗ 1902

The Kymin in Monmouthshire

Parking: limited parking on site with accessible parking bay adjacent to Round House.

Lord Nelson and Lady Hamilton were delighted with this Georgian banqueting house and Naval Temple when they visited in 1802. The Kymin is still a great spot from which to enjoy panoramic views of the Brecon Beacons and Wye Valley. The woods and pleasure grounds are also perfect for picnics. **Note**: access via steep winding single lane with passing places.

Eat, shop, stay: cakes and refreshments available during special events.
Picnics welcome.

Things to see and do: **Indoors** Friendly guides offer a taste of a Georgian gentleman's picnic club. **Outdoors** Self-guided walks, bluebells in spring. Children's nature quiz. Special events all year. **Dogs**: welcome in the Round House and grounds.

Access: ♿♿♿
Round House ♿♿ Naval Temple ♿ Grounds ➡

Find out more: 01600 719241 or kymin@nationaltrust.org.uk

The Kymin		M	T	W	T	F	S	S
Round House								
28 Mar–26 Oct*	11–4	M	·	·	·	·	S	S
Grounds								
Open all year	8–9	M	T	W	T	F	S	S

*Open Good Friday. Car park: open daylight hours only.

Llanbedrog Beach

Llanbedrog, Gwynedd

🏖 2000

Satnav: use LL53 7TT.
Parking: on site. Electric vehicle charging point beside visitor welcome hut.

This wonderful stretch of sand, best known for its colourful beach huts, has been enjoyed by generations. Its sheltered waters, fantastic views over Cardigan Bay and adjacent wooded and craggy landscape make this a real gem of Llŷn. **Note**: toilet (not National Trust).

Eat, shop, stay: shops and cafés at Llanbedrog and at nearby Pwllheli and Abersoch (not National Trust).

Things to see and do: events during summer months. Children's adventure packs, maps and guides available at the visitor welcome cabin. Second-hand bookshop. Beach huts for hire (subject to availability).
Dogs: welcome under close control.

Find out more: 01758 740561 or llanbedrog@nationaltrust.org.uk

Sandy Llanbedrog Beach, Gwynedd

Llanerchaeron

Ciliau Aeron, near Aberaeron,
Ceredigion SA48 8DG

🏛️📷♿🚶🛏️☕🍽️ 1989

Parking: 50 yards. Electric vehicle charging point in front of visitor reception/café.

A self-sufficient 18th-century Welsh minor gentry estate. The villa, designed in the 1790s, is the most complete example of the early work of John Nash. It has its own service courtyard with dairy, laundry, brewery and salting house, giving a full 'upstairs, downstairs' experience. The walled kitchen gardens, pleasure grounds, ornamental lake, woodland and parkland offer peaceful walks, while Home Farm has an impressive range of traditional, atmospheric outbuildings. The working farm has Welsh Black cattle, Llanwenog sheep and rare Welsh pigs as well as chickens, geese and turkeys.

Eat, shop, stay: café serving light meals and cakes (not National Trust). Picnic site. Fresh garden produce and plants, farm meat, gifts and books for sale. Second-hand bookshop. Two holiday cottages nearby.

Llanerchaeron in Ceredigion, clockwise from top right: walking on the estate, views across the farmland and the pretty villa

Things to see and do: family activities during local school holidays, including craft activities, gardening, nature activities and self-led trails. Special event days. **Dogs**: welcome on leads on the woodland walks and in the parkland.

Access: 🅿️♿🔔🔍📷📹♿
Visitor building 🦽♿ Villa 🚶♿♿ Grounds 🦽➡️♿

Find out more: 01545 570200 or llanerchaeron@nationaltrust.org.uk

Llanerchaeron		M	T	W	T	F	S	S
Whole property								
15 Feb–13 Mar	11:30–3:30	M	T	W	T	F	S	S
14 Mar–1 Nov	10:30–5:30*	M	T	W	T	F	S	S
Farm, shop and garden								
4 Jan–15 Feb	11:30–3:30						S	S
2 Nov–31 Dec	11:30–3:30**	M	T	W	T	F	S	S

Last admission one hour before closing. *Villa: open 11:30 to 4. **Closed 24 to 26 December. Geler Jones Rural Life Collection: open 12 to 4, Wednesday and Friday, 18 March to 30 October. Parkland and woodland walks: open daily.

Marloes Sands and Mere

Marloes, Pembrokeshire

🏛️🏖️🦅 1941

Satnav: use SA62 3BH. **Parking**: on site.

A hidden gem on the western edge of Pembrokeshire, Marloes Sands beach is a long sandy stretch that is perfect for making a splash. Join us for a beach clean, spot marine life and go for a clifftop walk along the coast path. The wetland of Marloes Mere, just inland, is bustling with birdlife. Bring binoculars and get closer to nature at our on-site bird hides. **Note**: nearest toilets by Runwayskiln farm, alongside the track from the car park to Marloes Mere.

Eat, shop, stay: Runwayskiln café (tenant-run) at Marloes Sands is open throughout the season. Snacks and beach goods available at the visitor hut in Marloes Sands car park.

Things to see and do: go for a walk along the coast path, visit the bird hide to watch wildlife and head to the beach for rock-pooling and sandy adventures. **Dogs**: welcome under close control.

Access: ♿🪑🦽📶➡️

Find out more: 01437 720385 or marloessands@nationaltrust.org.uk

Marloes Sands and Mere in Pembrokeshire: the Mere wetlands, below, and the long sandy beach right

Martin's Haven

near Marloes, Pembrokeshire

🏛 ⛰ 🚶 1981

Martin's Haven, Pembrokeshire: the waters here are a designated Marine Conservation Zone

Satnav: use SA62 3BJ. **Parking**: on site.

This fabulously wild headland with fine panoramic views of St Bride's Bay is also the gateway to Skomer Island. For a really varied and exciting day, why not combine spotting marine wildlife with discovering traces of ancient settlements? **Note**: nearest toilets by the slipway.

Eat, shop, stay: Runwayskiln café (tenant-run) at Marloes Sands is open throughout the season. Snacks and beach goods available at the visitor hut in Martin's Haven car park.

The deer park at Martin's Haven

Things to see and do: follow the coast path, visit the deer park to watch wildlife and discover Iron Age history. Join us for guided seal pup walks in autumn. **Dogs**: welcome under close control.

Access: ♿ ➡️

Find out more: 01437 720385 or martinshaven@nationaltrust.org.uk

Mwnt

near Cardigan, Ceredigion 1963

Beautiful secluded bay with a sandy beach – perfect for spotting dolphins, seals and other amazing wildlife. **Note**: small café and shop (not National Trust). Steep steps to beach. For satnav use SA43 1QH. Dogs not permitted on beach, 1 May to 30 September.

Find out more: 01545 570200 or mwnt@nationaltrust.org.uk

Ogwen Cottage

Nant Ffrancon, Bethesda, Gwynedd LL57 3LZ

♿ 2014

Parking: at Ogwen Lake (not National Trust).

Ogwen Cottage is nestled between the dramatic Carneddau and Glyderau mountain ranges, at the starting point for numerous walking routes in the area. It includes a base for our local ranger team and outdoor education centre. This iconic building has long been associated with mountaineering and adventure, a tradition we're maintaining by providing outdoor learning experiences on site in partnership with The Outward Bound Trust.

Eat, shop, stay: picnic benches outside ranger base. Food kiosk (not National Trust). Two holiday cottages at Dyffryn Mymbyr (7 miles), and one at Tal y Braich (3 miles).

Things to see and do: range of rock-climbing and mountain-walking routes available, as well as the National Cycle Network's Lon Las Ogwen. **Dogs**: welcome on leads.

Access: 🏞 **Ranger base** ♿

Find out more: 01248 605739 or
ogwen@nationaltrust.org.uk

Ogwen Cottage
Ogwen Cottage Ranger Base: usually open during office
hours, but opening times may vary (call for details).

**Ogwen Cottage, Gwynedd, below, is the
starting point for numerous walks, above**

Paxton's Tower

Llanarthne, near Dryslwyn,
Carmarthenshire 1965

Known as 'Golwg y Byd' (Eye of the World),
Paxton's Tower is said to offer views of seven
counties. **Note:** for satnav use SA32 8HX.
Sorry no toilet. Nearest National Trust
facilities at Dinefwr in Llandeilo.

Find out more: 01558 823902 or
paxtonstower@nationaltrust.org.uk

Penbryn

near Sarnau, Cardigan, Ceredigion 1967

One of Ceredigion's best-kept secrets, this
beautifully secluded sandy cove lies down
leafy lanes, edged with flower-covered banks.
Note: café serving a selection of snacks
and drinks (not National Trust). For satnav
use SA44 6QL. Electric vehicle charging
point. Dogs not permitted on beach,
1 May to 30 September.

Find out more: 01545 570200 or
penbryn@nationaltrust.org.uk

Pennard, Pwll Du and Bishopston Valley

near Southgate, Swansea

🏛🏖🗺 1954

Pennard, Pwll Du and Bishopston Valley, Swansea

Satnav: use SA3 2DH.
Parking: at Southgate car park.

Spectacular cliffs, caves where mammoth remains have been found, rare birds, an underground river, bat roosts, silver-lead mining, ancient woodland, smuggling and limestone quarrying are just a few of the wonders of this area. There are also numerous archaeological features and two important caves – Bacon Hole and Minchin Hole.
Note: due to dangerous rip tides, swimming in Three Cliffs Bay is not advised.

Eat, shop, stay: coffee shop, village stores, tea-rooms and a pub in Pennard (none National Trust). Picnics welcome.

Things to see and do: Pennard provides a great starting point for a variety of walks. Enjoy wild flowers and spot rare birds, such as choughs and Dartford warblers.
Dogs: welcome, but please be aware livestock graze freely across Pennard Burrows.

Access: 🅿

Find out more: 01792 390636 or pennard@nationaltrust.org.uk

Penrhyn Castle and Garden

Bangor, Gwynedd LL57 4HT

🏰🏚✝🏵🐕🍴 1951

Parking: 500 yards. Electric vehicle charging point in main car park, just below visitor reception.

Penrhyn Castle is a vast neo-Norman castle with many different tales to tell. Set against the dramatic backdrop of Snowdonia and the North Wales coast, the castle's dominating stone façade hides more than just its internal red-brick construction. Inside, the luxury of the exquisite carving and furnishings are deeply at odds with the links to slavery and bitter industrial dispute that changed Penrhyn's relationship with the local community for ever. Over the coming years Penrhyn will be exploring these difficult stories and presenting them within the castle.
Note: during this period of transformation, opening arrangements, room layout and tour availability may vary.

Neo-Norman Penrhyn Castle and Garden in Gwynedd: the dominating Keep, above, and Grand Hall, opposite

Eat, shop, stay: enjoy hot meals in the castle café or a lighter bite in the Stables. Browse through a range of National Trust and local products in our shop and find a bargain in our second-hand bookshop.

Things to see and do: **Indoors** Climb aboard one of our industrial locomotives or see what life was like in the Victorian kitchens. **Outdoors** Find peace in Walter Speed's famous walled garden. **Dogs**: welcome on leads in grounds. Assistance dogs only in the castle.

Access: 🅿️♿🚻♿♿♿🔊📷📱🖼️

Castle ♿♿♿ Stable block ♿♿

Grounds ♿♿

Find out more: 01248 353084 or penrhyncastle@nationaltrust.org.uk

Penrhyn Castle		M	T	W	T	F	S	S
Castle*								
29 Feb–1 Nov	11–5**	M	T	W	T	F	S	S
28 Nov–20 Dec	11–4						S	S
Garden, Railway Museum, café and shop								
4 Jan–9 Feb	11–3						S	S
15 Feb–1 Nov	10:30–5†	M	T	W	T	F	S	S
7 Nov–27 Dec	11–4						S	S
Victorian kitchens*								
15 Feb–1 Nov	10:30–5	M	T	W	T	F	S	S
7 Nov–27 Dec	11–4						S	S

*Last entry one hour before closing.
**Guided entry, 4 to 5. †Shop: opens 11.

Plas Newydd House and Garden

Llanfairpwll, Anglesey LL61 6DQ

🏠 🏛 ✿ ⛹ ⟋ 1976

Parking: 400 yards from main entrance.

Perfectly positioned on the shore of the Menai Strait with spectacular views of Snowdonia and Anglesey's coastline, Plas Newydd is surrounded by Grade I-listed gardens: the Italianate Terrace and Rhododendron Garden, Australasian Arboretum and extensive woodland. Transformed into a family home by the 6th Marquess of Anglesey during the 1930s, it houses Rex Whistler's famous 58-foot mural and numerous works of art. You can discover more about the life of the flamboyant 5th Marquess and enjoy outdoor activities for all ages, including the hand-built treehouse, nine-hole Frisbee™ golf course, adventure playground and the resident red squirrels. **Note**: due to reservicing works, some rooms may be closed; opening and tour arrangements may vary.

Eat, shop, stay: Plas Café serving hot and cold lunches. Light bites and cakes available from the Old Dairy. The Old Dairy Shop and Siop Newydd are the perfect place for gifts.

Things to see and do: **Indoors** Learn about the house and see Rex Whistler's masterpiece. **Outdoors** Enjoy walks and talks with the gardeners and a full calendar of events. **Dogs**: welcome on leads in wider garden.

Access: 🅿️ ♿ ♿ 👶 🦽 ♿ 🖥 📷 ⚓ 🛒
Building 🦽 🦽 ♿ Grounds 🦽 ➡️

Find out more: 01248 714795 or plasnewydd@nationaltrust.org.uk

Plas Newydd		M	T	W	T	F	S	S
Mansion								
29 Feb–6 Sep	11–4:30	M	T	W	T	F	S	S
7 Sep–1 Nov	12–4:30	M	T	W	T	F	S	S
Gardens, shop and café								
4 Jan–16 Feb	11–3	·	·	·	·	·	S	S
17 Feb–15 Nov	10:30–5	M	T	W	T	F	S	S
21 Nov–20 Dec	11–3	·	·	·	·	·	S	S

Opening times may vary and some rooms may close occasionally due to major reservicing project.

Plas Newydd House and Garden, Anglesey: the Grade I-listed garden, below, and south-facing side of the house, above

Plas yn Rhiw

Rhiw, Pwllheli, Gwynedd LL53 8AB

🏠❄♿🛏 1952

Parking: 100 yards (narrow lanes). Electric vehicle charging point in top car park beside tea-room.

Standing on a hillside overlooking Cardigan Bay, Plas yn Rhiw is a beautiful 16th-century manor house with Georgian additions. The house was rescued from neglect and lovingly restored by the three Keating sisters, who bought the property in 1938. The views from the grounds and gardens across the bay are among the most spectacular in Britain. The garden contains many beautiful flowering trees and shrubs, with beds framed by box hedges and grass paths – a real joy to explore and stunning whatever the season.

Eat, shop, stay: tea-room serving a selection of fresh sandwiches, soup, cakes, drinks and ice cream; picnics also available to take out. Shop selling gifts, plants, books and prints of Honora Keating's landscape watercolours. Three holiday cottages within walking distance.

Things to see and do: **Indoors** Virtual tour available on iPad and guided tours by arrangement. **Outdoors** Woodland walks and a native-apple orchard to explore. Links to the Wales Coast Path. **Dogs**: welcome on leads in woodland walk below the shop. Assistance dogs welcome elsewhere.

Access: 👓♿🦽📷🚻🎫:👤
Building 🏠♿ Grounds 🏠♿

Find out more: 01758 780219 or plasynrhiw@nationaltrust.org.uk

Plas yn Rhiw		M	T	W	T	F	S	S
19 Mar–30 Sep	11–5*	M	T	W	T	F	S	S
1 Oct–1 Nov	11–4*	M	T	W	T	F	S	S

*House: opens at 12.

Sitting in glorious gardens, 16th-century Plas yn Rhiw in Gwynedd, has spectacular views over Cardigan Bay

Porth Meudwy

near Aberdaron, Gwynedd

🏛️ ♿ 1990

Satnav: use LL53 8DA. **Parking**: ½ mile.

Nowhere expresses the essence of the area better than this sheltered cove on the wild and rocky coastline west of Aberdaron. It was from here that the pilgrims set out to Ynys Enlli (Bardsey Island). Today fishermen still bring the daily catch into the cove. Don't miss the unique Aberdaron boats: small wooden beach boats designed to dance nimbly through the waves along the craggy coastline.
Note: sorry no toilet.

Eat, shop, stay: shops, pubs and cafés in Aberdaron village (none National Trust). Four holiday apartments in Aberdaron.

Things to see and do: the Wales Coast Path – a birdwatchers' paradise – runs dramatically along the clifftop.
Dogs: welcome on leads (near livestock).

Find out more: 01758 760469 or porthmeudwy@nationaltrust.org.uk

The cove of Porth Meudwy, Gwynedd, below, offers protection from the wild seas on this rocky coast, above

Porth y Swnt

Henfaes, Aberdaron, Pwllheli,
Gwynedd LL53 8BE

🛏️ 🏛️ ⛽ 2010

Parking: on site. Electric vehicle charging point behind visitor centre.

This exciting interpretation centre, at the heart of the beautiful fishing village of Aberdaron, shines a light on Llŷn's unique culture, heritage and environment. You can experience the Bardsey Island lighthouse's retired optic up close, follow in the footsteps of pilgrims on a journey across the Sound in the video pod, catch up on what Llŷn's rangers are up to and form your reflective thoughts in the Sea of Words.

Eat, shop, stay: gift shop in visitor centre (not National Trust). Cafés, pubs and convenience stores in village (none National Trust). Henfaes holiday apartments (Meudwy, Enlli, Daron and Hywyn) are located at the centre of Aberdaron.

Things to see and do: **Indoors** Audio guide, children's scrapbooks, events during school holidays. **Outdoors** Walks and access to the Wales Coast Path. Adventure packs, beach fun days, guided walks and cycle rides.
Dogs: Porth y Swnt – assistance dogs only; local rules apply on beach (not National Trust).

Access: 🅿️ ♿ 🚼 ♿ Car park ♿ ♿

Find out more: 01758 703810 or porthyswnt@nationaltrust.org.uk

Porth y Swnt		M	T	W	T	F	S	S
2 Jan–31 Mar*	10–4	M	T	W	T	F	S	S
1 Apr–30 Jun	10–5	M	T	W	T	F	S	S
1 Jul–31 Aug	10–6	M	T	W	T	F	S	S
1 Sep–30 Sep	10–5	M	T	W	T	F	S	S
1 Oct–31 Dec**	10–4	M	T	W	T	F	S	S

*Closed 23 to 29 January. **Closed 24 to 26 December.

There is so much to discover at the exciting interpretation centre of Porth y Swnt, Gwynedd, above and below

Pretty Porthdinllaen in Gwynedd, above, boasts clear sheltered waters and a fine sandy beach, below

Porthdinllaen

Morfa Nefyn, Gwynedd

🏛️ 🛏️ 1994

Satnav: use LL53 6DA. **Parking**: on site for beach; 1 mile from village (no vehicular access to village). Electric vehicle charging point in Trust car park, beside visitor welcome hut.

This old fishing village really is a jewel. Perched on the end of a thin ribbon of land which stretches out into the Irish Sea, its clear sheltered waters lap against the stout stone houses. You can watch fishermen bring in the daily catch, while relaxing with a drink at the Tŷ Coch Inn. In the summer you can view the ecologically rich seagrasses from a paddle board – and have fun trying to stand up. **Note**: nearest toilet in village, which can only be reached by foot. Steps down to beach.

Eat, shop, stay: two holiday cottages available in the heart of the village. Refreshments available at our tenanted pub, Tŷ Coch Inn.

Things to see and do: summer events for all the family. Wonderful walking on the coastal path – maps and guides available at car-park welcome cabin. **Dogs**: under close control, 1 October to 31 March; on east side of beach in summer.

Access: 👤

Find out more: 01758 760469 or porthdinllaen@nationaltrust.org.uk

Why not share your pictures with us? #nationaltrust

Porthor

Aberdaron, Gwynedd

🏖️ 🛏️ 1981

Satnav: use LL53 8LG. **Parking**: on site. Electric vehicle charging point.

This wonderful beach is famous for its 'whistling sands' and glistening waters. The whistling happens because of the especially fine sand grains on the beach – perfect for building sandcastles. If the joys of sandcastles and sunbathing are not enough for you, then why not have a go at surfing? The sea here is perfect. In addition, the Wales Coast Path runs in both directions from the car park. **Note**: nearest toilet in car park. Please remember to scan your membership card.

Eat, shop, stay: National Trust tenanted beachside café and shop offering everything from lunch to sun cream. Four holiday apartments in Aberdaron.

Things to see and do: famous beach and glorious clifftop coast path to explore. Children's adventure pack available from car park. **Dogs**: welcome under close control from 1 October to 31 March.

Access: 🚻

Find out more: 01758 760469 or porthor@nationaltrust.org.uk

Porthor in Gwynedd, above, offers wonderful surf, while the fine sand on the beach is perfect for sandcastles, below

Powis Castle
and Garden

Welshpool, Powys

🏰 ✿ 🐾 ⛔ 1952

Satnav: postcode misdirects, enter Powis Castle. **Parking**: on site. Two electric vehicle charging points in car park.

Once the stark medieval fortress of Welsh princes, Powis Castle was transformed over centuries into a grand home for the Herbert family, reflecting their wealth and status. Furnished with sumptuous fabrics, world-class artworks, furniture, tapestries and the unique Clive collection of Indian treasures, the interior reflects the Elizabethan period through to the 1940s, when an evacuated girls' school made the castle its home. With breathtaking views across the Severn Valley, the garden is one of Britain's finest. Dating back more than 300 years, the garden includes Italianate terraces lined with vibrant herbaceous borders and gigantic clipped yews, an Edwardian formal garden with century-old apple trees and rose beds, and a woodland area which boasts several champion trees.

Eat, shop, stay: café serving lunch, light bites, snacks and cakes (licensed) and garden coffee shop. Gift shop, garden shop, plant sales and second-hand books. Holiday cottage, The Bothy, located in the heart of the garden.

Things to see and do: **Indoors** Introductory talks (April to September). Family trails. Welsh Girls' School interactive installation. **Outdoors** Garden tours and talks. Family trails. Additional children's activities during school holidays. **Dogs**: assistance dogs only March to October. Dogs on short leads welcome November to February.

Access: 🅿️ 🅿️ ♿ 🚹 ♿ 📶 📺 ⠿
Building 🔖 Grounds 🔖 🔖 ➡️ ♿

Find out more: 01938 551920 or
powiscastle@nationaltrust.org.uk
Welshpool, Powys SY21 8RF

Powis Castle		M	T	W	T	F	S	S
Castle and shop								
1 Jan–31 Mar	11–4*	M	T	W	T	F	S	S
1 Apr–30 Sept†	11–5*	M	T	W	T	F	S	S
1 Oct–31 Dec††	11–4*	M	T	W	T	F	S	S
Garden and café								
1 Jan–31 Mar	10–4	M	T	W	T	F	S	S
1 Apr–30 Sep	10–5**	M	T	W	T	F	S	S
1 Oct–31 Dec††	10–4	M	T	W	T	F	S	S

*Castle: last entry one hour before closing.
**Garden: open to 6. †Garden coffee shop and garden
shop open (opening times vary). ††Closed 25 December.

**Powis Castle and Garden, Powys, this page and left: an
astounding garden, incredible views and grand interiors**

Rhosili and South Gower Coast

on the Gower Peninsula, Swansea

🍽️🏛️♿🎨🐾🛏️ 1933

Satnav: use SA3 1PR. **Parking**: large pay and display car park at end of village. Suitable for motorhomes (no overnight stays). Electric vehicle charging point.

Lying at the far end of the beautiful Gower Peninsula, Rhosili is blessed with 3 miles of golden, award-winning sands and spectacular coastal views. It is the perfect base from which to explore the stunning South Gower coastline – most of which is in the care of the National Trust. From the historically and environmentally important medieval strip farm system known as The Vile, the instantly recognisable Worms Head tidal island, Iron Age earthworks, notable wildlife and geology, through to legends, shipwrecks and stories, there is so much to see. Once visited, Rhosili will stay with you for ever. **Note**: steep steps and a slope to the beach.

Eat, shop, stay: wide range of carefully selected gifts, souvenirs, outdoor essentials, home and kitchen accessories and refreshments available all year. Small outdoor catering offer, March to October (weather dependent). Three National Trust holiday cottages nearby.

Spectacular Rhosili and South Gower Coast, Swansea

Golden sunflowers at Rhosili and South Gower Coast

Things to see and do: you can walk along the Wales Coast Path and through The Vile, cross to Worms Head and explore the beach. Visitor information available all year. Regular free activities for all ages. **Dogs**: welcome (on leads near livestock please). Beach is dog-friendly all year.

Access: 🅿️♿🚻🅿️♿♿👁️🔊
Gallery 🖼️ Car park/viewpoint ♿➡️

Find out more: 01792 390707 or rhosili@nationaltrust.org.uk

Rhosili		M	T	W	T	F	S	S
Shop								
2 Jan–3 Apr	10–4:30*	M	T	W	T	F	S	S
4 Apr–17 Jul	10–5*	M	T	W	T	F	S	S
18 Jul–30 Aug	10–6*	M	T	W	T	F	S	S
31 Aug–4 Oct	10–5*	M	T	W	T	F	S	S
5 Oct–2 Nov	10–4:30*	M	T	W	T	F	S	S
3 Nov–23 Dec	10–4	M	T	W	T	F	S	S
26 Dec–30 Dec	11–4	M	T	W	·	·	S	S

*Outdoor food and beverages: open 1 March to 31 October (weather permitting). Car park: open daily, dawn to dusk.

St David's Visitor Centre and Shop

Captain's House, High Street,
St David's, Pembrokeshire SA62 6SD

🏛️ 📷 1974

Parking: none on site.

Overlooking the Celtic Old Cross in the centre of St David's, Wales's smallest historic city, the visitor centre and well-stocked shop are open all year. Have a browse of our retail collection and have a chat with the team about our special places and what's on. **Note**: sorry, no toilet.

Access: Building 🔨

Find out more: 01437 720385 or stdavidsshop@nationaltrust.org.uk

St David's Visitor Centre		M	T	W	T	F	S	S
2 Jan–21 Mar	10–4	M	T	W	T	F	S	.
23 Mar–31 Dec	9–5*	M	T	W	T	F	S	S

*Open 10 to 4 on Sundays. Closed 1 January and 25, 26 and 27 December.

St David's Visitor Centre and Shop, Pembrokeshire: the peninsula, top right, and St David's Head, above

Eat, shop, stay: the shop stocks a range of beautiful, local, Welsh and National Trust products. Porth Clais Kiosk (tenant-run) is nearby and offers a flavour of the area. Holiday cottages nearby.

Things to see and do: book onto one of our Pembrokeshire events and plan your visit with help from the team. St David's Head, Porth Clais, Solva and Abereiddi nearby.

Segontium

Caernarfon, Gwynedd 1937

Fort built to defend the Roman Empire against rebellious tribes. **Note**: under the guardianship of Cadw – Welsh Government's historic environment service. Museum not National Trust. For satnav use LL55 2LN. Please call for opening arrangements.

Find out more: 01443 336000 or segontium@nationaltrust.org.uk

Skenfrith Castle

Skenfrith, near Abergavenny, Monmouthshire NP7 8UH 1936

Remains of early 13th-century castle, built beside the River Monnow to command one of the main routes from England. **Note**: under the guardianship of Cadw – Welsh Government's historic environment service.

Find out more: 01874 625515 or skenfrithcastle@nationaltrust.org.uk

Southwood Estate

Newgale, Roch, Pembrokeshire

🐾⛰️📷 2003

Satnav: for Maidenhall car park use SA62 6BD; Southwood Farm car park use SA62 6AR.
Parking: on site.

A timeless landscape of wooded valleys, floral fields and craggy cliffs, the Southwood Estate is full of scenic surprises. Follow the waymarked walking trails and explore the best of coast and countryside; spot flora and fauna and see how we're working hard to safeguard this special place.

Southwood Estate, Pembrokeshire: scenic coast path

Eat, shop, stay: shop, café and pub in nearby Newgale and Roch (not National Trust). St David's Visitor Centre and Shop nearby. Holiday cottage at Southwood Farm.

Things to see and do: walking trails and events; guided walks, talks and children's activities. Information at Southwood Farm and Maidenhall car parks, with self-guided interpretation in the Shearing Shed.
Dogs: welcome under close control.

Access: 🅿️♿

Find out more: 01437 720385 or southwoodestate@nationaltrust.org.uk

Stackpole

near Pembroke, Pembrokeshire

🏠🏛️♿🐾⛰️🍴🛏️🍽️ 1976

Satnav: for Stackpole Quay use SA71 5LS; Broad Haven South SA71 5DR; Bosherston Lakes SA71 5DR; Stackpole Court SA71 5DE.
Parking: car parks at Stackpole Quay, Broad Haven South, Bosherston Lakes and Stackpole Court. Electric vehicle charging point at Stackpole Centre (SA71 5DQ) and Stackpole Quay (SA71 5LS).

A former grand estate stretching down to some of the most beautiful coastline in the world, including Broad Haven South, Barafundle Bay and Stackpole Quay. Today, Stackpole is a National Nature Reserve, recognised for its abundant flora and fauna; Bosherston Lakes are famous for their superb display of lilies and resident otters; and the dramatic cliffs of Stackpole Head are great for wildlife watching. You can uncover the history and heritage of this special place too; the former Stackpole Court site and nearby Lodge Park Woods reveal the story behind the magnificent designed landscape.

Eat, shop, stay: Boathouse tea-room offers drinks, light lunches, sandwiches, cakes and cream teas. A wide range of gifts and local goods available at the shop. Stay longer at Stackpole's holiday cottages, Stackpole Centre or Gupton campsite and surf lodge.

Things to see and do: walking trails, coarse fishing (close season 15 March to 15 June) and events, including runs, guided walks, talks and family nature adventures. Kayaking and coasteering available (not National Trust). **Dogs**: welcome under close control on the estate.

Access: 🅿♿🚻 Building 🏛 Landscape ♿➡♿

Find out more: 01646 623110 or stackpole@nationaltrust.org.uk

Stackpole		M	T	W	T	F	S	S
Estate								
Open all year	Dawn–dusk	M	T	W	T	F	S	S
Boathouse tea-room								
8 Feb–3 Apr*	11–4	M	T	W	T	F	S	S
4 Apr–27 Sep	10–5	M	T	W	T	F	S	S
28 Sep–1 Nov*	11–4	M	T	W	T	F	S	S
7 Nov–29 Nov*	11–4	.	.	.	.	.	S	S

*Reduced catering offer.

Stackpole in Pembrokeshire: the wide sandy bay of Broad Haven South beach with Church Rock beyond

Stackpole Centre

Old Home Farm Yard, Stackpole, near Pembroke, Pembrokeshire SA71 5DQ

🏠🏛♿🛶⛵🏕🔔🚻 1976

Kayaking fun at the Stackpole Centre in Pembrokeshire

Parking: free for guests.
Electric vehicle charging point available.

Located in the heart of the Stackpole Estate, our eco-award-winning centre provides residents with easy access to Bosherston Lakes, Stackpole Quay and award-winning beaches – including Barafundle and Broad Haven South – as well as the historic site of Stackpole Court. The recently refurbished centre can house up to 147 guests and offers flexible accommodation with modern facilities, including a theatre, meeting and classroom space. It is ideal for groups, corporate clients, celebrations and family holidays. **Note**: contact the centre for activity programmes, prices and availability.

Eat, shop, stay: self-catering or chef-catered options. Meals provided by in-house catering team. Full entertainment licence for events with bar. Shop selling wide range of gifts and local goods. Single and double rooms, surf lodge accommodation and campsite at nearby Gupton Farm.

Things to see and do: events, including rock-pool rambles, bushcraft, guided walks and talks. Explore the area from an alternative angle with kayaking and coasteering guided tours. **Dogs**: assistance dogs only.

Access: 🅿♿♿♿📷♿ Landscape 🏞➡♿

Find out more: 01646 623110 or stackpolecentre@nationaltrust.org.uk

---

Stackpole Centre

Please contact the centre for information on residential group bookings, courses and activities.

Schoolchildren exploring Bosherston Lakes at the eco-award-winning Stackpole Centre

Sugar Loaf and Usk Valley

near Abergavenny, Monmouthshire

🏠🏛♿ 1936

Sugar Loaf and Usk Valley in Monmouthshire

Satnav: for Llanwenarth car park, follow signs for Sugar Loaf vineyard and continue uphill.
Parking: at Llanwenarth car park for Sugar Loaf; numerous on-site car parks for Usk Valley.

Discover glorious views across Monmouthshire and the borders from the peaks of Sugar Loaf and The Skirrid. Alternatively explore seasonal changes through the ancient woodland that straddles their slopes. By contrast, meander through parkland at Clytha and the Usk Valley, perfect for picnics or short walks.
Note: sorry no toilets. Some car parks not National Trust (charge including members).

Eat, shop, stay: many shops and restaurants at nearby Abergavenny (none National Trust).

Things to see and do: Sugar Loaf and Skirrid are perfect for family adventures and '50 things' activities. Skenfrith Castle and the Georgian Round House at The Kymin are nearby. **Dogs**: welcome on leads.

Find out more: 01874 625515 or sugarloaf@nationaltrust.org.uk

Tredegar House

Newport NP10 8YW

🏠♿🔔👤 2012

Satnav: please enter 'Pencarn Way' as well as the postcode.
Parking: on site. One electrical charging point.

Tredegar House and the Morgan family have been an important part of the Newport community for more than 500 years. Captivating tales of war heroism, inheritance disputes, Russian princesses and sprawling influence bring alive a home designed to impress and entertain, while the modest but elegant contrasting formal gardens pay homage to life at Tredegar House. Those who keep the mansion, gardens and parkland running today are working in partnership with local organisations to combine colourful histories and modern programmes with an ambition to bring genuine benefit to the community and all who visit.

Eat, shop, stay: tea-room serving light lunches, homemade cakes and hot drinks. Gift shop selling souvenirs, books, gifts and plants.

Things to see and do: Indoors Beautiful architectural decoration and intriguing stories.
Outdoors Lakeside walks, formal gardens and programmed activities.
Dogs: well-behaved dogs welcome in the parkland, formal gardens and tea-room.

Access: 🅿♿♿♿♿♿♪
House ♿ ⬆ Reception ♿ Grounds ♿♿

Find out more: 01633 815880 or tredegar@nationaltrust.org.uk

Tredegar House		M	T	W	T	F	S	S
House and gardens*								
15 Feb–3 Apr	11–4	M	T	W	T	F	S	S
4 Apr–30 Sep	11–5	M	T	W	T	F	S	S
1 Oct–1 Nov	11–4	M	T	W	T	F	S	S
2 Nov–27 Nov**	Tour	M	T	W	T	F	S	S
28 Nov–22 Dec	11–4	M	T	W	T	F	S	S
28 Dec–31 Dec	11–4	M	T	W	T	·	·	·
Tea-room and shop								
4 Jan–14 Feb†	10–3:30	·	·	W	T	F	S	S
15 Feb–3 Apr	10–4	M	T	W	T	F	S	S
4 Apr–1 Nov	10–5	M	T	W	T	F	S	S
2 Nov–22 Dec	10–4††	M	T	W	T	F	S	S
28 Dec–31 Dec	11–4	M	T	W	T	·	·	·
Park								
Open all year	Dawn–dusk	M	T	W	T	F	S	S

*Gardens: open 10:30. Last entry one hour before closing.
**House: open for tours only, 11 to 4; gardens closed.
†Shop: open weekends only. ††Tea-room and shop:
2 November to 22 December, open to 5 at weekends.

Tredegar House, Newport: as well as the splendid 17th-century mansion, there are acres of parkland to discover

Tudor Merchant's House

Quay Hill, Tenby, Pembrokeshire SA70 7BX

⌂ 1937

Parking: very limited on-street parking. Several pay-and-display car parks, not National Trust (charge including members).

Over 500 years ago when Tenby was a busy trading port, a merchant built this three-storey house (below) to live in and trade from. Today, the house and shop have been furnished with exquisitely carved replicas and brightly coloured wall-hangings which recreate the atmosphere of life in Tudor Tenby. **Note**: sorry no toilet.

Eat, shop, stay: shop range includes specially made Tudor-style pottery (design based on finds at the house), pewterware, horn cups, glass, beeswax candles and books about the Tudors.

Things to see and do: you can lay the high table, see the wall-paintings, try on traditional costumes and play with replica games and toys. Tudor-themed family activities year-round. **Dogs**: assistance dogs only.

Access: ⃝⃝⃝ Building ⃝

Find out more: 01834 842279 or tudormerchantshouse@nationaltrust.org.uk

Tudor Merchant's House		M	T	W	T	F	S	S
15 Feb–1 Mar	11–3	M	T	W	T	F	S	S
7 Mar–5 Apr	11–3						S	S
6 Apr–1 Nov	11–5	M	T	W	T	F	S	S

Tŷ Isaf

Beddgelert, Gwynedd LL55 4YA

⌂⃝ 1985

Tŷ Isaf in Gwynedd lies at the heart of pretty Beddgelert

Parking: car parks in village, not National Trust (charge including members).

Brimming with character, Tŷ Isaf lies in the very heart of Beddgelert. Dating back to the late 17th century, this Grade II-listed building is the oldest property in the village and has fulfilled many roles over the centuries – from tavern to farmhouse and, now, shop.

Eat, shop, stay: fantastic range of local produce and crafts, alongside National Trust products, for sale. Second-hand books and gallery upstairs.

Things to see and do: free family adventure packs. Go for a ramble beside the river and see how many activities you can complete. **Dogs**: welcome on estate (on leads near livestock) and in shop.

Access: ⃝

Find out more: 01766 890545 or tyisaf@nationaltrust.org.uk

Tŷ Isaf		M	T	W	T	F	S	S
30 Mar–30 Oct	11–5*	M	T	W	T	F	S	S
31 Oct–20 Dec	11–4						S	S
21 Dec–23 Dec	11–4	M	T	W				

*Sunday: opens to 4.

Tŷ Mawr Wybrnant, Conwy: although humble, this farmhouse has enormous cultural significance for Welsh speakers

Tŷ Mawr Wybrnant

Betws-y-Coed, Conwy

🏠 ♿ 1951

Satnav: do not use. No access from A470.
Parking: 500 yards.

Modest 16th-century farmhouse with huge cultural significance. Birthplace to Bishop William Morgan, whose 10-year endeavour to translate the Bible into Welsh helped ensure the survival of the language. You can view an original copy of the 1588 Welsh Bible at the house, which is situated on the old drovers' road. **Note**: access via narrow road from Penmachno. Follow brown signs and avoid satnav.

Eat, shop, stay: picnics welcome. Four holiday cottages available near Betws-y-Coed and Hendre Isaf bunkhouse at Pentrefoelas (9 miles).

Things to see and do: **Indoors** Introductory talk, exhibition room and extensive Bible collection. Virtual tour available. **Outdoors** Tudor kitchen garden, woodland walk and animal puzzle trail. **Dogs**: welcome on leads.

Access: 🅿️ 🚻 🎦 ♿ Building 🦽 🚻 🚹

Find out more: 01690 760213 or tymawrwybrnant@nationaltrust.org.uk
Penmachno, Betws-y-Coed, Conwy LL25 0HJ

Tŷ Mawr Wybrnant		M	T	W	T	F	S	S
26 Mar–27 Sep	12–5				T	F	S	S
1 Oct–1 Nov	12–4				T	F	S	S

Open Bank Holiday Mondays.

Additional coastal and countryside car parks in Wales

Brecon Beacons
Cwm Gwdi   LD3 8LE

Ceredigion
Mwnt   SA43 1QH
Penbryn   SA44 6QL

Monmouthshire
Skirrid   NP7 8AP

Llŷn Peninsula
Uwchmynydd   LL53 8DD

Pembrokeshire
Broad Haven South   SA71 5DR
Bosherston Lakes   SA71 5DR
Porth Clais   SA62 6RR

Snowdonia
Cregennan   LL39 1LX
Nantmor   LL55 4YG

A budding photographer takes a snap of
wildlife at Castle Ward, County Down.
Competition entry from Minchen Liang

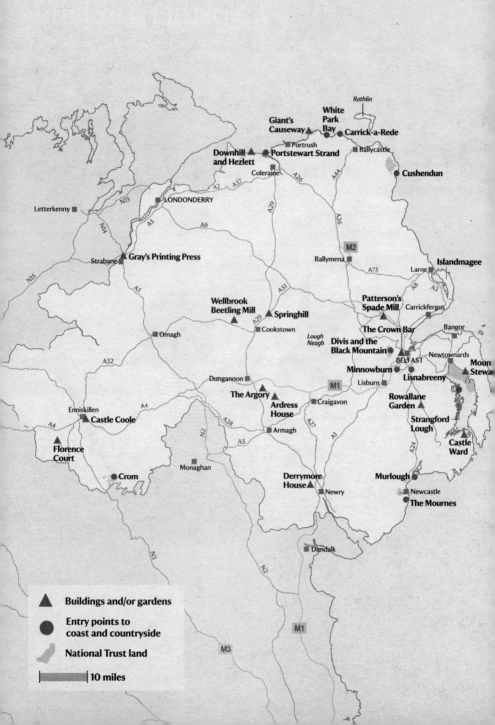

Giant's
Causeway

White
Park
Bay

Carrick-a-Rede

Rathlin

Portrush

Ballycastle

Downhill
and Hezlett

Portstewart Strand

Cushendun

Coleraine

A26

A44

A2   A37

A26

LONDONDERRY

A29

Letterkenny

N13

A5

A6

M2

N14

Ballymena

A75

Larne

Islandmagee

Strabane

Gray's Printing Press

A8   A2

Carrickfergus

N15

A5

A31

Patterson's
Spade Mill

Wellbrook
Beetling Mill

A29

Springhill

The Crown Bar

Bangor

Omagh

Cookstown

Lough
Neagh

Divis and the
Black Mountain

BELFAST

Newtownards

A32

Dungannon

Minnowburn

Lisburn

Lisnabreeny

Moun
Stewa

M1

Rowallane
Garden

The Argory

Craigavon

Ardress House

Enniskillen

Castle Coole

A28

Armagh

A24

Strangford
Lough

Castle
Ward

A4

N2

A3

A27

A1

Florence
Court

Crom

Monaghan

A32

Derrymore
House

Murlough

Newcastle

Newry

The Mournes

N3

Dundalk

M1

Buildings and/or gardens

Entry points to
coast and countryside

National Trust land

10 miles

M3

Ardress House

64 Ardress Road, Annaghmore, Portadown,
County Armagh BT62 1SQ

🏠🚻♿♿ 1959

Parking: 10 yards.

Set within 40 hectares (100 acres) of rolling
countryside, this 17th-century farmhouse,
with detailed plasterwork and fine Georgian
interiors, offers afternoons of fun and
relaxation for everyone. The cobbled farmyard
is the perfect spot for children to feed the
resident chickens, and the nearby apple
orchards (below) are great for exploring.

Eat, shop, stay: takeaway hot and cold drinks
and ice cream available. Picnics welcome
in the garden or woodlands.

Things to see and do: cobbled farmyard with
dairy, smithy and threshing barn. Miniature
Shetland ponies, donkeys, nanny goats
and chickens. Lady's Mile walking trail.
Children's outdoor and indoor play.
Dogs: on leads in garden only.

Access: 🏠 Building ♿♿ Grounds ♿➡

Find out more: 028 8778 4753 or
ardress@nationaltrust.org.uk

Ardress House		M	T	W	T	F	S	S
House and farmyard								
7 Mar–5 Apr	11–5	·	·	·	·	·	S	S
10 Apr–19 Apr	11–5	M	T	W	T	F	S	S
25 Apr–28 Jun	11–5	·	·	·	·	·	S	S
2 Jul–31 Aug	11–5	M	·	·	T	F	S	S
5 Sep–27 Sep	11–5	·	·	·	·	·	S	S
4 Oct–25 Oct	11–4	·	·	·	·	·	·	S
Lady's Mile Walk								
Open all year	Dawn–dusk	M	T	W	T	F	S	S

House: admission by guided tour (last tour one hour
before closing). Open Bank Holiday Mondays and all other
public holidays in Northern Ireland. Closed 25, 26 December
and 1 January 2021.

The Argory

144 Derrycaw Road, Moy, Dungannon,
County Armagh BT71 6NA

🏠♿♿ 1979

Parking: 100 yards.

This Irish gentry house (above) can trace more
than 190 years of history. Built in the 1820s for
the MacGeough Bond family, the house and
surrounding riverside estate came into
existence due to a quirky stipulation in a will.
The interior of this understated and intimate
house still evokes the eclectic tastes and
interests of the family. The small rose garden
with its unusual sundial, pleasure gardens
and wooded walks along the River Blackwater
are ideal for exploring (below).

Built in the 1820s, The Argory, County Armagh, still evokes the eclectic tastes and interests of the creator's family

Eat, shop, stay: Courtyard Café serving home-baked scones, sandwiches, paninis and cakes. Gift shop offering a wide range of products. Second-hand bookshop. Picnics welcome.

Things to see and do: **Indoors** Guided house tours and children's art trail. Discover Artificial Sunshine, the neon light installation in the house. **Outdoors** Variety of walks and trails. Children's play area with zip line. **Dogs**: welcome on leads in grounds and garden.

Access: ⓟ⚲ ⓓ⚲ ♿ ⓦ♿ Grounds ♿ ➡

Find out more: 028 8778 4753 or argory@nationaltrust.org.uk

The Argory		M	T	W	T	F	S	S
House, café and shop								
1 Feb–29 Feb*	11–5						S	S
1 Mar–5 Apr	11–5					F	S	S
6 Apr–19 Apr	11–5	M	T	W	T	F	S	S
24 Apr–26 Apr	11–5					F	S	S
1 May–31 May	11–5				T	F	S	S
3 Jun–28 Jun	11–5			W	T	F	S	S
1 Jul–31 Aug	11–5	M	T	W	T	F	S	S
3 Sep–27 Sep	11–5				T	F	S	S
3 Oct–25 Oct	11–4						S	S
26 Oct–1 Nov	11–4	M	T	W	T	F	S	S
7 Nov–29 Nov	11–4						S	S
Grounds								
Open all year**	11–5	M	T	W	T	F	S	S

*Also open 17 and 18 February for local half term.
Guided house tours available from 12. Open Bank Holiday Mondays and all public holidays in Northern Ireland.
**Grounds closed 25, 26 December and 1 January 2021.

Carrick-a-Rede

Ballintoy, County Antrim BT54 6LS

🏠 📷 1967

Parking: on site.

Connected to the cliffs by a rope bridge across the Atlantic Ocean, this rocky island is the ultimate clifftop experience. Jutting out from the Causeway Coastal Route, the 30-metre-deep and 20-metre-wide chasm separating Carrick-a-Rede from the mainland is traversed by an amazing rope bridge that was traditionally erected by salmon fishermen. Wildlife-rich and with views across the seas to Rathlin Island, this is also home to Larrybane old quarry, recently featured in the television series *Game of Thrones*. **Note**: timed-ticketing system (book online – free for members). Bridge access weather-dependent.

Cross it if you dare. The rope bridge at Carrick-a-Rede, County Antrim, is not for the faint-hearted

Eat, shop, stay: Weighbridge Tea-room offering great coffee, delicious scones and sweet treats, hot snacks and light lunches. Gift shop area showcasing local crafts and unique range of Carrick-a-Rede souvenirs.

Things to see and do: coastal path – part of the Causeway Coast Way walking route from Portstewart to Ballycastle. Birdwatching and coastal scenery. Unique flora and fauna. Guided tours (by arrangement). **Dogs**: welcome on leads (not permitted to cross bridge).

Access: 🅿️ ♿ ♿ 🏢 📷 Grounds ➡️

Find out more: 028 2073 3335 or carrickarede@nationaltrust.org.uk

Carrick-a-Rede		M	T	W	T	F	S	S
Bridge								
1 Jan–31 Jan	9:30–3:30	M	T	W	T	F	S	S
1 Feb–29 Feb	9:30–5	M	T	W	T	F	S	S
1 Mar–30 Apr	9:30–6	M	T	W	T	F	S	S
1 May–30 Jun	9:30–7	M	T	W	T	F	S	S
1 Jul–31 Aug	9:30–8	M	T	W	T	F	S	S
1 Sep–31 Oct	9:30–6	M	T	W	T	F	S	S
1 Nov–31 Dec	9:30–3:30	M	T	W	T	F	S	S

Bridge: open weather permitting; last entry 45 minutes before closing. Car park and North Antrim coastal path open all year. Closed 24 to 26 December.

Castle Coole

Enniskillen, County Fermanagh BT74 6HN

🏠 ♨ 🔔 🍴 1951

Parking: 150 yards.

Surrounded by a stunning landscape park, the majestic 18th-century home of the Earls of Belmore was created to impress. One of the finest examples of Neo-classical architecture in Ireland, the rooms at Castle Coole are brimming with opulence, luxury and colour. There are interesting pieces of history to explore, such as the servants' tunnel and ice house. The parkland, interspersed with mature oaks, woodlands and paths, is perfect for refreshing walks, while the outdoor play area is great for families.

Eat, shop, stay: Tallow House Tea-room serving snacks, lunch and afternoon tea. Picnics welcome on the Drying Green. Gift shop selling souvenirs, homeware, books and local crafts. Second-hand bookshop (volunteer-run).

Things to see and do: **Indoors** Events all year. 'Upstairs downstairs' guided tours of the mansion. **Outdoors** Events all year, including summer music sessions. Children's Tracker Packs available. Trails and walks.
Dogs: welcome under control.

Access: 👿 🅿 ♿ ♿ 🔍 📷 ⓧ
Building 🅿 ♿ ♿ Grounds ♿ ➡

Find out more: 028 6632 2690 or castlecoole@nationaltrust.org.uk

Castle Coole		M	T	W	T	F	S	S
House, tea-room and shop								
7 Mar–5 Apr	11–5						S	S
10 Apr–19 Apr	11–5	M	T	W	T	F	S	S
20 Apr–31 May	11–5	M		W	T	F	S	S
1 Jun–1 Sep	11–5	M	T	W	T	F	S	S
2 Sep–30 Sep	11–5	M		W	T	F	S	S
Grounds								
1 Jan–29 Feb	10–4	M	T	W	T	F	S	S
1 Mar–31 Oct	10–7	M	T	W	T	F	S	S
1 Nov–31 Dec	10–4	M	T	W	T	F	S	S

House: admission by guided tour (last tour one hour before closing). Open Bank Holiday Mondays, Monday 16 March and all other public holidays in Northern Ireland.

Castle Coole in County Fermanagh, above and below, is one of the finest Neo-classical buildings in Ireland

Castle Ward

Strangford, Downpatrick,
County Down BT30 7LS

🏠🏞🏛🚻♿🛥🐑⛵🛏⛺🔔🍴 1953

Parking: on site.

High on a hillside, with views across the tranquil waters of Strangford Lough, the Gothic and classical collide at Castle Ward. This eccentric 18th-century mansion within an extensive walled demesne, is one of the most peculiar architectural compromises between two people. The story behind the different façades of the former home of the Viscounts Bangor is revealed by guided tours. In the farmyard, visit the water-powered corn mill, or stroll among flowers and subtropical plants in the newly restored Sunken Garden.

The laundry, tack room and dairy give an insight into life 'below stairs'. Discover more on the 21 miles of multi-use trails, while the woodland and adventure playgrounds and Secret Shore Nature Trail are great for children. **Note**: 1 March to 30 November, access to livestock grazing areas may be restricted.

Eat, shop, stay: Stableyard tea-room and Coach House gift shop. Second-hand bookshop. Slaughterhouse shop offering HBO *Game of Thrones* merchandise. New dog-friendly Trailhead café. Holiday cottage, bunkhouse, caravan park and campsite with camping pods.

Things to see and do: **Indoors** Guided house tours. Victorian laundry, dairy and corn mill. **Outdoors** Network of multi-use trails. Bicycles for hire (not National Trust). Farmyard with animals. Woodland and Adventure playground and Secret Shore Nature Trail. Children's Tracker Packs. A series of family events all year, including Easter, Pumpkinfest and Christmas.

Gothic and classical collide at eccentric Castle Ward, County Down, which sits within an extensive walled demesne

Visit the iconic filming location of Winterfell in HBO's *Game of Thrones*. **Dogs**: welcome on leads (restrictions apply in livestock grazing areas). New dog exercise area.

Access: ⃞⃞⃞⃞⃞⃞⃞⃞⃞
Mansion ⃞⃞⃞ Grounds ⃞⃞⃞⃞

Find out more: 028 4488 1204 or castleward@nationaltrust.org.uk

Castle Ward		M	T	W	T	F	S	S
Parkland, trails and garden								
Open all year	10–6	M	T	W	T	F	S	S
House								
14 Mar–1 Nov	12–5	M	T	W	T	F	S	S
Tea-room, gift shop and second-hand bookshop								
1 Jan–13 Mar	11–4	M	T	W	T	F	S	S
14 Mar–1 Nov	10–5	M	T	W	T	F	S	S
2 Nov–31 Dec	11–4	M	T	W	T	F	S	S

House: admission by guided tour (last tour one hour before closing). Corn mill demonstration: 5 April to 20 September, Sundays, 2 to 5. Everything closed 25 and 26 December.

As well as the opulent interiors, above, there are miles of multi-use trails to discover at Castle Ward

Crom

Upper Lough Erne, Newtownbutler,
County Fermanagh BT92 8AJ

🚗🏊🎣🏠⛺🛶🍽 1987

Parking: 100 yards.

Home to islands, ancient woodland and historical ruins, this 800-hectare (2,000-acre) demesne sits in a tranquil landscape on the peaceful southern shores of Upper Lough Erne. One of Ireland's most important conservation areas, it has many rare species and is rich in wildlife, including fallow deer, red squirrels and pine martens. An ideal spot for relaxing walks, cycling and boat trips. Visit the outbuildings such as the summerhouse and boathouse. Jetty area available to use nearby. Turn your visit into a holiday with a stay in one of our holiday cottages (dog-friendly), award-winning glamping pods or campsites. **Note**: 19th-century castle not open to public.

Eat, shop, stay: homemade lunches, snacks and afternoon tea, cold drinks, ice cream. Selection of gifts, local books, maps and seasonal goods available in visitor centre. Convenience goods and outdoor clothing also for sale. Holiday cottages, campsite (tents only) and award-winning glamping pods.

Things to see and do: historic castle ruins. Cot trips (Bank Holiday Mondays). Boat and canoe hire. Children's Tracker Packs and GPS devices available. Events, including Summer Family Adventures and Music by the Lake. **Dogs**: under control.

Access: 🅿♿🔊♿👁
Building 🏠♿ Grounds 🏠➡♿♿

Find out more: 028 6773 8118 or crom@nationaltrust.org.uk

Crom		M	T	W	T	F	S	S
Grounds								
1 Jan–29 Feb	10–4	M	T	W	T	F	S	S
1 Mar–1 Nov	10–7	M	T	W	T	F	S	S
2 Nov–31 Dec	10–4	M	T	W	T	F	S	S
Visitor centre and tea-room								
7 Mar–30 Sep	11–5	M	T	W	T	F	S	S
3 Oct–1 Nov*	11–5						S	S

Open Bank Holiday Mondays and all other public holidays in Northern Ireland. Last admission one hour before closing.
*Tea-room closed October.

Crom in County Fermanagh, above and below, is set on the peaceful southern shores of Upper Lough Erne

The Crown Bar

46 Great Victoria Street, Belfast,
County Antrim BT2 7BA 1978

Belfast's most famous pub remains one
of the finest examples of a high-Victorian
gin palace complete with period features.
Note: run by Mitchells & Butlers. Open daily
all year. Monday to Saturday, 9 to midnight;
Sunday opens 11.

Find out more: 028 9024 3187 or
info@crownbar.com

The view over the bay at Cushendun

Cushendun

County Antrim

♿ 🏛 1954

Charming and historic Cushendun in County Antrim

Satnav: use BT44 0PH.
Parking: car park adjacent to Corner House
tea-room and at Glenmona House.

Set at the mouth of the River Dun (Brown
River) at the foot of Glendun, Cushendun
is a very charming historic village steeped
in character and folklore. The surrounding
hills are a patchwork of farms, small fields,
hedgerows and traditional stone walls.
Sheltered harbour and beautiful beach.
Views of Scotland.

Eat, shop, stay: pub and restaurant facilities
available in the village (none National Trust).
Stay at Strand House, a Cornish-style cottage
on the coast (sleeps five).

Things to see and do: Cornish-style houses
(designed by Clough Williams-Ellis) and
Glenmona House grounds to discover. Circular
walking trail. River fishing, sea angling, boating,
horse-riding and golf course nearby.

Find out more: 028 7084 8728 or
cushendun@nationaltrust.org.uk

Derrymore House

Bessbrook, Newry, County Armagh
BT35 7EF 1953

Resting peacefully in a landscape demesne, this
18th-century thatched cottage is rich in history
and a great place for walks. **Note**: sorry no
toilet. Drawing room open the last Saturday
of every month, March to September, 2 to 5.
Last admission 45 minutes before closing.

Find out more: 028 8778 4753 or
derrymore@nationaltrust.org.uk

Divis and the Black Mountain

Hannahstown, near Belfast, County Antrim

🏠🏞️👥 2004

Satnav: use BT17 0NG.
Parking: beside The Barn or on Divis Road, opposite entrance gates.

Sitting in the heart of the Belfast Hills, this 809-hectare (2,000-acre) mosaic of upland heath and blanket bog is a great place for a wild countryside experience. There are four walking trails to explore, affording panoramic views across Belfast and a wealth of flora, fauna and archaeological remains to discover.
Note: cattle roam freely during summer months. Mountain environment and weather conditions can change rapidly.

Eat, shop, stay: tea, coffee and light refreshments available in The Barn.

Things to see and do: walks and talks with a ranger. **Dogs**: welcome, but please note cattle roam freely during summer.

Access: 🅿️♿🚻📷🚶 Visitor centre ♿

Find out more: 028 9082 5434 or divis@nationaltrust.org.uk

Divis and the Black Mountain

Café: open daily all year (apart from 25 and 26 December), 9 to 3.

Divis and the Black Mountain in County Antrim, above and below, sits in the very heart of the Belfast Hills

Downhill Demesne and Hezlett House

Mussenden Road, Castlerock,
County Londonderry BT51 4RP

🏰 🏚 ♿ ❄ 🍽 🚗 🔔 🍴 1949

Satnav: use BT51 4TW for Hezlett House.
Parking: for Downhill Demesne at Lion's Gate;
on site at Hezlett House.

The sheltered gardens, cliff-edge landmark and striking ruins of a grand headland mansion bear testament to the eccentricity of the Earl Bishop who once made this 18th-century demesne his home. Mussenden Temple, perched atop sheer cliffs, offers panoramic views of the famous north coast and is a great place for walking and kite-flying. Nearby at Hezlett House, life in a rural 17th-century cottage is told through the people who once lived there. One of the oldest thatched cottages left standing in Northern Ireland, it boasts a rare cruck frame and houses the Downhill Marble Collection.

Eat, shop, stay: tea and coffee facilities at Hezlett House and Bishop's Gate. Picnics welcome in gardens. Coffee Bar at Lion's Gate (not National Trust). Book Nook in Bishop's Gate lodge.

Things to see and do: **Indoors** Hezlett House guided tours on request (booking essential). **Outdoors** Numerous events throughout year, including Easter hunts and Kite Festival. Bishop's Play Trail and new Bishop's Tree Trail. **Dogs**: on leads only.

Kite-flying at Downhill Demesne in County Londonderry, below, and Mussenden Temple, right

Access: 🅿️ ♿ Building 🏛️ Grounds 🏛️

Find out more: 028 7084 8728 or downhilldemesne@nationaltrust.org.uk
Hezlett House, 107 Sea Road, Castlerock, County Londonderry BT51 4TW

Downhill and Hezlett		M	T	W	T	F	S	S
Downhill Demesne grounds								
Open all year	Dawn–dusk	M	T	W	T	F	S	S
Downhill Demesne facilities								
14 Feb–18 Feb	10–3	M	T	·	·	F	S	S
7 Mar–4 Oct	10–5*	M	T	W	T	F	S	S
10 Oct–8 Nov	10–3	·	·	·	·	·	S	S
Hezlett House **								
29 Jun–31 Aug	Tour	M	T	W	T	F	S	S

Open Bank Holiday Mondays and all other public holidays in Northern Ireland. *29 June to 31 August: open until 6. **Tours by appointment only.

Florence Court

Enniskillen, County Fermanagh BT92 1DB

🏠🖼🌿♿🏞🔔🍽 1954

Parking: 200 yards to visitor centre.

Florence Court enjoys a majestic countryside setting in West Fermanagh, surrounded by lush parkland with Benaughlin Mountain rising in the background. There is something for everyone to enjoy at this extensive and welcoming place. On a guided tour of the Georgian mansion you can hear stories about the Earls of Enniskillen and their staff, who lived here for more than 250 years. Outdoors take a gentle walk or long cycle along 10 miles of trails in the adjoining forest park and see fascinating industrial heritage features, including the water-powered sawmill and blacksmith's forge. The gardens are home to the mother of all Irish yew trees, as well as the kitchen garden, which is being restored to its 1930s character.

Eat, shop, stay: Stables Tea-room serving snacks, lunch and afternoon tea. Coach House gift shop. Second-hand bookshop (volunteer-run). Visitor centre providing information, tour tickets, retail (including seasonal kitchen garden produce) and drinks-to-go. You can stay for longer in the Butler's Apartment.

Things to see and do: **Indoors** Guided house tours. Laundry yard with washroom, dairy, ironing and drying room. Explore the forge, sawmill and carpenters' shop.
Outdoors Events and ranger-led walks all year. Children's Tracker Packs. Network of 10 miles of multi-use trails. Bike hire available from the visitor centre. Why not relax in the Pleasure Grounds and enjoy stunning views of Benaughlin Mountain from the restored summerhouse? You can visit the kitchen garden to see the progress of the restoration project, driven by the local community and volunteers.
Dogs: welcome on leads in walled garden.

Access: 🅿♿🚻♿🐕🛗📷🚽🚭
Building 🚶♿♿ Grounds ♿➡♿

Find out more: 028 6634 8249 or florencecourt@nationaltrust.org.uk

Florence Court		M	T	W	T	F	S	S
House, tea-room, visitor centre* and shop								
10 Apr–19 Apr	11–5	M	T	W	T	F	S	S
20 Apr–31 May	11–5	M	T	W	T	·	S	S
1 Jun–31 Aug	11–5	M	T	W	T	F	S	S
1 Sep–30 Sep	11–5	M	T	W	T	·	S	S
3 Oct–1 Nov	11–5	·	·	·	·	·	S	S
Gardens and park								
1 Jan–29 Feb	10–4	M	T	W	T	F	S	S
1 Mar–31 Oct	10–7	M	T	W	T	F	S	S
1 Nov–31 Dec	10–4	M	T	W	T	F	S	S

House: admission by guided tour (last tour one hour before closing). Open Bank Holiday Mondays, 16 March and all other public holidays in Northern Ireland. Open Republic of Ireland Bank Holiday, 26 October. Grounds closed 25 December. *Visitor centre: also open November and December weekends.

This page and opposite, three views of Florence Court in County Fermanagh: something for everyone to enjoy

Why not share your pictures with us? #nationaltrust

Giant's Causeway

44 Causeway Road, Bushmills,
County Antrim BT57 8SU

🚻 ♿ 📶 🅿️ 1962

Parking: on site and park and ride in Bushmills village. Electric vehicle charging point in car park two.

Follow in the legendary footsteps of giants at Northern Ireland's iconic UNESCO World Heritage Site. The famous basalt columns of the Causeway landscape, left by volcanic eruptions 60 million years ago, are home to more than Finn McCool. Its nooks and crannies are dotted with dainty sea campion, and defensive fulmars protect their cliff nests. Windswept walking trails wind through this Area of Outstanding Natural Beauty, with an all-accessible walk at Runkerry Head and more challenging terrain along the Causeway Coast Way. The interactive exhibition and innovative audio-guides unlock secrets of the landscape and regale visitors with legends of giants.

Eat, shop, stay: light lunches and tasty snacks available in Visitor Centre café. Causeway Hotel bar and restaurant offer delicious lunch and evening meal menus based around fresh local produce. The award-winning gift shop showcases locally handcrafted gifts and exclusive Giant's Causeway souvenirs.

Things to see and do: Indoors Interactive exhibition brings the stories of the Causeway to life. **Outdoors** Audio-guides (11 languages) reveal the landscape's secrets. Walking trails for all abilities. Entertaining guided tours. Family fun events. **Dogs**: on leads only.

Access: 🅿️♿🚻♿🔊♿♿♿:·👁️ Grounds ➡️
Visitor Centre ♿♿ Causeway Hotel ♿♿

Find out more: 028 2073 1855 or giantscauseway@nationaltrust.org.uk

Giant's Causeway		M	T	W	T	F	S	S
Stones and coastal path								
Open all year	Dawn–dusk	M	T	W	T	F	S	S
Visitor Centre								
1 Jan–31 Jan	9–4	M	T	W	T	F	S	S
1 Feb–29 Feb	9–5	M	T	W	T	F	S	S
1 Mar–31 May	9–6	M	T	W	T	F	S	S
1 Jun–30 Sep	9–7	M	T	W	T	F	S	S
1 Oct–31 Oct	9–6	M	T	W	T	F	S	S
1 Nov–31 Dec	9–4	M	T	W	T	F	S	S

Visitor Centre: last admission one hour before closing.
Closed 24 to 26 December.

The Giant's Causeway in County Antrim, above and below, is an iconic UNESCO World Heritage Site

Gray's Printing Press

49 Main Street, Strabane,
County Tyrone BT82 8AU 1966

The indelible story of printing is told behind
this Strabane Georgian shop front, once
reputed to be Ireland's printing capital.
Note: open the last Saturday of the month,
March to September (times subject to change).
Last admission 45 minutes before closing.

Find out more: 028 8674 8210 or
grays@nationaltrust.org.uk

Islandmagee

near Larne, County Antrim 1996

An Area of Special Scientific Interest,
the peninsula at Islandmagee has some
of Northern Ireland's largest colonies of
cliff-nesting seabirds. **Note**: for satnav
use BT40 3TP. Paths are uneven and
steep in places.

Find out more: 028 9064 7787 or
islandmagee@nationaltrust.org.uk

Lisnabreeny

near Belfast, County Down 1938

On the edge of Belfast, paths through a
wooded glen cross farmland, emerging
at a rath on the Castlereagh Hills.
Note: for satnav use BT8 6SA.
Uneven paths and steps.

Find out more: 028 9064 7787 or
lisnabreeny@nationaltrust.org.uk

Minnowburn

near Belfast, County Down

1952

Satnav: use BT8 8LD. **Parking**: on site.

Cycling at Minnowburn in County Down

Nestled in the heart of Lagan Valley Regional
Park, where meadows and woodlands roll down
to the River Lagan. Perfect for a short stroll or
longer walk. Climb Terrace Hill to discover the
garden built by linen merchant Ned Robinson,
and stop for a picnic and to admire the views.
Note: trails are uneven and steep in places.

Eat, shop, stay: coffee van (not National Trust)
in car park serving refreshments six days a
week. Lock Keeper's Inn (not National Trust),
¾ mile along riverside path. Terrace Hill
garden picnic tables.

Things to see and do: guided walks, including
heritage, history and woodlands. Natural play
area and walking trails to discover, including
the Giant's Ring and Terrace Hill trails.
Dogs: on leads only.

Find out more: 028 9064 7787 or
minnowburn@nationaltrust.org.uk

Mount Stewart

Portaferry Road, Newtownards,
County Down BT22 2AD

🏠🏛️✤🐾🚗🔔🍴 1976

Satnav: access via second gate into
Mount Stewart identified by brown sign.
Parking: 200 yards from main car park.
Overflow car park approximately 465 yards.
Two electric vehicle charging points in rear
car park. Accessible and family parking
spaces in main car park.

Voted one of the world's top 10 gardens,
Mount Stewart reflects a rich tapestry of
design and planting artistry bearing the
hallmark of its creator. Edith, Lady
Londonderry's passion for bold planting
schemes coupled with the mild climate of
Strangford Lough mean rare and tender plants
from across the globe thrive in this celebrated
garden, with the formal gardens exuding a
distinct character and appeal. Explore the
exquisite house, recently restored to glory.

Hear fascinating stories about the Londonderry
family, and enjoy a world-class collection of
paintings and many other internationally
significant items. For a different view of Mount
Stewart, stroll around miles of new walking
trails and discover a landscape lost in time.

Eat, shop, stay: gift shop selling local gifts.
Garden shop offering a range of plants specially
propagated from our world-class garden.
Second-hand bookshop. Tea-room serving
a range of homemade seasonal hot and
cold food. Coffee and ice-cream kiosk
in the courtyard.

Things to see and do: **Indoors** Explore the
house and discover the impressive collection of
artwork and objects. Guided tours on selected
days. **Outdoors** World-class gardens, walking
trails, red squirrel hide, natural play area and
garden tours. The natural play area and walking
trails will take you through a magical landscape
of woodland and farmland, set within the
iconic drumlin landscape of Strangford Lough.
Events throughout the year: Jazz in the
Gardens (April to September), Teddy Bears'
Picnic (July), Mount Stewart Conversations
Festival and Red Squirrel Day (both in
September). **Dogs**: welcome on short leads
in grounds, trails and gardens. Elsewhere,
assistance dogs only.

Access: 🅿️ 🐕 ♿ 🚹 ♿ 🔁
Reception, shop and tea-room 🏠♿
House 🏠⬆️🚹♿ Grounds 🏞️♿➡️♿♿

Find out more: 028 4278 8387 or
mountstewart@nationaltrust.org.uk

Mount Stewart		M	T	W	T	F	S	S
Formal and lakeside gardens, trails, tea-room and shop								
1 Jan–1 Mar	10–4*	M	T	W	T	F	S	S
2 Mar–1 Nov	10–5	M	T	W	T	F	S	S
2 Nov–31 Dec	10–4*	M	T	W	T	F	S	S
House								
2 Jan–14 Feb	11–3**				T	F	S	S
15 Feb–8 Mar	11–3**						S	S
14 Mar–1 Nov	11–5†	M	T	W	T	F	S	S
5 Nov–27 Dec	11–3**				T	F	S	S

*Tea-room, shop and visitor reception: close 5 at weekends,
Bank Holidays and public holidays. Everything closed
25 and 26 December. **House: access by guided tours only.
†Guided tours and freeflow available at selected times
(tours subject to availability). Temple of the Winds: opens
once a month for guided tours.

**Mount Stewart in County Down, this page and opposite:
the exquisite house is surrounded by glorious gardens**

The Mournes

near Newcastle, County Down

🏛️🏊‍♂️🚠 1992

Rocky path at Slieve Donard in The Mournes, County Down

Satnav: use BT33 0EU for Slieve Donard and BT33 0LA for Bloody Bridge.
Parking: for Slieve Donard, park in Newcastle; for Bloody Bridge, park on A2.

These famous, wildlife-rich mountains are crossed by coastal and mountain paths. Great for exploring, the National Trust-maintained paths stretch from the shore into the heart of the Mournes, offering views over Dundrum Bay to the Isle of Man on a clear day.

Eat, shop, stay: picnics welcome. Shops, restaurants and cafés in nearby Newcastle (none National Trust).

Things to see and do: outstanding views from Bloody Bridge or the coastal path to St Mary's Chapel ruins. Birdwatching.
Dogs: welcome under control and on leads.

Find out more: 028 4375 1467 or mournes@nationaltrust.org.uk

Murlough National Nature Reserve

near Dundrum, County Down

🏛️🏊‍♂️🚠👤 1967

Satnav: use BT33 0NQ. **Parking**: on site.

Home to seals, Neolithic sites and Ireland's first nature reserve, Murlough is one of the most extensive examples of dune landscape in the country (below) and an important wildlife conservation site. A network of paths and boardwalks winds through ancient dunes, woodland and heath, making the reserve ideal for relaxed walks and spotting wildlife. **Note**: limited toilet facilities with seasonal opening.

Eat, shop, stay: beach café (seasonal opening, not National Trust). Picnics welcome on beach or in car park.

Things to see and do: explore the dune network and discover the wildlife of Murlough on one of the ranger-led guided walks. Family activities all year and new natural play area.
Dogs: welcome on leads, restrictions apply when ground-nesting birds are breeding or cattle grazing.

Access: 🚻➡️

Find out more: 028 4375 1467 or murlough@nationaltrust.org.uk

Murlough		M	T	W	T	F	S	S
Nature reserve								
1 Jan–29 Feb	8–5	M	T	W	T	F	S	S
1 Mar–30 Sep	8–7	M	T	W	T	F	S	S
1 Oct–31 Dec	8–5	M	T	W	T	F	S	·
Facilities								
14 Mar–5 Apr	10–6	·	·	·	·	·	S	S
10 Apr–19 Apr	10–6	M	T	W	T	F	S	S
25 Apr–31 May	10–6	·	·	·	·	·	S	S
1 Jun–31 Aug	10–6	M	T	W	T	F	S	S
5 Sep–27 Sep	10–6	·	·	·	·	·	S	S

Facilities also open Bank Holidays. Car park gates: open for exit until 8 in summer and 6 in winter. Separate pay and display all year.

Patterson's Spade Mill

751 Antrim Road, Templepatrick, County Antrim BT39 0AP

🏠🏛️♿🔔🍴 1991

Patterson's Spade Mill, County Antrim: still water-driven

Parking: 50 yards.

Travel back in time and witness history literally forged in steel at the last working water-driven spade mill in daily use in the British Isles. Dig up the history and culture of the humble spade and discover the origin of the phrase 'a face as long as a Lurgan spade'.

Eat, shop, stay: handcrafted spades on sale and made to specification.

Things to see and do: guided tours and demonstrations for all the family.
Dogs: on leads only.

Access: 🅿️🚪🚻♿ Building 🏛️♿ Grounds 🏛️

Find out more: 028 9443 3619 or pattersons@nationaltrust.org.uk

Patterson's Spade Mill		M	T	W	T	F	S	S
10 Apr–19 Apr	12–4	M	T	W	T	F	S	S
22 Apr–31 Dec	12–4	·	·	W	T	F	S	S

Admission by guided tour, last admission one hour before closing. Open Bank Holiday Mondays and all other public holidays in Northern Ireland from 10 April. Closed 25 and 26 December.

Portstewart Strand

Portstewart, County Londonderry

🏚️♿🏖️👓⛴️ 1981

Satnav: use BT55 7PG. **Parking**: on beach.

Sweeping along the edge of the north coast, this 2-mile stretch of golden sand is one of Northern Ireland's finest beaches and affords uninterrupted views of the coastline. It's an ideal place for lazy picnics, surfing and long walks into the wildlife-rich sand dunes (above).

Eat, shop, stay: award-winning Harry's Shack restaurant (not National Trust). Mobile beach information service.

Things to see and do: waymarked nature trail. Barmouth Estuary bird hide. Events during peak season. **Dogs**: welcome on leads before post 10; exercise area beyond.

Access: 🅿️♿♿♿ Café ♿ Beach ♿➡️

Find out more: 028 7083 6396 or portstewart@nationaltrust.org.uk

Portstewart Strand		M	T	W	T	F	S	S
Beach								
Open all year*	Dawn–dusk	M	T	W	T	F	S	S
Facilities								
1 Jan–5 Jan	10–2			W	T	F	S	S
11 Jan–15 Mar	10–3						S	S
16 Mar–5 Apr	10–4	M	T	W	T	F	S	S
6 Apr–28 Jun	10–7	M	T	W	T	F	S	S
29 Jun–31 Aug	10–8	M	T	W	T	F	S	S
1 Sep–8 Nov	10–4	M	T	W	T	F	S	S
14 Nov–20 Dec	10–3						S	S
21 Dec–31 Dec	10–2	M	T	W	T	F	S	S

*Open to pedestrians. Beach closed to vehicles one hour after last admission time. Opening times vary depending on weather and tides. Closed 25 December.

Rowallane Garden

Saintfield, County Down BT24 7LH

✿♿👓⛴️ 1956

Parking: on site.

Carved into the County Down drumlin landscape since the mid-1860s, this inspirational 21-hectare (52-acre) garden is waiting to be discovered. The passion and shared vision of the Reverend John Moore, and later his nephew Hugh Armytage Moore, created a garden where you can leave the outside world behind and immerse yourself in nature's beauty. The formal and informal garden spaces are home to magical features mingled with native and exotic plants, such as drifts of rare rhododendrons. Follow in the footsteps of plant hunters and explore the sights and scents of their discoveries in the garden today.

Rowallane Garden in County Down, above and below

Eat, shop, stay: garden café with new open-air tea garden seating area. Café/gift shop. Second-hand bookshop. Pottery providing unique Rowallane Garden items and garden pots.

Things to see and do: exciting activities and events connected to the seasons for all ages throughout the year.
Dogs: welcome on leads in garden.

Access: ♿🅿️🚻🔄🎵 Grounds ♿♿

Find out more: 028 9751 0131 or rowallane@nationaltrust.org.uk

Rowallane Garden		M	T	W	T	F	S	S
Garden								
1 Jan–29 Feb	10–4	M	T	W	T	F	S	S
1 Mar–30 Apr	10–6	M	T	W	T	F	S	S
1 May–31 Aug	10–8	M	T	W	T	F	S	S
1 Sep–31 Oct	10–6	M	T	W	T	F	S	S
1 Nov–31 Dec	10–4	M	T	W	T	F	S	S
Café								
1 Jan–29 Feb	11–3:30	M	T	W	T	F	S	S
1 Mar–30 Apr	11–4	M	T	W	T	F	S	S
1 May–31 Aug	10–5	M	T	W	T	F	S	S
1 Sep–31 Oct	11–4	M	T	W	T	F	S	S
1 Nov–31 Dec	11–3:30	M	T	W	T	F	S	S

Open Bank Holiday Mondays and all other public holidays in Northern Ireland. Closed 25 and 26 December.

Springhill

20 Springhill Road, Moneymore, Magherafelt, County Londonderry BT45 7NQ

🏠 ✲ ♿ 1957

Parking: 50 yards.

Home to the Lenox-Conyngham family for 10 generations, this 17th-century plantation house is regarded as 'one of the prettiest houses in Ulster'. The stories of this family home are brought to life on a guided tour, and the old laundry houses a celebrated costume collection that captures its enthralling past.

Eat, shop, stay: soup, scones, hot and cold drinks, snacks and ice cream available from the Barn Café. Retail area with a range of items for the home and garden. Second-hand bookshop.

Things to see and do: **Indoors** Guided house tours and children's indoor Pest Quest. Costume museum and children's dressing-up area. **Outdoors** Woodland walks and children's natural play. **Dogs**: welcome on leads in grounds.

Springhill in County Londonderry, above and below, is a 17th-century plantation house

Access: 🅿 ♿ 🚻 ♿ 🔊 📷 ♿ Building 🔥

Find out more: 028 8674 8210 or springhill@nationaltrust.org.uk

Springhill		M	T	W	T	F	S	S
House, visitor centre, café and costume museum								
1 Feb–5 Apr*	11–5	·	·	·	·	·	S	S
6 Apr–19 Apr	11–5	M	T	W	T	F	S	S
25 Apr–26 Apr	11–5	·	·	·	·	·	S	S
1 May–28 Jun	11–5	·	·	·	·	F	S	S
1 Jul–31 Aug	11–5	M	T	W	T	F	S	S
5 Sep–27 Sep	11–5	·	·	·	·	·	S	S
4 Oct–25 Oct	11–4	·	·	·	·	·	·	S
26 Oct–1 Nov	11–4	M	T	W	T	F	S	S
Visitor centre and café								
8 Nov–29 Nov	11–4	·	·	·	·	·	·	S
Grounds								
Open all year	11–5	M	T	W	T	F	S	S

*Also open 17 and 18 February for local half term.
House: guided tour available from 12. Open Bank Holiday Mondays and all other public holidays in Northern Ireland. Closed 25, 26 December and 1 January 2021.

Strangford Lough

County Down 1969

The tidal treasures of Britain's largest sea lough and one of Europe's key wildlife habitats await discovery. **Note**: for satnav use BT22 1RG. Small car park at Ballyquintin or parking around Lough.

Find out more: 028 4278 7769 or strangford@nationaltrust.org.uk

Cattle on the beach at White Park Bay, County Antrim

Wellbrook Beetling Mill

20 Wellbrook Road, Corkhill, Cookstown, County Tyrone BT80 9RY 1968

Discover how yarn was spun at Northern Ireland's last working water-powered linen beetling mill and enjoy a woodland river walk. **Note**: open weekends, 7 March until 27 September, 1 to 5. Admission by guided tour, last tour one hour before closing. Open Bank Holiday Mondays and all other public holidays in Northern Ireland.

Find out more: 028 8674 8210 or wellbrook@nationaltrust.org.uk

Eat, shop, stay: shops, restaurants and cafés in nearby towns (none National Trust). Picnics welcome.

Things to see and do: so much history to discover, including Druid's Altar (not on National Trust land). Part of the Causeway Coast Way, a section of the Ulster Way. **Dogs**: welcome on leads.

Access: ♿

Find out more: 028 7084 8728 or whiteparkbay@nationaltrust.org.uk

White Park Bay

near Ballintoy, County Antrim

1939

Satnav: use BT54 6NH. **Parking**: on site.

Embraced by ancient dunes and once home to Neolithic settlements, this arc of white sand nestles between two headlands on the North Antrim coast. Home to a range of rich habitats for a myriad of wildlife, its secluded location makes it ideal for quiet relaxation and peaceful walks.

Additional coastal and countryside car parks in Northern Ireland	
Belfast	
Glenoe	BT40 3LG
East Down	
Kearney	BT22 1QF
Strangford Lough (Greyabbey)	BT22 2RU
Mid Ulster	
Ballymoyer	BT60 2LA
North Coast	
Cushendun	BT44 0PH
Dunseverick	BT57 8SY
Fair Head and Murlough Bay	BT54 6RG
South Down	
Dundrum Coastal Path	BT33 0NG

Themed index

General interest

1 Adventure playgrounds/play areas
2 Boat hire
3 Bicycle hire
4 Camping and caravanning
5 Gardens
6 Ghosts
7 Industrial heritage
8 UNESCO World Heritage Sites

Springhill, County Londonderry

Arlington Court in Devon

Notable people

People with connections to places listed in this *Handbook*.

Admiral Anson

Thomas Carlyle

Octavia Hill

General James Wolfe

Film and television

This is a small selection of the largest and most popular films and TV dramas filmed at National Trust places.

Mullion Cove in Cornwall

Osterley Park and House in London

Alphabetical index

Photography credits

Accessibility: notes and information

- You can find information on access and facilities for every place listed in this *Handbook* in their entry. For the key to the symbols, please see the bookmark at the front of this book.

- If you have specific requirements, please ring before you visit in case something needs to be booked in advance.

- Disabled people can bring up to two essential companions free of charge. Get in touch with our Supporter Services team on **0344 800 1895** or **enquiries@nationaltrust.org.uk** for a companion card, so you can bring the person or people you need. Alternatively, on arrival just let our reception team know that you need someone to accompany you.

- Blue Badge holders park free.

- Assistance dogs are welcome at virtually all of our places.

- All the places we care for are writing their own access statements with more detailed accessibility information. These can be found on our website.

We're constantly working to improve accessibility at the places we look after, for example:

- We have around 150 powered mobility vehicles which visitors can use free of charge at more than 75 places. We are increasing this number, together with organisations such as Countryside Mobility South West.

- Seven locations have Changing Places toilets, which include hoists and changing tables. We have more opening this year and we're working with Mobiloo to continue to offer mobile changing places.